APPROVED TEXTBOOK

SEP 15 1964

ORBAN'S ORAL HISTOLOGY AND EMBRYOLOGY

EDITED BY **HARRY SICHER, M.D., D.Sc.**

Professor Emeritus
School of Dentistry, Loyola University
Chicago, Illinois

ORBAN'S ORAL HISTOLOGY AND EMBRYOLOGY

With 283 text illustrations
and 4 color plates

FIFTH EDITION

Saint Louis

THE C. V. MOSBY COMPANY

1962

CONTRIBUTORS

MYRON S. AISENBERG, D.D.S.

Baltimore College of Dental Surgery
University of Maryland
Baltimore, Maryland

GERRIT BEVELANDER, Ph.D.

College of Dentistry
New York University
New York, New York

LEROY R. BOLING, Ph.D.

School of Dentistry
Washington University
St. Louis, Missouri

MARVIN S. BURSTONE, M.S., D.D.S.

National Institutes
of Health
Bethesda, Maryland

SAMUEL W. CHASE, A.B., A.M., Ph.D.

School of Dentistry
Western Reserve University
Cleveland, Ohio

HARRY E. FRISBIE, D.D.S.

College of Dentistry
University of California
San Francisco, California

DONALD A. KERR, A.B., M.S., D.D.S.

School of Dentistry
University of Michigan
Ann Arbor, Michigan

GEORGE A. KRIKOS, D.D.S., Ph.D.

School of Dentistry
University of Pennsylvania
Philadelphia, Pennsylvania

†EDGAR B. MANLEY, M.Sc., B.D.S., F.D.S.R.C.S.(Eng.)

Department of Dental Pathology
Medical School
University of Birmingham
Birmingham, England

JULIA MEYER, Ph.D.

School of Dentistry
University of Illinois
Chicago, Illinois

†Deceased

5

MARIE U. NYLEN,
D.D.S.
  National Institute of Dental
  Research
  Bethesda, Maryland

ALFRED L. OGILVIE, M.S.
D.D.S.
  School of Dentistry
  University of Washington
  Seattle, Washington

†BALINT J. ORBAN, D.D.S.,
M.D.
  School of Dentistry
  Loyola University
  Chicago, Illinois

DOROTHY PERMAR, B.S.,
M.S.
  School of Dentistry
  Ohio State University
  Columbus, Ohio

HAMILTON B. G. ROBINSON,
M.S., D.D.S.
  College of Dentistry
  University of Kansas City
  Kansas City, Missouri

ISAAC SCHOUR, M.S.,
D.D.S., Ph.D.
  College of Dentistry
  University of Illinois
  Chicago, Illinois

DAVID B. SCOTT, A.B.,
M.S., D.D.S.
  National Institute of Dental
  Research
  Bethesda, Maryland

HARRY SICHER, M.D., D.Sc.
  School of Dentistry
  Loyola University
  Chicago, Illinois

REIDAR F. SOGNNAES,
D.M.D., Ph.D.
  School of Dentistry
  University of California
  Los Angeles, California

†JOSEPH P. WEINMANN,
M.D.
  College of Dentistry
  University of Illinois
  Chicago, Illinois

FRANK M. WENTZ, M.S.
D.D.S., Ph.D.
  School of Dentistry
  Loyola University
  Chicago, Illinois

†Deceased

To **BALINT J. ORBAN**

A clinician of consummate skill; a researcher of an incomparable power of observation and an unprejudiced intellect in interpretation; a teacher of unlimited patience and unstinting generosity

PREFACE TO FIFTH EDITION

Long before Dr. Orban's untimely death on the first of June, 1960, he had started preparation for this, the fifth, edition of *Oral Histology and Embryology*. He had asked me to join him in editing the latest revision and we had discussed some of the more radical changes. Wherever possible, I have followed his ideas and tried to execute his plans.

A separate chapter on the Histochemistry of Oral Tissues by Marvin S. Burstone has been added to this edition. Furthermore, the following chapters have been entirely rewritten: Development of the Face and Oral Cavity (by Hamilton B. G. Robinson); Enamel and Dentin, including a discussion of electron microscope findings with significant alterations made in the text as a result of these findings (by Reidar F. Sognnaes, David B. Scott, and Marie U. Nylen); Salivary Glands (by George A. Krikos); and Maxillary Sinus (by Dorothy Permar). The counsel of Julia Meyer was invaluable in pointing out some inconsistencies and in adding some new important findings on the oral epithelium.

In addition, minor changes have been made throughout which we hope will contribute materially to the didactic value of the book.

In revising the text, the leading thought was that *although there cannot be a best or perfect way of teaching, orally or through the printed word, there always will be a better way of doing it.*

I cannot close these remarks without paying tribute to Balint Orban and Joseph P. Weinmann. Of Dr. Orban, one can truly say: he planned as if he would live forever and worked as if he would die the next day. Dental research has suffered an equally great loss with the death of Dr. Weinmann, whose wide knowledge and critical counsel were essential in the planning and editing of this book.

CHICAGO   *Harry Sicher*

CONTENTS

COLOR PLATES

ORBAN'S ORAL HISTOLOGY
AND EMBRYOLOGY

Chapter I • DEVELOPMENT OF THE FACE AND ORAL CAVITY*

INTRODUCTION

The development of the face and oral cavity involves a dynamic series of events that begin during the second month of intrauterine life. The complex origin of this region from different growth centers, with the development of seven different processes which grow at varying rates and which unite to varying degrees, makes the relatively infrequent occurrence of malformations remarkable. Critical changes lead to formation of the embryonic face, the nasal duct, and the tongue and to the separation of the oral and nasal cavities by formation of the palate. This period can be divided into two phases.

In the first phase, during the fifth and sixth weeks, the building blocks of the face are prepared, communication between the oral cavity and foregut is established, and the nasal ducts are formed. At the end of this period, the nasal cavity and the oral cavity communicate freely, and the tongue has developed. In the second phase, during the seventh and eighth weeks, the development of the palate takes place, leading to the separation of the oral and nasal cavities. The most common malformations of the face, cleft lip (harelip) and cleft palate, originate during the first and second phases, respectively.

DEVELOPMENT OF THE FACE

Early development. In the human embryo (Plate 1, A) that is 3 mm. long (3 weeks old), the greater part of the face consists of the rounded prominence formed by the forebrain (prosencephalon). The forebrain is covered by a thin layer of mesoderm and by ectoderm. Below the rounded prominence (Fig. 1) there is a deep groove, the primary oral groove (stomodeum, oral fossa). The stomodeum is bounded caudally by the mandibular arch (first branchial arch),

---

Rewritten by Hamilton B. G. Robinson.

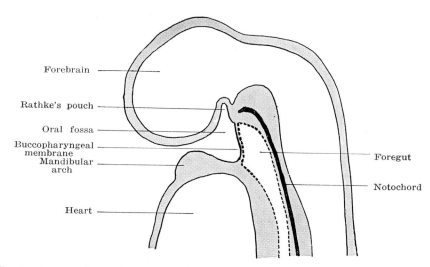

Fig. 1. Diagram of a median section through the head of a human embryo of 3 mm. length. Oral fossa separated from foregut by a double layer of epithelium, the buccopharyngeal membrane.

laterally by the maxillary processes, and cephalically by the frontonasal process (Plate 1, *B*). During early phases of development, two bulges may be observed laterally and anteriorly on the mandibular arch, united centrally by a copula (Plate 1, *A* to *E*). Later these bulges disappear (Plate 1, *F*).

The stomodeum (oral groove) deepens to meet the blind end of the foregut (Fig. 1). The stomodeum and the foregut are separated by the buccopharyngeal membrane, consisting of two epithelial layers only. There is an additional ecto-dermal pouch (Fig. 1), which is derived from the stomodeum, Rathke's pouch, which gives rise to the anterior lobe of the pituitary gland. The lining of the stomodeum is ectodermal; therefore, the lining of the nasal and the oral cavities, the enamel of the teeth, and the salivary glands are of ectodermal origin. The pharyngeal lining is entodermal since it is formed from the foregut. Communica-tion between the primary oral cavity and the foregut is established at about the third or fourth week when the buccopharyngeal membrane ruptures.

Essentially, the face is derived from seven primordia: the two mandibular processes, which unite very early, the two maxillary processes, the two lateral nasal processes, and the medial nasal process (Plate 1). The mandibular and maxillary processes originate from the first branchial arch, whereas the medial nasal and the two lateral nasal processes arise from the frontonasal process, which in turn arose in the prominence covering the forebrain.

The first significant change in the configuration of the face results from the rapid proliferation of the mesoderm covering the anterior portion of the brain (Plate 1, *A* and *B*). This prominence, the frontonasal process (Plate 1), will give rise to most of the structures of the upper and the middle portion of the face. Next, the formation and deepening of the stomodeum (Plate 1 and Fig. 1)

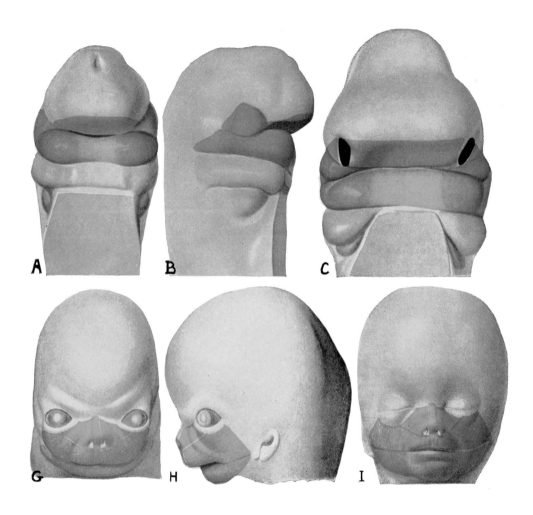

Plate 1. Development of the human face. **A** and **B**, Embryo 3 mm. long, third week: Fronto-nasal process (blue) undivided. Caudal to mandibular arch (yellow), the hyoid arch, and the third branchial arch. Depression on top of figure is neuropore. **C**, Embryo 6.5 mm. long, fourth week: Nasal pits divide the frontonasal process into medial nasal process (blue) and lateral nasal processes (red). **D**, Embryo 9 mm. long, fifth week: Fusion of medial nasal and maxillary processes has narrowed entrance into nasal pit. **E**, Embryo 9.2 mm. long, sixth week: Fusion of medial and lateral nasal processes has further narrowed the nostrils. Medial nasal process reduced in relative width. Eyes at lateral edges of face.

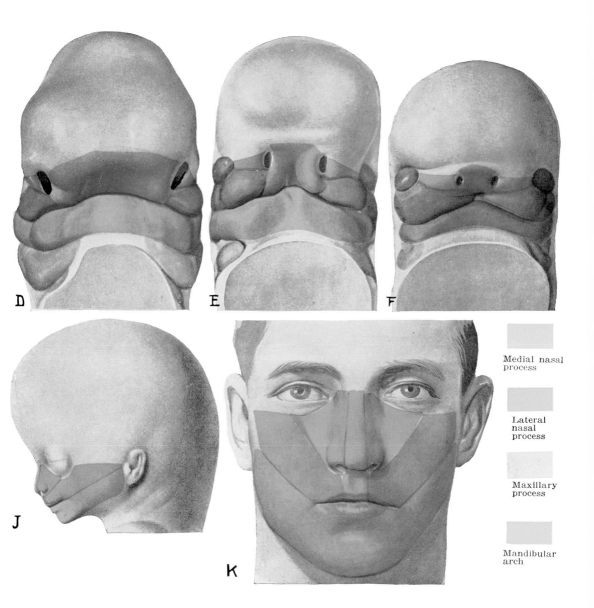

Medial nasal process

Lateral nasal process

Maxillary process

Mandibular arch

F, Embryo 14.5 mm. long, seventh week: Nasal area slightly prominent. Nasal septum further reduced in relative width. Eyes on anterior surface of face. G and H, Embryo 18 mm. long, eighth week: Lidless eyes on anterior surface of face. Their distance relatively reduced, mandible short. I and J, Embryo 60 mm. long, twelfth week: Lids closed. Nostrils closed by epithelial proliferation. Relation of mandible to maxilla normal. K, Adult face: The derivatives of medial nasal process (blue), lateral nasal processes (red), maxillary processes (green), and mandibular arch (yellow). (Modified after Sicher, H., and Tandler, J.: Anatomie für Zahnärzte [Anatomy for Dentists], Vienna and Berlin, 1928, Julius Springer.)

and olfactory (nasal) pits (Plate 1) and the division of the caudal portion of the frontonasal process into the medial nasal and two lateral nasal processes (Plate 1, *C* to *F*) are most striking. The lateral nasal processes are adjacent to the maxillary processes (Plate 1, *C*) and are separated from them by shallow furrows, the nasomaxillary grooves (Fig. 2). These grooves formerly were called the nasolacrimal grooves, but it is now recognized that the nasolacrimal grooves, which give origin to the nasolacrimal ducts, originate parallel and medial to the nasomaxillary grooves[8] (Fig. 2).

The medial nasal process is at first larger than the lateral nasal processes (Plate 1, *C* and *D*), but it later lags in its growth (Plate 1, *E* to *G*). Its rounded and prominent inferolateral corners are known as the globular processes (Plate 1, *D*). The globular processes are primarily united with the maxillary processes on both sides; here, a fusion does not occur (Plate 1, *E*). The lateral nasal processes do not contribute to the upper boundary of the oral orifice.

The subsequent changes that occur are due only in part to union of primarily separated processes. Careful examination of Plate 1 will show that the processes, in most instances, were separated by shallow grooves (e.g., the maxillary and mandibular processes) or by pits (e.g., the lateral and the medial nasal processes). For this reason, most of the changes that are commonly considered as "fusions" are the result of decreasing depth and disappearance of grooves or pits.

Formation of the primary palate. During the fifth and sixth weeks of intra-uterine life, a structure known as the primary palate is formed. From it will

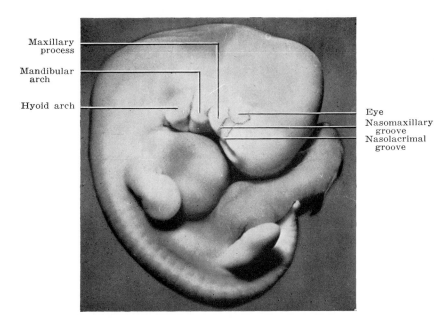

Maxillary process
Mandibular arch
Hyoid arch
Eye
Nasomaxillary groove
Nasolacrimal groove

Fig. 2. Photograph of human embryo of 10 mm. length. Nasomaxillary and nasolacrimal grooves. (Courtesy Dr. P. Gruenwald.)

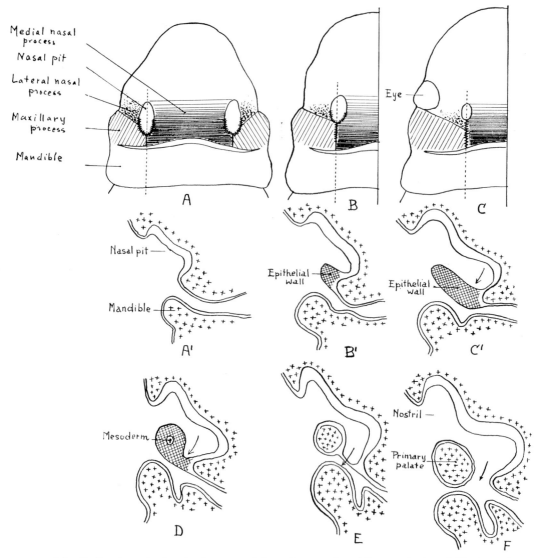

Fig. 3. Six stages in the development of the primary palate (diagrams). **A** and **A′**, Face of a human embryo of 6.5 mm. length (compare Plate 1, **C**). The zigzag line on the inferior border of the nasal pit marks the line of later fusion of medial nasal process to maxillary and lateral nasal processes. The broken line marks the plane of section **A′**. **B** and **B′**, Human embryo of 9 mm. length (compare Plate 1, **D**). The median nasal process has fused with the maxillary process. By this fusion, an epithelial wall has been formed which is visible in section **B′**. The nasal pit is closed in its inferior part to form a short, blind olfactory sac. **C** and **C′**, Human embryo, 9.5 mm. in length (compare Plate 1, **E**). The medial nasal process is now fused to maxillary and lateral nasal processes. The epithelial wall has lengthened (**C′**). The arrow in **C′** points to the area in which the epithelial wall separates olfactory sac from oral cavity. **D**, Human embryo of 12 mm. length. The plane of seciton is as in **A′**, **B′**, and **C′**. The mesoderm has broken through the superior part of the epithelial wall, thus strengthening the primarily epithelial fusion of medial nasal process to maxillary and lateral nasal processes. The inferior part of the epithelial wall has thinned out (arrow). **E**, Human embryo of 14 mm. length. The destruction of the superior part of the epithelial wall by proliferating mesoderm (crosses) has advanced. The inferior part of the epithelial wall is thinned out to form the nasobuccal membrane (arrow). **F**, Human embryo of 15 mm. length. The nasobuccal membrane has disappeared. Nasal cavity communicates with oral cavity through the primary choana (arrow). The superior part of the epithelial wall is entirely replaced by proliferating mesoderm forming the primary palate between nasal and oral cavities. **A′**, **B′**, **C′**, **D**, **E**, and **F** represent sagittal sections corresponding to the broken lines in **A**, **B**, and **C** and comparable sections of three older embryos.

develop the upper lip and the anterior portion of the maxillary alveolar process. The first step in its formation is the elevation of the borders of the olfactory (nasal) pits along the inferior (caudal) half (Fig. 3, *A* and *A'*). The borders of the olfactory pit are formed from the medial nasal process medially and from the lateral nasal and maxillary processes laterally. The inferior margins of the olfactory pit grow toward each other until they touch and unite (Fig. 3, *B* and *C*), reducing the size of the external opening of the pits, the primary nostrils, and transforming the pits into blind ending sacs (Fig. 3, *B'* and *C'*).

At this stage of development, the blind ends of the nasal sacs correspond to positions on the embryonic face just above the oral orifice. If the blind ends were to open at this period, the nasal ducts would open into the face instead of into the oral cavity. A change in the topographic relation of the nasal sac (Fig. 3, *B'* and *C'*) precedes the final stages, and the opening is into the oral cavity (Fig. 3, *F*). These changes are effected through differential growth with bulging of the mesoderm parallel to the oral orifice (Fig. 3, *D*) and continued forward growth of the mandibular arch (Fig. 3, *A'* to *F*). As the region immediately above the oral orifice enlarges (Fig. 3, *B'* and *C'*, epithelial wall, and Fig. 3, *D*, mesoderm), the base of the sac is brought into position adjacent to the primitive oral cavity.

The lateral and medial borders of the lower portion of the olfactory pit first are joined by epithelial union (Fig. 3, *B* and *C*), but the proliferating mesoderm (Fig. 3, *D*) invades the epithelial lamina and makes this union permanent. However, at the blind end of the sac that is formed from the olfactory pit, the epithelium is thinned out by growth of adjacent parts and is not replaced by mesoderm. The resulting nasobuccal membrane (Fig. 3, *E*) separates the primitive oral cavity from the olfactory sac. When this membrane ruptures (Fig. 3, *F*), the olfactory sac becomes the olfactory duct leading from the nostril to the opening into the oral cavity, the primary choana. The horizontal bar of tissue (seen in cross section in Fig. 3, *F*) formed by union of the median nasal process with the lateral nasal processes and the maxillary processes is the primary palate (Figs. 3, *C*, and 4).

While the primary palate is being formed, the mandibular arch undergoes developmental changes that lead to the appearance of a median furrow and two small pits on either side of the midline. The furrow and median pits seem to disappear by union of the epithelium lining their walls.

The continued development of the future mature facial characteristics is the result of differential growth of the regions of the face (Plate 1). The most dramatic change is brought about by the slower growth in breadth of the derivatives of the medial nasal process in comparison with those from the lateral nasal and maxillary processes during later stages of embryonic life, while the middle third of the face increases in an anterior direction to bulge beyond the other surface areas (compare *F, G, H, I,* and *J* in Plate 1). The external nose is formed in this manner, and the eyes, which were situated on the lateral aspect

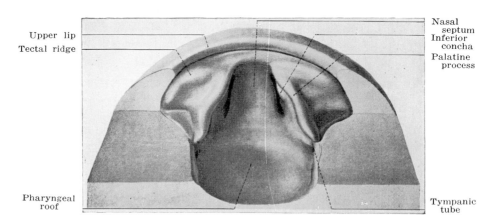

Nasal
septum
Inferior
concha
Palatine
process

Upper lip
Tectal ridge

Pharyngeal
roof

Tympanic
tube

Fig. 4. Reconstruction of the roof of the primitive oral and pharyngeal cavities of a human embryo of 23 mm. length (eighth week). Primary palate and internal surface of maxillary process form a horseshoe-shaped and incomplete roof of the oral cavity. In the center, the oral cavity communicates with the nasal cavities. At the edges of maxillary processes, the palatine processes develop. (From Sicher, H., and Tandler, J.: Anatomie für Zahnärzte [Anatomy for Dentists], Vienna and Berlin, 1928, Julius Springer.)

of the head (Plate 1, *E*), come into their position close to, and on either side of, the nose (Plate 1, *I*).

The nose is not fully developed in the newborn infant, the nose of a young child being flat. Not until puberty does the nose develop its inherited size and shape.

The growth of the mandible follows a peculiar curve. During early development it is small (Fig. 3, *B*) by comparison with the upper portions of the face, and then its growth in width and length spurts with some of the stages of palatal development (Fig. 3, *D* and *E*). Later, mandibular growth again lags (Plate 1, *G* and *H*). The fetus shows a physiologic micrognathia that disappears at, or soon after, birth. In early embryonic life, the oral orifice is very wide, but as the maxillary and mandibular processes unite to form the cheeks, the width of the oral opening is reduced.

DEVELOPMENT OF THE SECONDARY PALATE

Palatine processes. At the time the primary palate is completed, the primary nasal cavity is a short duct leading from the nostril into the primitive oral cavity (Fig. 3, *F*). Its outer openings and inner openings (primary choanae) are separated from the face and oral cavity by the primary palate. As pointed out, the primary palate will develop into the upper lip, the anterior part of the alveolar process, and the anteriormost part of the palate.

As the primitive oral cavity increases in height, the tissue that separates the two primitive nostrils grows backward and downward to form the future nasal septum. The oral cavity has an incomplete, horseshoe-shaped roof (Fig. 4) formed anteriorly by the primary palate and laterally by the oral surface of the maxillary processes. On either side of the nasal septum, the oral cavity communicates with the nasal cavities (Figs. 4 and 5).

Folds develop from the medial edge of the maxillary processes at the lateral portions of the oral roof. They grow downward almost vertically (Fig. 5) on either side of the tongue. The vertically disposed extension, which grows from the maxillary process, is the palatine process (Figs. 4 and 5). It extends posteriorly to the lateral walls of the pharynx. At this stage of development the tongue is narrow and high and reaches the nasal septum (Fig. 5).

The secondary palate, which is destined to separate the oral and nasal cavities, is formed by union of the two palatine processes (Figs. 6 and 7), after the tongue assumes a more inferior position and the palatine processes have assumed horizontal positions. The anterior portion of the palatine processes also unites with the nasal septum (Fig. 7). In this anterior region the hard palate develops. In the posterior region, where the soft palate and uvula develop, there is no attachment to the nasal septum.

The transposition and union of the palatine processes can occur only when the tongue has moved downward, evacuating the space between the palatine processes. This takes place simultaneously with a marked growth spurt of the mandible in both length and width. This protrusion of the mandible is visible

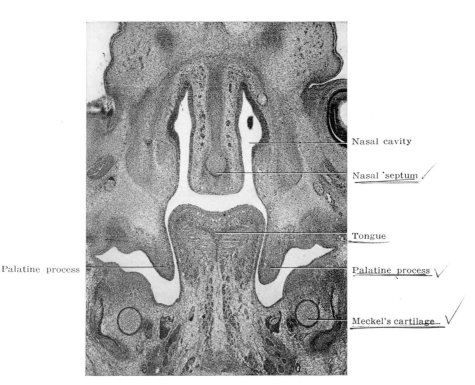

Nasal cavity

Nasal septum

Tongue

Palatine process

Palatine process

Meckel's cartilage

Fig. 5. Frontal section through the head of a human embryo of 24 mm. length (eighth week). Tongue high and narrow between the vertical palatine processes. (Courtesy Dr. P. Gruenwald.)

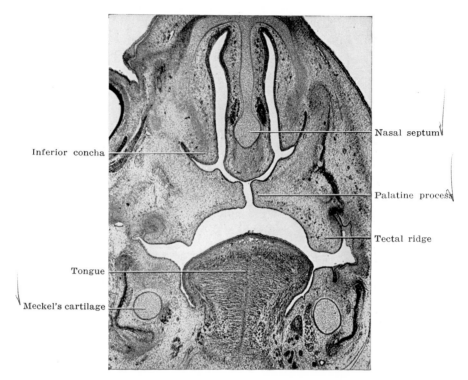

Inferior concha

Nasal septum

Palatine process

Tectal ridge

Tongue

Meckel's cartilage

Fig. 6. Frontal section through the head of a human embryo of 30 mm. length (ninth week). Tongue has left the space between the palatine processes and lies flat and wide within the mandibular arch. The palatine processes have assumed a horizontal position. (Courtesy Dr. P. Gruenwald.)

(Plate 1, *H* and *J*). The tongue moves into the wide space within the mandibular arch and assumes its natural shape with its width greater than its height (Figs. 5 to 7). The transposition of the palatine processes can occur because of accentuated growth of the mesoderm at the lateral aspect of these processes (Fig. 5). The dense arrangement of the cells and the presence of many mitotic figures identify this region as one of rapid growth.

When the palatine processes assume their horizontal position, they touch the lower border of the nasal septum but are still separated from each other by a median cleft (Fig. 6) which is wider posteriorly than it is toward the anterior aspect. The cleft gradually closes from the anterior to the posterior region. In earlier phases, an epithelial suture is present between the two processes that formed the palate (Fig. 7). Later, most of this epithelium is invaded by the growing mesoderm, and, as it breaks up, epithelial rests are formed that may persist through later life. The epithelium persists at the anterior end where the palatine processes unite with, and partially overgrow, the primitive palate on its oral aspect. The persisting epithelium in this region forms two strands that begin in the nasal cavity and unite, below, with the oral epithelium. These are

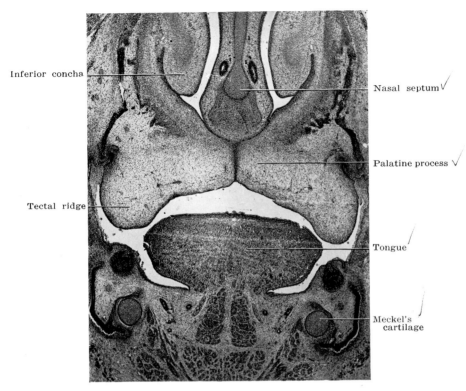

Fig. 7. Frontal section through the head of a human embryo slightly older than that in Fig. 6. The horizontal palatine processes have fused with each other and with the nasal septum. Secondary palate separates nasal from oral cavities.

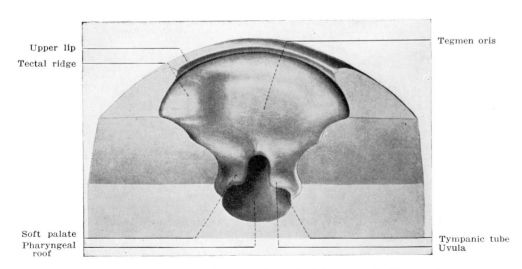

Fig. 8. Reconstruction of palate of a human embryo of 28.5 mm. length. The palatine processes fused in the area of the hard palate. The fusion has not reached the soft palate and uvula. (From Sicher, H., and Tandler, J.: Anatomie für Zahnärzte [Anatomy for Dentists], Vienna and Berlin, 1928, Julius Springer.)

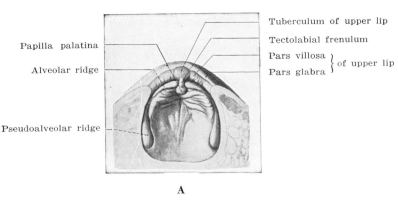

Papilla palatina

Alveolar ridge

Pseudoalveolar ridge

Tuberculum of upper lip

Tectolabial frenulum

Pars villosa } of upper lip
Pars glabra

A

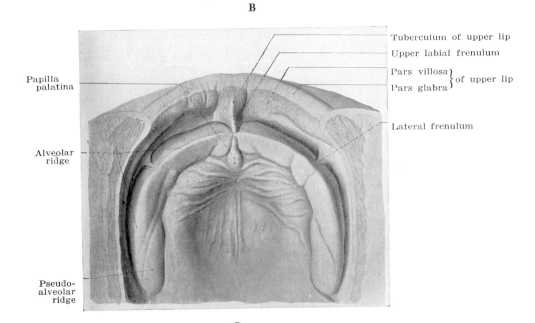

Papilla palatina

Alveolar ridge

Pseudoalveolar ridge

Tuberculum of upper lip

Tectolabial **frenulum**

Pars villosa } **of upper lip**
Pars glabra

B

Papilla palatina

Alveolar ridge

Pseudo-alveolar ridge

Tuberculum of upper lip

Upper labial frenulum

Pars villosa } of upper lip
Pars glabra

Lateral frenulum

C

Fig. 9. Advanced stages in the development of the hard palate. **A,** Human fetus, 3 months old. **B,** Human fetus, 4 months old. **C,** Human newborn infant. Note the changes in the relationship of palatine papilla and frenulum and those between the alveolar ridge and pseudoalveolar ridge. (From Sicher, H., and Tandler, J.: Anatomie für Zahnärzte [Anatomy for Dentists], Vienna and Berlin, 1928, Julius Springer.)

the primordia of the nasopalatine ducts, which are vestigial in man (see Chapter IX). It should be emphasized that not all of the palate arises from the palatine processes. Only the soft palate and the central portion of the hard palate (tegmen oris, oral roof) are formed from the palatine processes; the horseshoe-shaped peripheral parts (tectal ridge) originate from the maxillary processes (Fig. 8).

The palate is separated from the lip by a shallow sulcus in the depths of which two epithelial laminae arise (Fig. 15). The outer lamina is the vestibular lamina; the inner is the dental lamina (see Chapter II). Later, the alveolar process forms from the mesoderm between these laminae.

The palatine papilla develops quite early as a round prominence at the anterior part of the palate (Fig. 9). The palatine rugae cross the anterior aspect of the palate as transverse, irregular folds. At this stage, the lip shows a definite division into an outer smooth zone, pars glabra, and an inner zone beset with fine villi, pars villosa (Fig. 9). In the upper lip, the central portion of the pars villosa is prominent and forms the tubercle of the upper lip. A fold, tectolabial frenum, connects the palatine papilla with the labial tubercle (Fig. 9, *A* and *B*).

When, in later stages, the growing alveolar process increases in size, the tectolabial frenum is separated from the palatine papilla and persists as the upper labial frenum, connecting the alveolar ridge with the upper lip (Fig. 9, *C*).

During these phases of development, a bulge appears in the molar region that may be mistaken for the alveolar ridge (Fig. 9). This structure, the pseudo-alveolar ridge, disappears as the true alveolar process grows posteriorly.

The development of the mandibular alveolar ridge is simple. There is no precedent pseudoalveolar ridge, the alveolar process gradually growing into the oral cavity within the limits of the labial sulcus. The labial sulcus deepens to form the oral vestibule, which extends posteriorly into the regions bounded by the cheeks.

DEVELOPMENT OF THE TONGUE

Branchial arches. Because of the role of the branchial arches in formation of the tongue, the development of those structures should be understood. The branchial arches develop as four pairs of curved structures in the fetal neck. They are separated by shallow branchial grooves externally and by deeper pharyngeal pouches internally (Fig. 10, *A*). Only the first and second arches extend to the midline, and each arch is successively smaller from the first to the fourth.

The entodermal epithelium of the pharyngeal pouches gives rise to a variety of organs. From the first pouch the auditory tube and the cavities of the middle ear are formed; in the second pouch the palatine tonsil originates; from the third pouch the inferior parathyroid gland and the thymus develop; and from the fourth pouch the superior parathyroid gland arises.

From the cartilaginous skeleton of the first arch, Meckel's cartilage, the malleus and the incus arise; from the second, the stapes, the styloid process, and the lesser horn of the hyoid; from the third, the remainder of the hyoid; and from the fourth, the thyroid cartilage.

Cervical sinus. Externally, the third and fourth arches are overgrown by a caudal outgrowth from the second arch (Plate 1, *C*) corresponding to the closing of the caudal arches by the operculum in gill-bearing vertebrates. This places the last three arches in a deep recess, the cervical sinus. Later, this is closed when the operculum-like structure unites with the lateral wall of the neck.

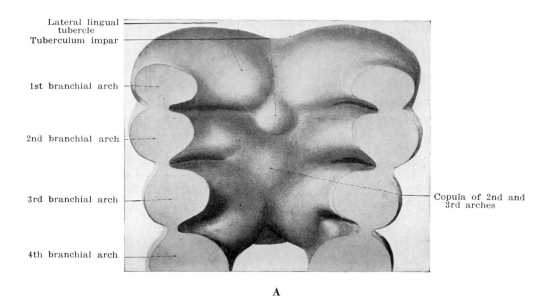

Lateral lingual tubercle
Tuberculum impar
1st branchial arch
2nd branchial arch
3rd branchial arch
Copula of 2nd and 3rd arches
4th branchial arch

A

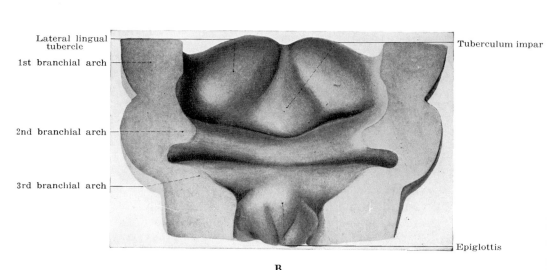

Lateral lingual tubercle
Tuberculum impar
1st branchial arch
2nd branchial arch
3rd branchial arch
Epiglottis

B

Fig. 10. Development of the tongue. Anterior wall of pharynx and floor of the oral cavity seen from within. **A,** Human embryo of 3.5 mm. length (third week). **B,** Human embryo of 6.5 mm. length (fourth week).

The cavity soon disappears, but its epithelium, if it persists, may give rise to branchial cysts.

Tongue. The tongue is derived from the first, second, and third branchial arches. The structures derived from the first branchial arches are divided, throughout life, from those from the more caudal arches by the terminal sulcus in the area of the vallate papillae (Fig. 209). The body and apex of the tongue originate in three prominences on the inner aspect of the mandibular or first branchial arch, as shown in Fig. 10. There are two lateral lingual prominences and one middle unpaired prominence, the tuberculum impar (Fig. 10, *A*). The base of the tongue develops from a prominence formed by the union of the bases of the second and third branchial arches, the copula (yoke). The tuberculum impar, which is at first prominent, is soon reduced in relative size (Fig. 10, *C*), and later almost disappears (Fig. 10, *D*).

In the midline at the base of the first arch and between the derivatives of the

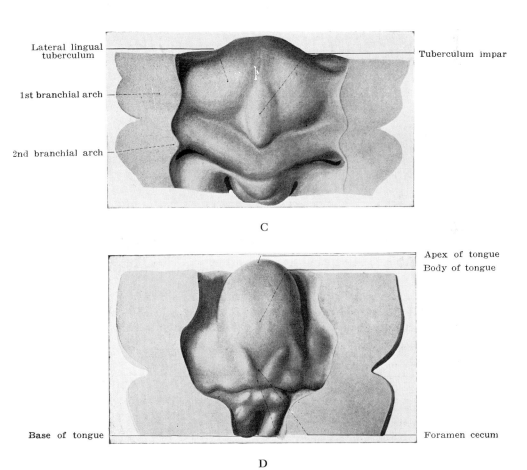

Fig. 10 (cont'd). **C,** Human embryo of 8 mm. length (fifth week). **D,** Human embryo of 11 mm. length (sixth week). (From Sicher, H., and Tandler, J.: Anatomie für Zahnärzte [Anatomy for Dentists], Vienna and Berlin, 1928, Julius Springer.)

first and second branchial arches, the thyroid gland develops by progressive downward growth and differentiation. A transitory duct, the thyroglossal duct, originates in this region, growing downward through the developing tongue to the future site of the gland. Its oral end is marked on the adult tongue by the foramen cecum (Fig. 209). Thyroglossal duct cysts may develop in the region from the foramen cecum to the isthmus of the thyroid gland.

In later stages of development, the tongue grows very rapidly, and various types of papillae are differentiated in the anterior part, whereas lymphatic tissue develops in the posterior part of the lingual mucosa (Chapter IX). The extrinsic muscles of the tongue grow into its primitive mesoderm, and the intrinsic muscles differentiate from the mesenchyme within the tongue.

CLINICAL CONSIDERATIONS

Facial malformations. The most frequent malformations of the face are clefts. Clefts of the lip, jaw, or palate, usually in some combination, occur once in about eight hundred births. Cleft lip (cheiloschisis, harelip) is a cleft, lateral to the midline, cutting through the lip. It may be bilateral or unilateral and is between the derivatives of the medial nasal and lateral processes (Plate 1, *K*). Gnathoschisis (cleft jaw) occurs in the maxilla between the derivatives of the same processes and likewise may be unilateral or bilateral. Uranoschisis (cleft palate) commonly involves both the hard and the soft palate. When only the soft palate is involved, the term staphyloschisis is used. Cleft palate is due to failure of union between the two palatine processes. The oblique facial cleft begins at some point in the upper lip and courses obliquely over the cheek to the eye along the line of junction of the maxillary and lateral nasal processes (Plate 1, *K*). Failure of complete union of the maxillary and mandibular processes produces macrostomia, an abnormally wide mouth.

Cleft lip and jaw. In most instances, both lip and jaw are cleft, cheilognathoschisis. This cleft extends from the lower border of the nostril, lateral to the midline, through the upper lip and the maxillary alveolar process, to the region of the incisive foramen. This malformation was long considered simply as a lack of fusion of the median nasal process with the lateral nasal process. It has been shown[12] that epithelial fusion does occur in cases of cleft lip and jaw, but the epithelial wall is not perforated by mesoderm, and the epithelial union opens. Cleft lip and jaw would be evident at 6 to 7 weeks in utero.

The relation of cleft jaw to the teeth and bone varies. In some instances the cleft is in the position between the premaxilla and the maxilla, usually lateral to the second incisor. Occasionally, it is medial to this site and medial to the second incisor. At other times the second incisor may be missing or a supernumerary tooth may develop. The skeletal parts and the teeth begin their development after the normal union of the facial processes has occurred; hence, the teeth and skeletal parts develop in a uniform tissue regardless of the *exact* location of the former boundaries between the processes.

Cleft palate. In cleft palate there may be lack of union of both palatine processes with each other and with the nasal septum, or one palatine process may unite with the nasal septum but not with its counterpart. Palatal union, if it is to occur, usually is completed before the third month. Since union begins in the anterior region and progresses posteriorly, the degree of cleft may vary from complete nonunion to the relatively innocuous notched or bifid uvula.

Cleft palate is associated with cleft lip in 84 per cent of patients. In bilateral cleft lip and palate there may be a protruding mass of tissue formed from the medial nasal process, or there may be an atrophy of this tissue. Then a wide cleft results that may erroneously be diagnosed as a median cleft.

Heredity probably is a major factor in cleft formation, although nutritional deficiencies, infectious diseases, trauma in utero, and other factors may contribute. Other anomalies, such as cranioschisis, spina bifida, polydactylism, or clubfoot, are found frequently associated with facial clefts.

Labial pits. Small pits may persist on either side of the midline of the lower lip. They are due to the failure of the embryonic labial pits to disappear.

Lingual anomalies. Median rhomboid glossitis, an innocuous, secondarily often inflamed smooth zone of the tongue in the midline in front of the foramen cecum, is considered the result of persistence of the tuberculum impar. Lack of fusion between the two lateral lingual prominences may produce a bifid tongue. Thyroid tissue may develop in the base of the tongue, or part of the thyroglossal duct may persist and form cysts.

Developmental cysts. Epithelial rests in lines of union of facial or oral processes or from epithelial organs, i.e., vestigal nasopalatine ducts, may give rise to cysts lined with epithelium.

Branchial cleft (cervical) cysts or fistulas may arise from the rests of branchial pouches or the cervical sinus. They usually are laterally disposed on the neck. Thyroglossal duct cysts may occur at any place along the course of the duct, usually at or near the midline.

Cysts may arise from epithelial rests after the fusion of medial and lateral nasal processes. Wrongly, they are called globulomaxillary cysts. Cysts in the maxilla between lateral incisor and canine may be primordial cysts from a supernumerary tooth germ.

"Anterior palatine" cysts are situated in the midline of the maxillary alveolar process. Once believed to be from remnants of the fusion of two processes, they are now considered as primordial cysts of odontogenic origin. The term "anterior palatine cyst" is misleading and should be avoided.

Nasolabial cysts, originating in the base of the wing of the nose and bulging into nasal and oral vestibule and root of upper lip, sometimes causing a flat depression on the anterior surface of the alveolar process, are also explained as originating from epithelial remnants in the harelip line. It is, however, more probable that they derive from excessive epithelial proliferations that normally, for some time in embryonic life, plug the nostrils. It is also possible that they are retention cysts of vestibular nasal glands or that they develop from the epithelium of the nasolacrimal duct.

References

1. Arey, L. B.: Developmental Anatomy, ed. 6, Philadelphia, 1957, W. B. Saunders Co.
2. Burket, L. W.: Nasopalatine Duct Structures and Peculiar Bony Patterns in the Anterior Maxillary Region, Arch. Path. **23**: 793, 1937.
3. Grace, L. G.: Frequency of Occurrence of Cleft Palate and Hare Lips, J. D. Res. **22**: 495, 1943.
4. Hochstetter, F.: Beiträge zur Entwicklungsgeschichte des menschlichen Gaumens (Contributions to the Development of the Human Palate), Morphol. Jahrb. **77**: 179, 1936.
5. Keibel, F., and Mall, F. P.: Manual of Human Embryology, Philadelphia and London, 1910, J. B. Lippincott Co.
6. Kraus, Bertram S.: Prenatal Growth and Morphology of the Human Bony Palate, J. D. Res. **39**: 1177, 1960.
7. Peter, K.: Die Entwicklung des Saugetiergaumens (Development of the Mammalian Palate), Ergebn. d. Anat. Entwicklngsgesch. **25**: 448, 1924.
8. Politzer, G.: Die Grenzfurche des Oberkieferfortsatzes und die Tränennasenrinne beim Menschen (The Limiting Sulcus of the Maxillary Process and the Nasolacrimal Groove in Man), Ztschr. f. Anat. u. Entwcklngsgesch. **105**: 329, 1936.
9. Robinson, H. B. G.: Classification of Cysts of the Jaws, Am. J. Orthodont. & Oral Surg. **31**: 370, 1945.
10. Sicher, H., and Pohl, L.: Zur Entwicklung des menschlichen Unterkiefers (Development of the Human Mandible—A Contribution to the Origin of the Fistulae of the Lower Lip), Ztschr. f. Stomatol. **32**: 552, 1934.
11. Sicher, H., and Tandler, J.: Anatomie für Zahnärzte (Anatomy for Dentists), Vienna and Berlin, 1928, Julius Springer.
12. Veau, V., and Politzer, G.: Embryologie du bec-de-lièvre; le palais primaire (Embryology of the Harelip: The Primary Palate. Formation and Anomalies), Ann. d' anat. path. **13**: 275, 1936.

Chapter II • DEVELOPMENT AND GROWTH OF THE TEETH*

INTRODUCTION

By the time the human embryo is 3 weeks of age, the stomodeum has formed at its cephalic end (see Chapter I). The ectoderm that lines the stomodeum comes in contact with the endoderm of the foregut, and the union of these two layers forms the buccopharyngeal membrane. This membrane soon ruptures, and there is produced an opening from the primitive oral cavity into the foregut.

The ectoderm of the primitive oral cavity consists of a basal layer of high cells and a surface layer of flattened cells. These cells appear empty in routine preparations of slides because of the loss of glycogen in their cytoplasm by the usual methods of microtechnique.

The oral ectoderm rests upon the underlying mesenchyme. The two tissues are separated by a basement membrane.

Each tooth develops from a tooth bud that forms deep beneath the surface in the area of the primitive mouth that will become the jaws. A tooth bud consists of three parts: (1) a *dental organ,* which is derived from the oral ectoderm; (2) a *dental papilla,* which is derived from the mesenchyme; and (3) a *dental sac,* which is also derived from the mesenchyme (Fig. 18). The dental organ produces the tooth enamel; the dental papilla produces the tooth pulp and the dentin; the dental sac produces not only the cementum but also the periodontal ligament.

Two or three weeks after the rupture of the buccopharyngeal membrane, when the embryo is 5 or 6 weeks old, the first sign of tooth development is seen. In

---

*First draft submitted by Isaac Schour in collaboration with Maury Massler.

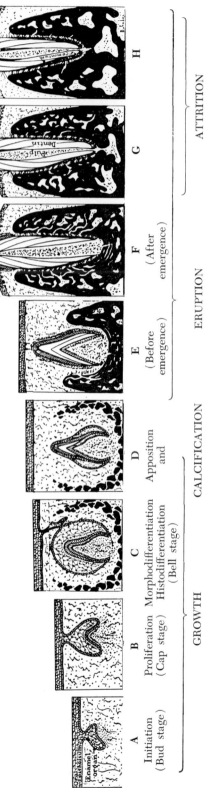

Fig. 11. Diagrammatic illustration of the life cycle of the tooth. (Modified from Schour, I., and Massler, M.: J. A. D. A. **27**: 1785, 1940.)

the oral ectoderm, which will, of course, give rise to the oral epithelium, certain areas of basal cells begin to proliferate at a more rapid rate than do cells in adjacent areas. The result is the formation of a band, an ectodermal thickening in the region of the future dental arches extending along a line that represents the margin of the jaws (Fig. 13). This band of thickened ectoderm is the *dental lamina*.

At certain points on the dental lamina, each representing the location of one of the ten mandibular and ten maxillary deciduous teeth, the ectodermal cells of the dental lamina multiply still more rapidly and form a little knob that presses slightly into the underlying mesenchyme (Figs. 12 and 14). Each of these little downgrowths on the dental lamina represents the beginning of the dental organ of the tooth bud of a deciduous tooth. Not all of these dental organs start to develop at the same time; the first to appear are in the anterior mandibular region.

As cell proliferation continues, each dental organ increases in size and changes in shape. As it develops, a dental organ takes on a shape that somewhat resembles a cap, with the outside of the cap directed toward the oral surface (Figs. 15 to 17).

Inside of the cap (i.e., inside the depression of the dental organ), the mesenchymal cells increase in number, and the tissue here appears more dense than the surrounding mesenchyme. With this cell modification, this area of mesenchyme becomes the dental papilla.

Now, surrounding the deeper side of this structure (i.e., the combined dental organ and dental papilla), the third part of the tooth bud forms. The mesenchyme in this area becomes somewhat fibrous in appearance, the fibers encircling the deep side of the papilla and the dental organ. These encircling fibers are the dental sac (Fig. 18).

During and after these developments, the shape of the dental organ continues to change. The depression in the dental organ occupied by the dental papilla deepens until the dental organ assumes a shape which has been described as resembling that of a bell. And as these developments take place, the dental lamina, which has thus far connected the dental organ to the oral epithelium, breaks up, and the tooth bud loses its connection with the epithelium of the primitive oral cavity.

DEVELOPMENTAL STAGES

Despite the obvious fact that tooth development (as the development of any other organ) is a continual process, it is not only traditional but also didactically necessary to divide the developmental history of a tooth into several "stages." They are named from the shape of the epithelial part of the tooth germ. Since the odontogenic epithelium not only produces enamel but also is indispensable for the initiation of dentin formation, the terms enamel organ and outer and inner enamel epithelium are best replaced by the terms *dental* organ and *dental* epithelium.

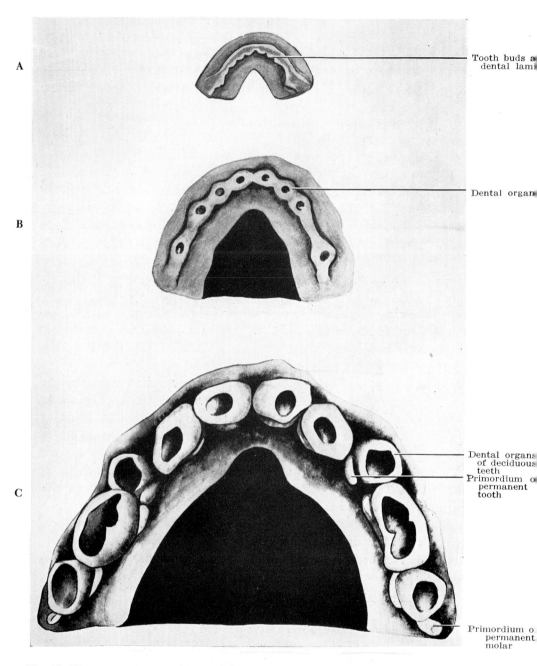

A   Tooth buds a
dental lami

B   Dental organ

C   Dental organs
of deciduous
teeth
Primordium o
permanent
tooth

Primordium o
permanent
molar

Fig. 12. Diagrammatic reconstruction of the dental lamina and dental organs of the mandible. **A,** 22 mm. embryo, bud stage (eighth week). **B,** 43 mm. embryo, cap stage (tenth week). **C,** 163 mm. embryo, bell stage (about 4 months old). The primordia of permanent teeth are seen as thickenings of the dental lamina on the lingual side of each tooth germ. Distal extension of the dental lamina with the primordium of the first molar. (Modified from Norberg, O.: Untersuchungen über das dento-gingivale Epithelleistensystem im intrauterinen Leben des Menschen [Investigations of the Dentino-Gingival Epithelium in Human Intra-Uterine Life], Stockholm, 1929, A. B. Fahlcrantz' Boktrycheri.)

Dental lamina and bud stage

Dental lamina. The first sign of human tooth development is seen during the sixth week of embryonic life (11 mm. embryo). At this stage the oral epithelium consists of a basal layer of high cells and a surface layer of flattened cells. The glycogen droplets in their cytoplasm are lost in routine preparations; this gives them an empty appearance. The epithelium is separated from the connective tissue by a basement membrane. Certain cells in the basal layer of the oral epithelium begin to proliferate at a more rapid rate than do the adjacent cells. An epithelial thickening arises in the region of the future dental arch and extends along the entire free margin of the jaws (Figs. 12 and 13). It is the primordium of the ectodermal portion of the teeth known as the dental lamina. Mitotic figures are seen not only in the epithelium but also in the subjacent mesoderm (Fig. 13).

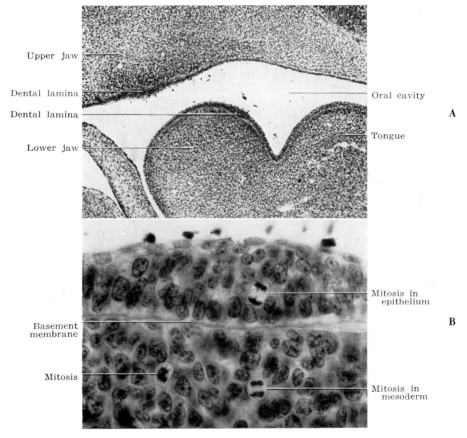

Fig. 13. Initiation of tooth development. Human embryo 13.5 mm. long, fifth week. **A,** Sagittal section through upper and lower jaws. **B,** High magnification of thickened oral epithelium. (From Orban, B.: Dental Histology and Embryology, Philadelphia, 1929, P. Blakiston's Son & Co.)

Tooth buds (primordia of teeth). Simultaneous with the differentiation of the dental lamina there arise from it in each jaw round or oval swellings at ten different points, corresponding to the future position of the deciduous teeth, the primordia of the dental organs, the tooth buds (Fig. 14). Thus the development of the tooth germs is initiated, and the cells continue to proliferate faster than

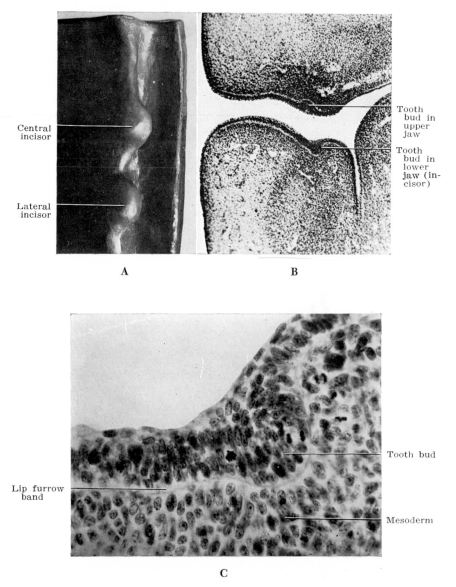

Fig. 14. Bud stage of tooth development, proliferation stage. Human embryo 16 mm. long, sixth week. **A,** Wax reconstruction of the germs of the lower central and lateral incisors. **B,** Sagittal section through upper and lower jaws. **C,** High magnification of the tooth germ of the lower incisor in bud stage. (From Orban, B.: Dental Histology and Embryology, Philadelphia, 1929, P. Blakiston's Son & Co.)

the adjacent cells. The dental lamina is shallow, and microscopic sections often show the tooth buds close to the oral epithelium.

Cap stage

As the tooth bud continues to proliferate, it does not expand uniformly into a larger sphere. Unequal growth in the different parts of the bud leads to formation of the cap stage, which is characterized by a shallow invagination on the deep surface of the bud (Figs. 12, *B*, and 15).

Outer and inner dental epithelium. The peripheral cells of the cap stage form the outer dental epithelium at the convexity, consisting of a single row of cuboidal cells, and the inner dental epithelium at the concavity, consisting of a layer of tall cells (Figs. 15 and 16).

Stellate reticulum (enamel pulp). The cells in the center of the epithelial dental organ, situated between the outer and inner epithelia, begin to separate by an

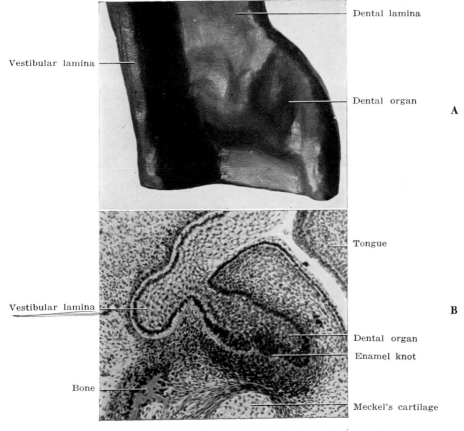

Fig. 15. Cap stage of tooth development. Human embryo 31.5 mm. long, ninth week. **A,** Wax reconstruction of the dental organ of the lower lateral incisor. **B,** Labiolingual section through the same tooth. (From Orban, B.: Dental Histology and Embryology, Philadelphia, 1929, P. Blakiston's Son & Co.)

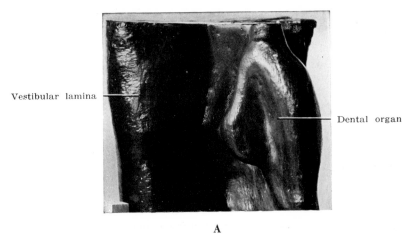

Vestibular lamina

Dental organ

A

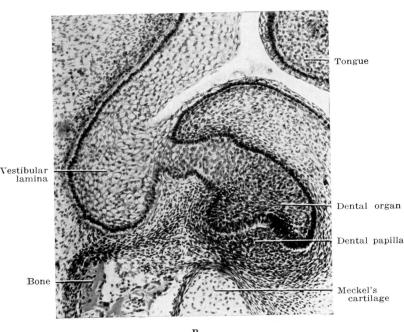

Tongue

Vestibular
lamina

Dental organ

Dental papilla

Bone

Meckel's
cartilage

B

Fig. 16. Cap stage of tooth development. Human embryo 41.5 mm. long, tenth week. **A,** Wax reconstruction of the dental organ of the lower central incisor. **B,** Labiolingual section through the same tooth. (From Orban, B.: Dental Histology and Embryology, Philadelphia, 1929, P. Blakiston's Son & Co.)

increase of the intercellular fluid and arrange themselves in a network called the stellate reticulum (Figs. 18 and 19). The cells assume a branched reticular form. The spaces in this reticular network are filled with a mucoid fluid rich in albumin, giving the stellate reticulum a cushionlike consistency that later supports and protects the delicate enamel-forming cells.

The cells in the center of the dental organ are densely packed and form the enamel knot (Fig. 15). It projects in part toward the underlying dental papilla, so that the center of the epithelial invagination shows a slightly knoblike enlargement that is bordered by the labial and lingual enamel grooves (Fig. 15). At the same time, there arises in the increasingly high dental organ a vertical extension of the enamel knot, called the enamel cord (Fig. 18). Both are temporary structures that disappear before enamel formation begins.

Dental papilla. Under the organizing influence of the proliferating epithelium of the dental organ, the mesenchyme, partially enclosed by the invaginated portion of the inner dental epithelium, proliferates; it condenses to form the dental papilla, which is the formative organ of the dentin and the primordium of the pulp (Figs. 15 and 16). The changes in the dental papilla occur concomitantly with the development of the epithelial dental organ. While the epithelium exerts a dominating influence over the adjacent connective tissue, the condensation of the latter should not be considered as a passive crowding by the proliferating epithelium. The dental papilla shows active budding of capillaries and mitotic figures, and its peripheral cells adjacent to the inner dental epithelium enlarge and later differentiate into the odontoblasts.

Dental sac. Concomitant with the development of the dental organ and the dental papilla, there is a marginal condensation in the mesenchyme surrounding the dental organ and dental papilla. In this zone, gradually a denser and more fibrous layer develops, which is the primitive dental sac.

The epithelial dental organ, the dental papilla, and the dental sac are the formative tissues for an entire tooth and its periodontal ligament.

Bell stage

As the invagination of the epithelium deepens and its margins continue to grow, the enamel organ assumes a bell shape (Figs. 12, *C*, 17, and 18).

Inner dental epithelium. The inner dental epithelium consists of a single layer of cells that differentiate prior to amelogenesis into tall columnar cells, the ameloblasts (Figs. 18 and 19). They are 4 to 5 microns in diameter and about 40 microns high. In cross section they assume a hexagonal shape, similar to that seen later in transverse sections of the enamel rods.

The cells of the inner dental epithelium exert an organizing influence upon the underlying mesenchymal cells, which differentiate into odontoblasts.

Stratum intermedium. Several layers of squamous cells, called stratum intermedium, appear between the inner dental epithelium and stellate reticulum (Fig. 19). This layer seems to be essential to enamel formation. It is absent in the part of the tooth germ that outlines the root portions of the tooth but does not form enamel.

Stellate reticulum. The stellate reticulum expands further, mainly by increase of the intercellular fluid. The cells are star-shaped with long processes that anastomose with those of adjacent cells (Fig. 19). Before enamel formation

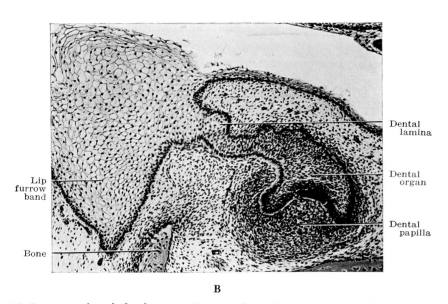

Lip furrow band

Dental organ

A

Dental lamina

Lip furrow band

Dental organ

Dental papilla

Bone

B

Fig. 17. Cap stage of tooth development. Human embryo 60 mm. long, eleventh week. **A,** Wax reconstruction of the dental organ of the lower lateral incisor. **B,** Labiolingual section through the same tooth. (From Orban, B.: Dental Histology and Embryology, Philadelphia, 1929, P. Blakiston's Son & Co.)

begins, the stellate reticulum shrinks by loss of the intercellular fluid. Its cells then are hardly distinguishable from those of the stratum intermedium. This change begins at the height of the cusp or the incisal edge and progresses cervically (Figs. 59 and 94).

Outer dental epithelium. The cells of the outer dental epithelium flatten to a low cuboidal form. At the end of the bell stage, preparatory to and during the formation of enamel, the formerly smooth surface of the outer dental epithelium is laid in folds. Between the folds, the adjacent mesenchyme of the dental sac forms papillae that contain capillary loops and thus provide a rich nutritional supply for the intense metabolic activity of the avascular enamel organ.

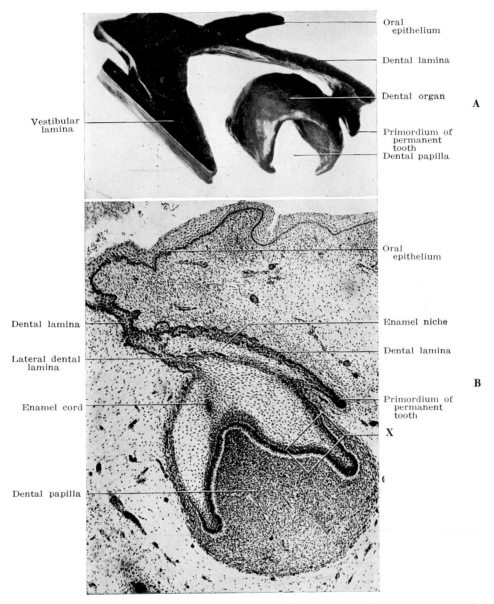

Fig. 18. Bell stage of tooth development. Human embryo 105 mm. long, fourteenth week. **A,** Wax reconstruction of lower central incisor. **B,** Labiolingual section of the same tooth. **X,** See Fig. 19. (From Orban, B.: Dental Histology and Embryology, Philadelphia, 1929, P. Blakiston's Son & Co.)

Dental lamina. In all teeth except the permanent molars, the dental lamina proliferates at its deep end to give rise to the dental organ of the permanent tooth, while it disintegrates in the region between the dental organ and the oral epithelium. The dental organ is gradually separated from the dental lamina at about the time when the first dentin is formed.

Dental papilla. The dental papilla is enclosed in the invaginated portion of the dental organ. Before the inner dental epithelium begins to produce enamel, the peripheral cells of the mesenchymal dental papilla differentiate into odontoblasts under the organizing influence of the epithelium. They assume a cuboidal and later a columnar form and acquire the specific potentiality to produce dentin.

The basement membrane separating the epithelial dental organ and dental papilla at the time just preceding dentin formation is called membrana preformativa.

Dental sac. Before formation of dental tissues begins, the dental sac shows a circular arrangement of its fibers and resembles a capsular structure. With the development of the root, the fibers of the dental sac differentiate into the periodontal fibers that become embedded in the cementum and alveolar bone.

Advanced bell stage. During the advanced bell stage, the boundary between inner dental epithelium and odontoblasts outlines the future dentinoenamel junction (Figs. 18 and 20). In addition, the junction of the inner and outer dental epithelia at the basal margin of the epithelial organ, in the region of the cervical line, will give rise to the epithelial root sheath of Hertwig.

Function of dental lamina. The functional activity of the dental lamina and its chronology may be considered in three phases. The first phase is concerned with the initiation of the entire deciduous dentition that occurs during the second month in utero (Fig. 12, *A* and *B*). The second phase deals with the initiation of the successors of the deciduous teeth. It is preceded by the growth of the free end of the dental lamina (successional lamina), lingual to the dental

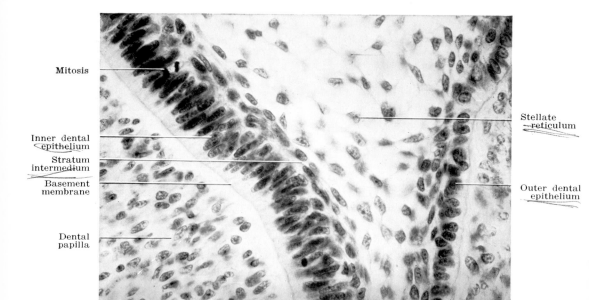

Mitosis

Inner dental epithelium
Stratum intermedium
Basement membrane

Dental papilla

Stellate reticulum

Outer dental epithelium

Fig. 19. The layers of the epithelial dental organ in high magnification. Area **X** of Fig. 18.

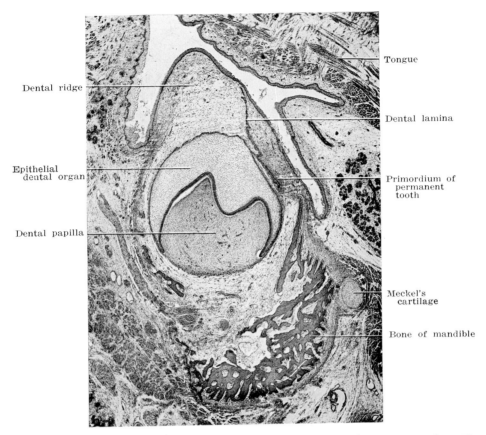

Tongue

Dental ridge

Dental lamina

Epithelial
dental organ

Primordium of
permanent
tooth

Dental papilla

Meckel's
cartilage

Bone of mandible

Fig. 20. Advanced bell stage of tooth development. Human embryo 200 mm. long, about 18 weeks. Labiolingual section through the deciduous lower first molar.

organ of each deciduous tooth, and occurs from about the fifth month in utero for the permanent central incisors to 10 months of age for the second premolar (Fig. 12, C). The third phase is preceded by the extension of the dental lamina distal to the dental organ of the second deciduous molar, which begins in the 140 mm. embryo (Fig. 12, C). The permanent molars arise directly from the distal extension of the dental lamina. The time of initiation is about 4 months of fetal life (in 160 mm. embryo) for the first permanent molar, the first year for the second permanent molar, and the fourth to fifth year for the third permanent molar.

It is thus evident that the total activity of the dental lamina extends over a period of about five years. Any particular portion of it functions for a much briefer period, since only a relatively short time elapses after initiation before the dental lamina begins to disintegrate at that particular location. However, the dental lamina may still be active in the third molar region after it has disappeared elsewhere except for occasional epithelial remnants. The distal proliferation of

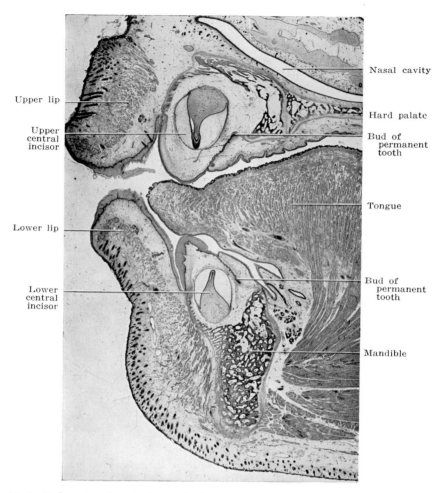

Upper lip

Upper central incisor

Lower lip

Lower central incisor

Nasal cavity

Hard palate

Bud of permanent tooth

Tongue

Bud of permanent tooth

Mandible

Fig. 21. Sagittal section through the head of a human fetus 200 mm. long, about 18 weeks of age, in the region of the central incisors.

the dental lamina is responsible for the peculiar location of the germs of the permanent molars. They develop in the ramus of the mandible and in the tuberosity of the maxilla.

Fate of the dental lamina. During the cap stage the dental lamina maintains a broad connection with the dental organ but, in the bell stage, it begins to break up by mesenchymal invasion, which first penetrates its central portion and divides it into the lateral lamina and the dental lamina proper. The mesenchymal invasion is at first incomplete and does not perforate the dental lamina (Fig. 18). The dental lamina proper proliferates only at its deeper margin, which becomes a free end situated lingually to the dental organ and forms the primordium of the permanent tooth (Fig. 18). The epithelial connection of the dental organ with the oral epithelium is severed by the proliferating mesoderm. Remnants of the dental lamina may persist as epithelial pearls.

Vestibular lamina. Labial and buccal to the dental lamina, another epithelial thickening develops independently and somewhat later. It is the vestibular lamina, also termed lip-furrow band. (Figs. 16 and 17.) It subsequently hollows out and forms the oral vestibule between the alveolar portion of the jaws and the lips and cheeks (Figs. 20 and 21).

Hertwig's epithelial root sheath and root formation

The development of the roots begins after enamel and dentin formation has reached the future cementoenamel junction. The epithelial dental organ plays an important part in root development by forming Hertwig's epithelial root sheath, which molds the shape of the roots and initiates dentin formation. Hertwig's root sheath consists only of the outer and inner dental epithelia, without a stratum intermedium and stellate reticulum.[2] The cells of the inner layer remain short and, normally, do not produce enamel. When these cells have induced the differentiation of connective tissue cells into odontoblasts and the first layer of dentin has been laid down, the epithelial root sheath loses its continuity and its close relation to the surface of the tooth. Its remnants persist as epithelial rests of Malassez in the periodontal ligament.

There is a marked difference in the development of Hertwig's epithelial root sheath in teeth with one root and those with two or more roots. Prior to the beginning of root formation, the root sheath forms the epithelial diaphragm (Fig. 22). The outer and inner dental epithelia bend at the future cementoenamel junction into a horizontal plane, narrowing the wide cervical opening of the tooth germ.[13] The plane of the diaphragm remains relatively fixed during the development and growth of the root[8] (see Chapter XI). The proliferation of the cells of the epithelial diaphragm is accompanied by proliferation of the cells of the connective tissue of the pulp, which occurs in the area adjacent to the diaphragm. The free end of the diaphragm does not grow into the connective tissue, but the epithelium proliferates coronally to the epithelial diaphragm (Fig. 22, *B*). The differentiation of odontoblasts and the formation of dentin succeed the lengthening of the root sheath. At the same time, the connective tissue of the dental sac surrounding the sheath proliferates and divides the continuous double epithelial layer (Fig. 22, *C*) into a network of epithelial strands (Fig. 22, *D*). The epithelium is moved away from the surface of the dentin so that connective tissue cells come into contact with the outer surface of the dentin and differentiate into cementoblasts, which deposit a layer of cementum onto the surface of the dentin. The rapid sequence of proliferation and destruction of Hertwig's root sheath explains the fact that it cannot be seen as a continuous layer on the surface of the developing root (Fig. 22, *D*). In the last stages of root development, the proliferation of the epithelium in the diaphragm lags behind that of the pulpal connective tissue. The wide apical foramen is reduced first to the width of the diaphragmatic opening itself and later further narrowed by apposition of dentin and cementum at the apex of the root.

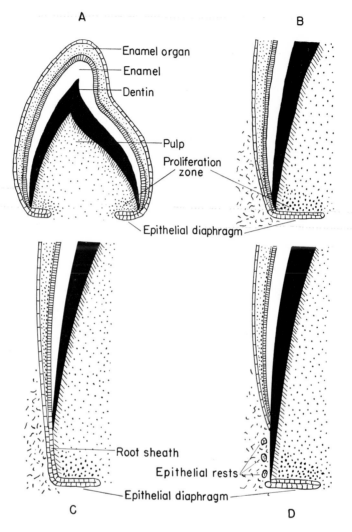

Fig. 22. Three stages in root development (diagrams). **A,** Section through a tooth germ. Note the epithelial diaphragm and proliferation zone of pulp. **B,** Higher magnification of the cervical region of **A. C,** "Imaginary" stage showing the elongation of Hertwig's epithelial sheath coronal to diaphragm. Differentiation of odontoblasts in the elongated pulp. **D,** In the area of proliferation, dentin has been formed. The root sheath is broken up into epithelial rests and is separated from the dentinal surface by connective tissue. Differentiation of cementoblasts.

Differential growth of the epithelial diaphragm in multirooted teeth causes the division of the root trunk into two or three roots.[10] During the general growth of the coronal epithelial dental organ, the expansion of its cervical opening occurs in such a way that long tonguelike extensions of the horizontal diaphragm develop (Fig. 23). Two such extensions are found in the germs of lower molars, three in the germs of upper molars. Before the division of root trunk occurs, the free ends of these horizontal epithelial flaps grow toward each other and fuse. The single cervical opening of the coronal enamel organ is then divided into two or three openings. On the pulpal surface of the dividing epithelial bridges, dentin formation starts (Fig. 24, A), and on the periphery of each opening root development follows in the same way as described for single-rooted teeth (Fig. 24, B).

If cells of the epithelial root sheath remain adherent to the dentin surface, they may differentiate into fully functioning ameloblasts and produce enamel. Such droplets of enamel, called enamel pearls, are sometimes found in the area of furcation of the roots of permanent molars. If the continuity of Hertwig's root sheath is broken or is not established prior to dentin formation, a defect in the dentinal wall of the pulp ensues. Such defects are found in the pulpal floor corresponding to the furcation if the fusion of the horizontal extensions of the diaphragm remains incomplete, or on any point of the root itself. This accounts for the development of accessory root canals opening on the periodontal surface of the root (see Chapter V).

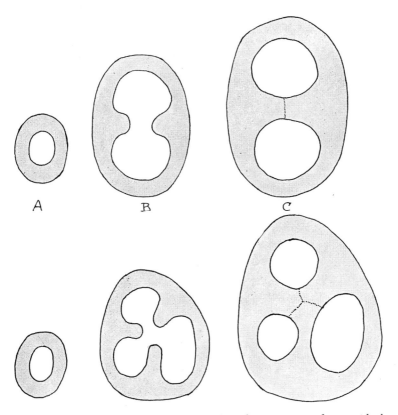

Fig. 23. Three stages in the development of a tooth with two roots and one with three roots. Surface view of the epithelial diaphragm. During growth of the tooth germ, the simple diaphragm, **A,** expands eccentrically so that horizontal epithelial flaps are formed, **B.** Later these flaps proliferate and unite (dotted lines in **C**) and divide the single cervical opening into two or three openings.

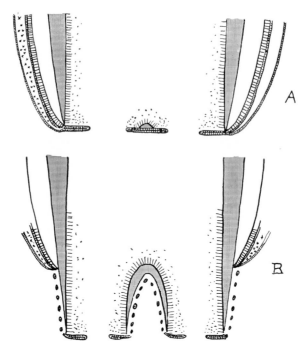

Fig. 24. Two stages in the development of a two-rooted tooth. Diagrammatic mesiodistal sections of a lower molar. **A,** Beginning of dentin formation at the bifurcation. **B,** Formation of the two roots in progress. (Details as in Fig. 22.)

HISTOPHYSIOLOGY AND CLINICAL CONSIDERATIONS

A number of physiologic growth processes participate in the progressive development of the teeth (Table 1). Except for initiation, which is a momentary event, these processes overlap considerably, and many are continuous over several histologic stages. Nevertheless, each tends to predominate in one stage more than in another.

For example, the process of histodifferentiation characterizes the bell stage in which the cells of the inner dental epithelium differentiate into functional ameloblasts. However, proliferation still progresses at the deeper portion of the dental organ.

Initiation. The dental lamina and tooth buds represent that part of the oral epithelium which has potencies for tooth formation. Specific cells contain the entire growth potential of certain teeth and respond to those factors which initiate tooth development. Different teeth are initiated at definite times. Initiation is set off by unknown factors just as the growth potential of the ovum is set off by the fertilizing spermatozoon.

Teeth may develop in abnormal locations, for instance, in the ovary (dermoid tumors or cysts) or in the hypophysis. In such instances, the tooth undergoes similar stages of development as in the jaws.

Table 1. Stages in tooth growth

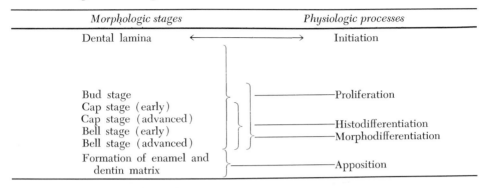

Morphologic stages	Physiologic processes
Dental lamina ← →	Initiation
Bud stage	Proliferation
Cap stage (early)	
Cap stage (advanced)	Histodifferentiation
Bell stage (early)	Morphodifferentiation
Bell stage (advanced)	
Formation of enamel and dentin matrix	Apposition

A lack of initiation results in the absence of teeth. This may involve single teeth, most frequently the permanent upper lateral incisors, third molars, and lower second premolars; or there may be a complete lack of teeth, anodontia. On the other hand, abnormal initiation may result in the development of single or multiple supernumerary teeth.

Proliferation. Marked proliferative activity ensues at the points of initiation and results successively in the bud, cap, and bell stages of the odontogenic organ. Proliferative growth causes regular changes in the size and proportions of the growing tooth germ (Figs. 13 and 17).

During the stage of proliferation, the tooth germ has the potentiality to progress to more advanced development. This is illustrated by the fact that explants of these early stages continue to develop in tissue culture through the subsequent stages of histodifferentiation and appositional growth. A disturbance or experimental interference has entirely different effects, according to the time of occurrence and the stage of development that it affects.

Histodifferentiation. Histodifferentiation succeeds the proliferative stage. The formative cells of the tooth germs developing during the proliferative stage undergo definite morphologic as well as functional changes and acquire their functional assignment (the appositional growth potential). The cells become restricted in their potencies; they give up their capacity to multiply as they assume their new function (a law that governs all differentiating cells). This phase reaches its highest development in the bell stage of the dental organ, just preceding the beginning of formation and apposition of dentin and enamel (Fig. 18).

The organizing influence of the inner dental epithelium on the mesenchyme is evident in the bell stage and causes the differentiation of the adjacent cells of the dental papilla into odontoblasts. With the formation of dentin, the cells of the inner dental epithelium differentiate into ameloblasts, and enamel matrix is formed opposite the dentin. Enamel does not form in the absence of dentin as demonstrated by the failure of transplanted ameloblasts to form enamel when no dentin is present.[3] Dentin formation therefore precedes and is essential to enamel formation. The differentiation of the epithelial cells precedes and is essential to the differentiation of the odontoblasts and the initiation of dentin formation.

In vitamin A deficiency the ameloblasts fail to differentiate properly. In consequence, their organizing influence upon the adjacent mesenchymal cells is disturbed, and atypical dentin, known as osteodentin, is formed.

Morphodifferentiation. The morphologic pattern or basic form and relative size of the future tooth is established by morphodifferentiation, i.e., by differential growth. Morphodifferentiation, therefore, is impossible without proliferation. The advanced bell stage marks not only active histodifferentiation but also an important stage of morphodifferentiation of the crown, by outlining the future dentinoenamel junction (Figs. 18 and 20).

The dentinoenamel and dentinocemental junctions, which are different and characteristic for each type of tooth, act as a blueprint pattern. In conformity with this pattern, the ameloblasts, odontoblasts, and cementoblasts deposit enamel, dentin, and cementum, and thus give the completed tooth its characteristic form and size. For example, the size and form of the cuspal portion of the crown of the first permanent molar are established at birth, prior to formation of hard tissues.

The frequent statement in the literature that endocrine disturbances affect the size or form of the crown of teeth is not tenable unless such effects occur during morphodifferentiation, i.e., in utero or in the first year of life. Size and shape of the root, however, may be altered by disturbances in later periods. Clinical examination shows that the retarded eruption that occurs in hypopituitary and hypothyroid cases results in a small clinical crown that is often mistaken for a small anatomic crown.

Disturbances in morphodifferentiation may affect the form and size of the tooth without impairing the function of the ameloblasts or odontoblasts. New parts may be differentiated (supernumerary cusps or roots), twinning may result, a suppression of parts may occur (loss of cusps or roots), or the result may be a peg or malformed tooth (e.g., Hutchinson's incisor) with enamel and dentin that may be normal in structure.[11]

Apposition is the deposition of the matrix of the hard dental structures; it will be described in separate chapters on the formation of enamel, dentin, and cementum. This chapter deals with certain aspects of apposition, in order to complete the discussion of the physiologic processes concerned in the growth of teeth.

Apposition. Appositional growth of enamel and dentin is a layerlike deposition of an extracellular matrix. This type of growth is, therefore, additive. It is the fulfillment of the plans outlined at the stages of histo- and morphodifferentiation. Appositional growth is characterized by regular and rhythmic deposition of the extracellular material, which is of itself incapable of further growth. Periods of activity and rest alternate at definite intervals.

The matrix is deposited by the cells along the site outlined by the formative cells at the end of morphodifferentiation, determining the future dentinoenamel and dentinocemental junctions, and according to a definite pattern of cellular activity that is common to all types and forms of teeth.

References

1. Brunn, A. v.: Ueber die Ausdehnung des Schmelzorganes und seine Bedeutung für die Zahnbildung (Concerning the Extent of the Enamel Organ and Its Significance in Tooth Development), Arch. f. mikr. Anat. **29:** 367, 1887.
2. Diamond, M., and Applebaum, E.: The Epithelial Sheath, J. D. Res. **21:** 403, 1942.
3. Hahn, W. E.: The Capacity of Developing Tooth Germ Elements for Self-Differentiation When Transplanted, J. D. Res. **20:** 5, 1941.
4. Johnson, P. L., and Bevelander, G.: The Role of the Stratum Intermedium in Tooth Development, Oral Surg., Oral Med., & Oral Path. **10:** 437, 1957.
5. Manley, E. B.: Adamantinoma in Relation to Tooth Development, Australian J. Dent. **58:** 137, 1954.
6. Marsland, E. A.: Histological Investigation of Amelogenesis in Rats, Brit. D. J. **91:** 251, 1951; **92:** 109, 1952.
7. Norberg, O.: Untersuchungen über das dento-gingivale Epithelleistensystem im intrauterinen Leben des Menschen (Investigations of the Dentino-Gingival Epithelium in Human Intra-Uterine Life), Stockholm, 1929, A. B. Fahlcrantz' Boktryckeri.
8. Orban, B.: Growth and Movement of the Tooth Germs and Teeth, J. A. D. A. **15:** 1004, 1928.
9. Orban, B.: Dental Histology and Embryology, Philadelphia, 1929, P. Blakiston's Son & Co.
10. Orban, B., and Mueller, E.: The Development of the Bifurcation of Multirooted Teeth, J. A. D. A. **16:** 297, 1929.
11. Sarnat, B. C., Schour, I., and Heupel, R.: Roentgenographic Diagnosis of Congenital Syphilis in Unerupted Permanent Teeth, J. A. M. A. **116:** 2745, 1941.
12. Schour, I., and Massler, M.: Studies in Tooth Development: The Growth Pattern of Human Teeth, J. A. D. A. **27:** 1785, 1918, 1940.
13. Sicher, H.: Tooth Eruption: Axial Movement of Teeth With Limited Growth, J. D. Res. **21:** 395, 1942.

Chapter III • ENAMEL*

HISTOLOGY

Physical characteristics

Enamel forms a protective covering of variable thickness over the entire surface of the crown. On the cusps of human molars and premolars, the enamel attains a maximum thickness of about 2 to 2.5 mm., thinning down to almost a knife edge at the neck of the tooth. The shape and contour of the cusps receive their final modeling in the enamel.

Due to its high content of mineral salts and their crystalline arrangement, enamel is the hardest calcified tissue in the human body. The specific function of the enamel is to form a resistant covering of the teeth, rendering them suitable for mastication.

The enamel varies in hardness from apatite, which is fifth in the scale of Mohs,† to topaz, which is eighth. The specific structure and hardness of the enamel render it brittle, which is particularly apparent when the enamel loses its foundation of sound dentin. The specific density of enamel is 2.8.

Another physical property of enamel is its permeability. It has been found

---

* First draft submitted by Charles F. Bodecker; revised by Reidar F. Sognnaes and by David B. Scott and Marie U. Nylen.

†In this scale hardness is compared to that of 10 different minerals: (1) talc, (2) gypsum, (3) calcite, (4) fluorite, (5) apatite, (6) orthoclase (feldspar), (7) quartz, (8) topaz, (9) sapphire (corundum), and (10) diamond.

with radioactive tracers that the enamel can act in a sense like a semipermeable membrane, permitting complete or partial passage of certain molecules—C^{14} (urea), I^{131}, etc.[2, 73, 81] The same phenomenon has also been demonstrated by means of dyestuffs.[34, 38]

The color of the enamel-covered crown ranges from yellowish white to grayish white. It has been suggested that the color is determined by differences in the translucency of enamel, yellowish teeth having a thin, translucent enamel through which the yellow color of the dentin is visible and grayish teeth having a more opaque enamel (Fig. 25).[11] The translucency may be due to variations in the degree of calcification and homogeneity of the enamel. Grayish teeth frequently show a slightly yellowish color at the cervical areas, presumably because the thinness of the enamel permits the light to strike the underlying yellow dentin and be reflected. Incisal areas may have a bluish tinge where the thin edge consists only of a double layer of enamel.

Chemical properties

The enamel consists mainly of inorganic material (96 per cent) and only a small amount of organic substance and water (4 per cent). The inorganic

Table 2. Chemical contents of enamel, dentin, cementum, and bone*

	Enamel	*Dentin*	*Cementum* *Compact bone*
Water	2.3%	13.2%	32%
Organic matter	1.7	17.5	22
Ash	96.0	69.3	46
In 100 Gm. of ash:			
Calcium	36.1 Gm.	35.3 Gm.	35.5 Gm.
Phosphorus	17.3	17.1	17.1
Carbon dioxide	3.0	4.0	4.4
Magnesium	0.5	1.2	0.9
Sodium	0.2	0.2	1.1
Potassium	0.3	0.07	0.1
Chloride	0.3	0.03	0.1
Fluorine	0.016	0.017	0.015
Sulfur	0.1	0.2	0.6
Copper	0.01		
Silicon	0.003		0.04
Iron	0.0025		0.09
Zinc	0.016	0.018	
	Whole teeth		Bone
Lead	0.0071 to 0.037		0.002 to 0.02
Small amounts of:	Ce, La, Pr, Ne, Ag, Sr, Ba, Cr, Sn, Mn, Ti, Ni, V, Al, B, Cu, Li, Se,		

*The editor is indebted to Dr. Harold C. Hodge, University of Rochester, School of Medicine and Dentistry, Rochester, N. Y., for compiling this table.

The chemical constituents of ash are here given as elements, whereas they are in reality present in different compounds, e.g., phosphorus and phosphate. The neglect of these other elements, e.g., oxygen, hydrogen, nitrogen, accounts for the difference between 100 and the actual grams.

material of the enamel is similar to apatite.[51, 76, 77] Table 2 shows the most reliable data on the chemical contents of enamel. Some values for dentin and compact bone are added for comparison.

The figures shown in the table represent *dry weights*. The relative *volume* of the organic framework and the entire enamel are almost equal. Fig. 26 illustrates this by comparing a stone and a sponge of approximately *equal volume*. The stone represents the mineral content, and the sponge represents the organic

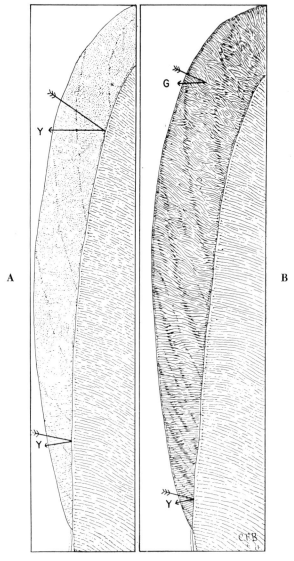

Fig. 25. Influence of thickness and calcification of enamel upon the color of the tooth. **A,** Thin, well-calcified translucent enamel giving the tooth a yellowish appearance, **Y. B,** Thick, less calcified opaque enamel giving the tooth a grayish appearance, **G.** In the cervical area, enamel thin, color yellow, **Y.** (From Bodecker, C. F.: Internat. J. Orthodontia **19:** 386, 1933.)

Fig. 26. A sponge, **A**, and a stone, **B**, are comparable to the organic and mineral elements of enamel. Their volumes are approximately equal, but their weights differ greatly. (From Bodecker, C. F.: D. Rev. **20**: 317, 1906.)

framework of the enamel. Although their volume is almost equal, their weights are vastly different. The stone is more than one hundred times heavier than the sponge, or, expressed in percentage, the weight of the sponge is less than 1 per cent of that of the stone.

The nature of the organic elements of enamel is incompletely understood. In development and histologic staining reactions, the enamel matrix resembles keratinizing epidermis. More specific methods have revealed sulfhydryl groups and other reactions suggestive of keratin. Similarly, hydrolysates of mature enamel matrix have shown a ratio of amino acids (histidine 1 : lysine 3 : arginine 10) suggestive of a keratin.[9, 75] In addition, histochemical reactions have suggested that the enamel-forming cells of developing teeth also contain a carbohydrate protein,[17] and that an acid mucopolysaccharide enters the enamel itself at the time when calcification becomes a prominent feature.[83] Tracer studies have indicated that the enamel of erupted teeth of rhesus monkeys can transmit and exchange radioactive isotopes originating from the saliva and the pulp.[73] Considerable investigation is still required to determine the normal physiologic characteristics and the age changes that occur in the enamel.

Structure

Rods. The enamel is composed of enamel rods or prisms, rod sheaths, and a cementing interprismatic substance. The number of enamel rods has been estimated[15] as ranging between 5 million in the lower lateral incisors and 12 million in the upper first molars. From the dentinoenamel junction the rods run outward to the surface of the tooth. The length of most rods is greater than the thickness of the enamel because of the oblique direction and the wavy course of the rods. The rods located in the cusps, the thickest part of the enamel, are longer than those at the cervical areas of the teeth. It is stated generally that the diameter of the rods averages 4 microns, but this measurement necessarily varies, since the outer surface of the enamel is greater than the dentinal surface where the rods originate. It is claimed[15, 48] that the diameter of the rods increases from the dentinoenamel junction toward the surface of the enamel at a ratio of about 1:2.

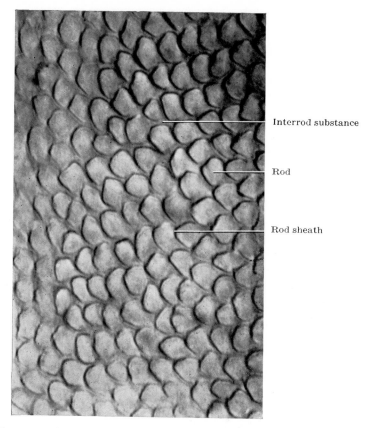

Interrod substance

Rod

Rod sheath

Fig. 27. Decalcified section of enamel of a human tooth germ. Rods cut transversely appear like fish scales.

The enamel rods were first described by Retzius[52] in 1837. They are tall columns or prisms passing through the entire thickness of the enamel. Normally they have a clear crystalline appearance, permitting the light to pass through them. In cross section the enamel rods occasionally appear hexagonal; sometimes they appear round or oval. Many rods resemble fish scales in cross sections of human enamel (Fig. 27).

Submicroscopic structure. The structural elements which make up the enamel rods are so small that they cannot be observed directly under the light microscope. With the advent of the electron microscope, which has now been applied to tooth structure for some fifteen years, new information about both the organic matrix and the crystalline component of the enamel has been gained. The examination of sections of decalcified mature enamel has revealed the presence of a network of fine organic fibrils throughout the rods.[19, 63] (Fig. 28.) There is some evidence that the apatite crystals may not only be laid down within the openings in this fibrillar mesh but that they may also form around the fibrils themselves.[20]

Under the electron microscope, the apatite crystals appear flat and ribbonlike, and they are arranged with their long axes in the main roughly paralleling the long axis of the rod (Fig. 29).[21, 66] This direct observation of parallelism among the crystals corroborates similar conclusions drawn earlier from birefringence studies made with polarized light[14] and from orientation studies made by means of roentgen ray diffraction.[76] The parallel arrangement within rods is far from perfect, and groups of crystals may diverge as much as 40 degrees from the axial plane of the rod.[29, 40] (Fig. 30.) The dimensions of the basic enamel crystals are not yet well defined, and reported lengths have varied between 0.05 and 1 micron.[21, 22]

Rod sheaths. A thin peripheral layer of each rod shows a different refractory

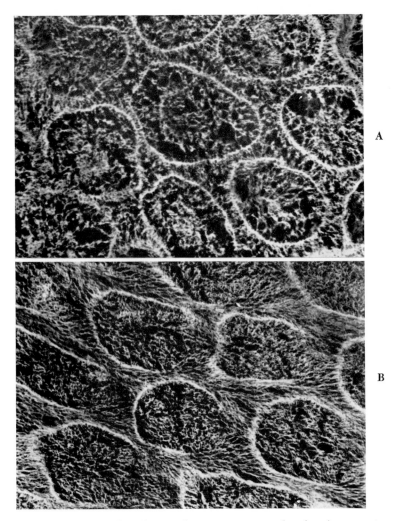

Fig. 28. Oval, **A,** and scale-shaped, **B,** rod contours seen under the electron microscope in cross sections of demineralized mature human enamel. (×5,000.) (From Scott, D. B.: Internat. D. J. **4:** 1953.)

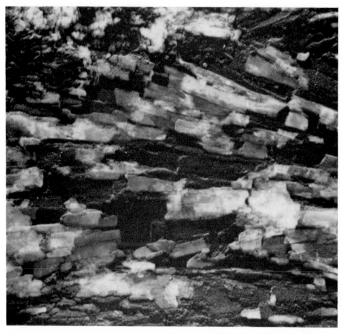

Fig. 29. Hydroxyapatite crystals within a single longitudinally sectioned enamel rod. In this type of electron microscopic preparation, which is a replica, or reproduction, of the surface of a ground section, small groups of individual crystals are removed from the enamel for observation. (×57,000.) (From Scott, D. B.: The Crystalline Component of Dental Enamel, Fourth International Conference on Electron Microscopy, Berlin, 1960, Springer-Verlag.)

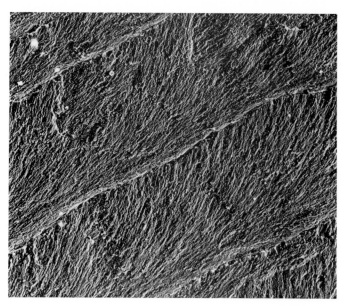

Fig. 30. An electron micrograph illustrating the orientation of crystals at an angle to the long axes of the enamel rods. Note also the minimal interprismatic substance in this particular region. (×8,000.)

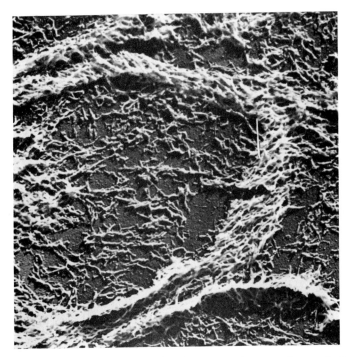

Fig. 31. The fibrillar character of the rod sheath, as seen electron microscopically in the sectioned matrix of demineralized human enamel. (×15,000.) (From Scott, D. B., Ussing, M. J., Sognnaes, R. F., and Wyckoff, R. W. G.: J. D. Res. 31: 74, 1952.)

index, stains darker than the rod, and is relatively acid-resistant. It may be concluded that it is less calcified and contains more organic substance than the rod itself. This layer is interpreted by some as a rod sheath (Figs. 27 and 31).[10, 72] Recent investigations with the electron microscope have shown that this structure is often incomplete.[64]

Striations. Each enamel rod is built up of segments separated by dark lines that give it a striated appearance (Fig. 32). These transverse striations demarcate rod segments and become more visible by the action of mild acids. The striations are more marked in enamel that is insufficiently calcified. The rods are segmented because the enamel matrix is formed in a rhythmic manner. In man these segments seem to be of uniform length of about 4 microns.[59]

Interprismatic substance. Enamel rods are not in direct contact with each other but are cemented together by the interprismatic substance, which has a slightly higher refractive index than the rods.[69] Discussion is still active concerning the structure of the interprismatic substance. (Fig. 33.) It appears to be at a minimum in the enamel of human teeth; in some animals, such as the dog or pig, however, the enamel contains a considerable amount of interprismatic substance.

Under the electron microscope, the structures observed in this region have

Fig. 32. Ground section through enamel. Rods cut longitudinally. Cross striation of rods.

appeared identical to those within the rods in every respect except their spatial orientation.[63, 65] Between adjacent rods both the organic matrix fibrils and the apatite crystals are arranged at sharply oblique angles to the long axes of the rods (Fig. 34). Whether or not there is a lower proportion of mineral in the interprismatic region, as usually stated, still remains to be settled.

Direction of rods. Generally the rods are oriented at right angles to the dentin surface. In the cervical and central parts of the crown of a deciduous tooth they are approximately horizontal (Fig. 35, A); near the incisal edge or tip of the cusps they change gradually to an increasingly oblique direction, until they are

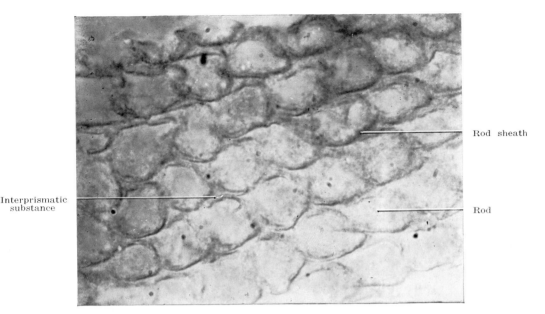

Fig. 33. Decalcified section of enamel. Rods, rod sheaths, and interprismatic substance are well differentiated. Photographed with ultraviolet light. (From Bodecker, C. F.: D. Rev. **20**: 317, 1906.)

almost vertical in the region of the edge or tip of the cusps. The arrangement of the rods in permanent teeth is similar in the occlusal two-thirds of the crown. In the cervical region, however, the rods deviate from the horizontal in an apical direction. (Fig. 35, *B*.)

The rods are rarely, if ever, straight throughout; they follow a wavy course from the dentin to the enamel surface. The most significant deviations from a straight radial course can be described as follows: If the middle part of the crown is divided into thin horizontal discs, the rods in the adjacent discs bend in opposite directions. For instance, in one disc the rods start from the dentin in an oblique direction and bend more or less sharply to the left side (Fig. 36, *A*). In the outer third of the enamel they change often to an almost straight radial course. In the adjacent disc the rods bend toward the right (Fig. 36, *B*). This alternating clockwise and counterclockwise deviation of the rods from the radial direction can be observed at all levels of the crown if the discs are cut in the planes of the general rod direction (Fig. 35).

If the discs are cut in an oblique plane, especially near the dentin in the region of the cusps or incisal edges, the rod arrangement appears to be further complicated—the bundles of rods seem to intertwine more irregularly; this optical appearance of enamel is called gnarled enamel.

The enamel rods forming the developmental fissures and pits, as on the occlusal surface of molars and premolars, converge in their outward course.

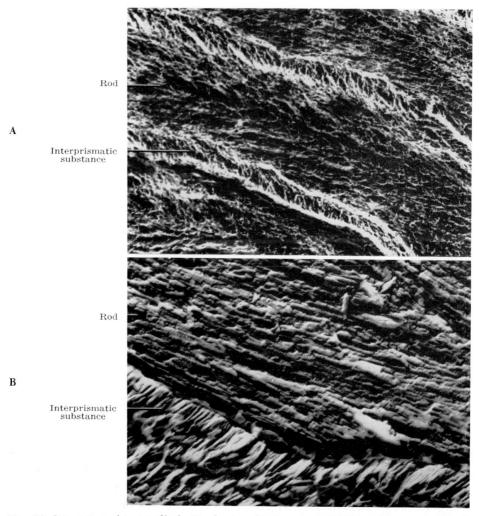

Fig. 34. Orientation of matrix fibrils (**A,** demineralized section, ×7,000) and inorganic crystals (**B,** undemineralized ground section, ×20,000) of the interprismatic substance at a sharp angle to the longitudinal rod axis. (Courtesy Dr. D. B. Scott.)

Hunter-Schreger bands. The more or less regular change in the direction of rods may be regarded as a functional adaptation, minimizing the risk of cleavage in the axial direction under the influence of occlusal masticatory stresses. The change in the direction of rods is responsible for the appearance of the Hunter-Schreger bands. These are alternating dark and light strips of varying widths (Figs. 37 and 38) that can best be seen in a longitudinal ground section under oblique reflected light. They originate at the dentinoenamel border and pass outward, ending at some distance from the outer enamel surface. Some investigators claim that there are variations in calcification of the enamel which coincide with the distribution of the bands of Hunter-Schreger. Careful decalcification and staining of the enamel have provided further evidence that these structures may

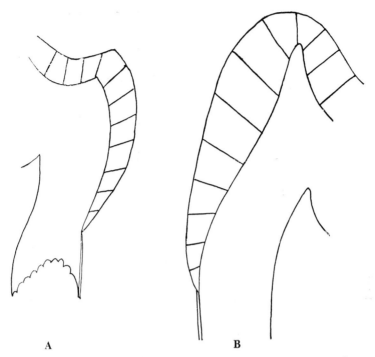

Fig. 35. Diagrams indicating the general direction of enamel rods. **A,** Deciduous tooth. **B,** Permanent tooth.

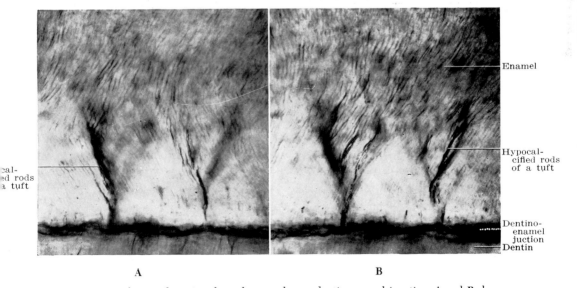

Fig. 36. Horizontal ground section through enamel near dentinoenamel junction. **A** and **B** show change in the direction of rods in two adjacent layers of enamel, made visible by a change in the focus of the microscope.

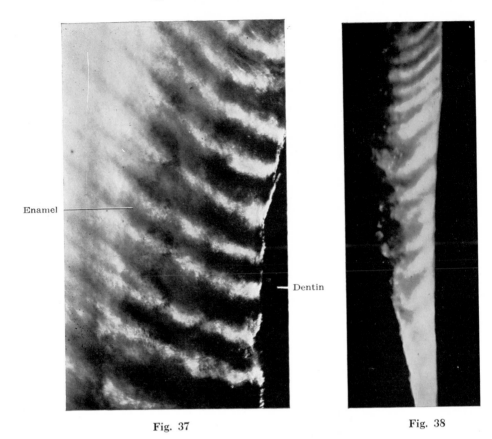

Fig. 37

Fig. 38

Fig. 37. Longitudinal ground section through enamel photographed by reflected light. Hunter-Schreger bands.

Fig. 38. Decalcified enamel, photographed by reflected light, showing Hunter-Schreger bands.

not be the result solely of an optical phenomenon, but that they are composed of alternate zones having a slightly different permeability and a different content of organic material.[33, 72, 83]

Incremental lines of Retzius. The incremental lines of Retzius appear as brownish bands in ground sections of the enamel. They illustrate the incremental pattern of the enamel, i.e., the successive apposition of layers of enamel matrix during formation of the crown. In longitudinal sections they surround the tip of the dentin. (Fig. 39, *A.*) In the cervical parts of the crown they run obliquely; from the dentinoenamel junction to the surface they deviate occlusally. (Fig. 39, *B.*) In transverse sections of a tooth the incremental lines of Retzius appear as concentric circles. (Fig. 40.) They may be compared to the growth rings in the cross section of a tree. The term "incremental lines" designates these structures appropriately, for they do, in fact, reflect variations in structure and mineralization that occur during growth of the enamel. The exact nature of these developmental changes is not known. The incremental lines have been attributed

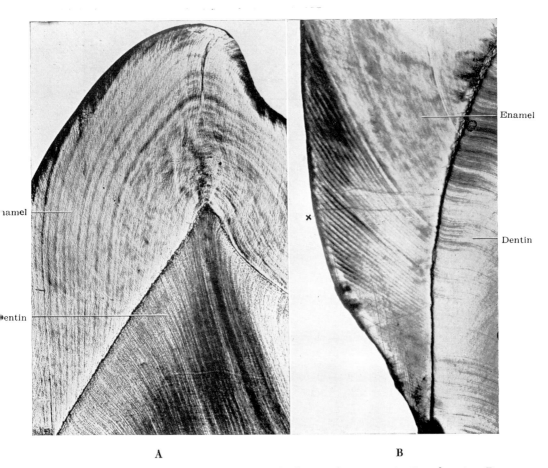

ıamel

ьentin

Enamel

Dentin

×

A   B

Fig. 39. Incremental lines of Retzius in longitudinal ground sections. **A,** Cuspal region. **B,** Cervical region (**X**).

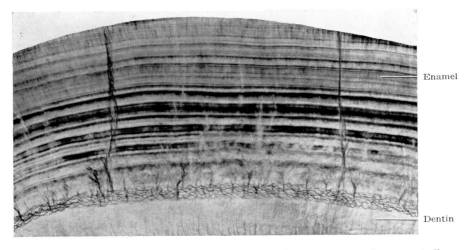

Enamel

Dentin

Fig. 40. Incremental lines of Retzius in transverse ground section, arranged concentrically.

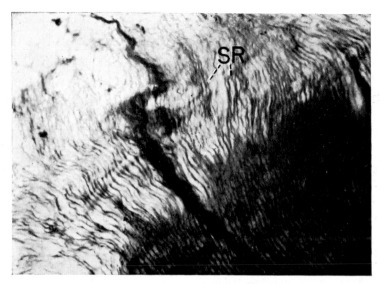

Fig. 41. Carefully decalcified section through enamel. Thickening of the interrod substance (SR) in Retzius lines. (From Bodecker, C. F.: D. Rev. **20:** 317, 1906.)

to periodic bending of the enamel rods,[27, 28, 52, 57] to variations in the basic organic structure (Fig. 41),[4, 34, 70] or to a physiologic calcification rhythm.[59]

Surface structures. The principal microscopic details that have been observed on outer enamel surfaces of newly erupted teeth are perikymata, rod ends, and cracks, lamellae.[60-62, 85]

Perikymata are transverse, wavelike grooves, thought to be the external manifestations of the striae of Retzius. They are continuous around a tooth and usually lie parallel to each other and to the cementoenamel junction. (Figs. 42 and 43.) Ordinarily there are about 30 perikymata per millimeter in the region of the cementoenamel junction, and their concentration gradually decreases to about 10 per millimeter near the occlusal or incisal edge of a surface. Their course usually is quite regular, but in the cervical region it may be quite irregular.

The enamel rod ends are concave and vary in depth and shape. They are shallowest in the cervical regions of surfaces and deepest near the incisal or occlusal edges.

The term "cracks" originally was used to describe the narrow, fissurelike structures that are seen on almost all surfaces (Fig. 44). It has since been demonstrated that they are actually the outer edges of lamellae (see section on Enamel Lamellae).[62] They extend for varying distances along the surface, at right angles to the cementoenamel junction, from which they originate. Most of them are less than a millimeter in length, but some are longer, and a few reach the occlusal or incisal edge of a surface. They are fairly evenly spaced, but long lamellae appear wider than short ones.

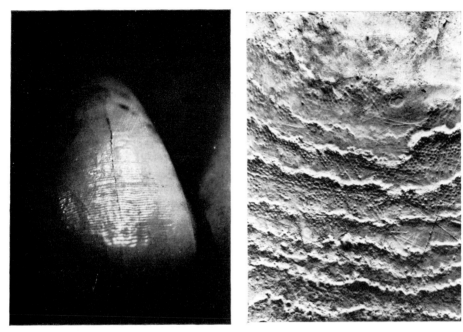

Fig. 42   Fig. 43

Fig. 42. Perikymata on a lateral incisor.

Fig. 43. Shadowed replica of the surface of intact enamel (buccal surface of upper left second molar showing the perikymata). (×1,500.) (From Scott, D. B., and Wyckoff, R. W. G.: Pub. Health Rep. **61**: 1397, 1946.)

The incremental lines of Retzius, if present in moderate intensity, are considered normal. However, the rhythmic alternation of periods of enamel matrix formation and of rest can be upset by metabolic disturbances, causing the rest periods to be unduly prolonged and close together. Such an abnormal condition is responsible for the broadening of the incremental lines of Retzius, rendering them more prominent. At the incremental lines of Retzius the interprismatic substance seems to be thickened at the expense of the rods (Fig. 41).

The enamel of the deciduous teeth develops partly before and partly after birth. The boundary between the two portions of enamel in the deciduous teeth is marked by an accentuated incremental line of Retzius, the neonatal line or neonatal ring.[58] It appears to be the result of the abrupt change in the environment and nutrition of the newborn. The prenatal enamel usually is better developed than the postnatal. (Fig. 45.) This is explained by the fact that the fetus develops in a well-protected environment with an adequate supply of all the essential materials, even at the expense of the mother. Because of the undisturbed and even development of the enamel prior to birth, perikymata are absent in the occlusal parts of the deciduous teeth, whereas they are present in the postnatal

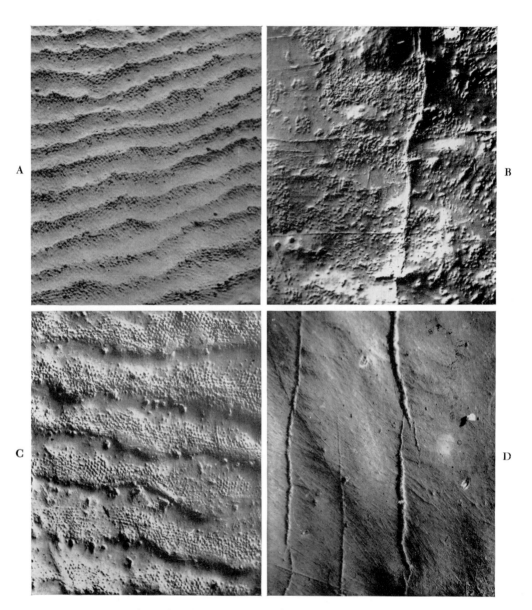

Fig. 44. Progressive loss of surface structure with advancing age. **A,** Surface of a recently erupted tooth, showing pronounced enamel prism ends and perikymata. Patient 12 years of age. **B,** Early stage of structural loss which occurs during the first few years (wear is more rapid on anterior teeth than on posterior ones and more rapid on facial or lingual surfaces than on proximal surfaces). Note small regions where prism ends are worn away. Patient 25 years of age. **C,** Later stage. Here the elevated parts between perikymata are worn smooth, while the structural detail in the depths of the grooves is still more or less intact. Eventually wearing proceeds to the point where all prism ends and perikymata disappear. Patient 52 years of age. [N. B. Since these are negative replicas, surface details appear inverted. Raised structures represent depressions in the actual surface.] **D,** Surface worn completely smooth, showing only "cracks," which actually represent the outer edges of lamellae. Patient 50 years of age. (All magnifications ×105.) (From Scott, D. B., and Wyckoff, R. W. G.: J. A. D. A. **39:** 275, 1949.)

cervical parts. The diagram in Fig. 46 shows the amount of enamel matrix formed during prenatal and postnatal periods.

Enamel cuticle. A delicate membrane, called Nasmyth's membrane[37] after its first investigator, covers the entire crown of the newly erupted tooth. When the ameloblasts have produced the enamel rods, they produce a thin, continuous layer, now termed the primary enamel cuticle, which covers the entire surface of the enamel. Because this cuticle is more resistant to acid than the enamel it-self, it can be floated off. It is worn off early from all exposed surfaces. Examination of the primary enamel cuticle of unerupted teeth under the electron micro-

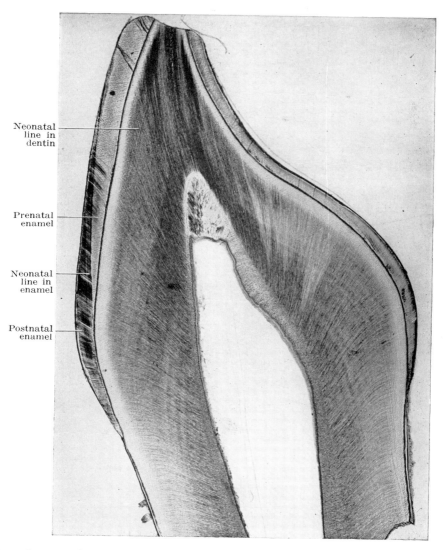

Neonatal line in dentin

Prenatal enamel

Neonatal line in enamel

Postnatal enamel

Fig. 45. Neonatal line in the enamel. Longitudinal ground section of a deciduous canine. (From Schour, I.: J. A. D. A. **23:** 1946, 1936.)

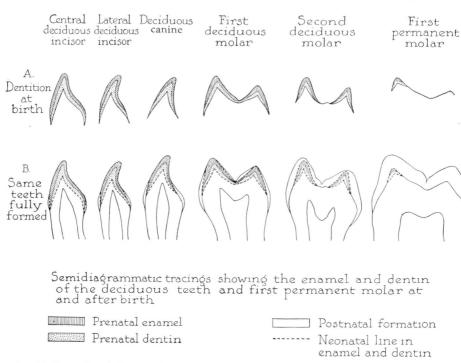

| Central deciduous incisor | Lateral deciduous incisor | Deciduous canine | First deciduous molar | Second deciduous molar | First permanent molar |

A. Dentition at birth

B. Same teeth fully formed

Semidiagrammatic tracings showing the enamel and dentin of the deciduous teeth and first permanent molar at and after birth

▓ Prenatal enamel

▒ Prenatal dentin

☐ Postnatal formation

------- Neonatal line in enamel and dentin

Fig. 46. Enamel and dentin of deciduous teeth and first permanent molar at and after birth. (From Schour, I.: J. A. D. A. **23**: 1946, 1936.)

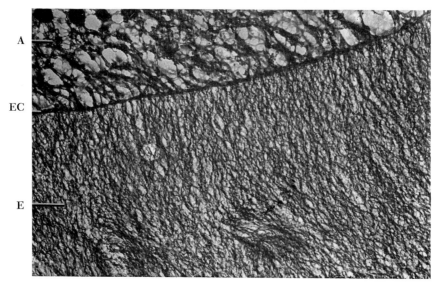

A

EC

E

Fig. 47. Section from an unerupted mouse molar, showing enamel matrix, **E**, enamel cuticle, **EC**, and ameloblasts, **A**. The enamel cuticle is intimately connected with both the enamel matrix and the ameloblasts. (×9,400.) (From Ussing, Marie J.: Acta odont. scandinav. **13**: 123, 1955; reprinted J. West. Soc. Periodont. **3**: 71, 1955.)

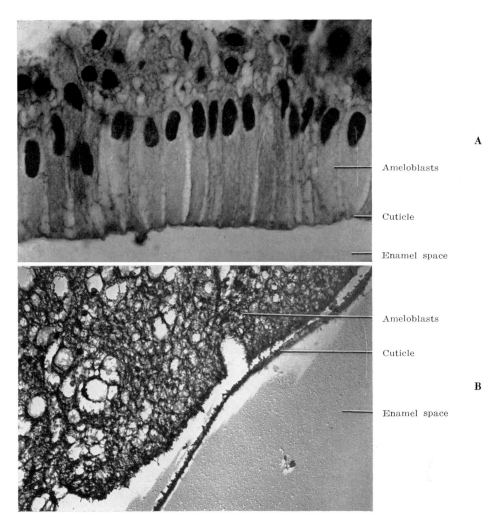

A

Ameloblasts

Cuticle

Enamel space

Ameloblasts

Cuticle

B

Enamel space

Fig. 48. A, Paraffin section through the enamel epithelium isolated by acid flotation from the surface of an unerupted human tooth. The enamel cuticle appears as a thin membrane at the ends of the ameloblasts. (Hematoxylin and eosin stain; ×1,300.) **B,** An electron micrograph from a thin section through a similar cuticular isolate. The enamel cuticle has become separated from the ameloblasts and appears as a continuous membrane across the ends of the cells. (×12,000.) (From Ussing, Marie J.: Acta odont. scandinav. **13:** 123, 1955; reprinted J. West. Soc. Periodont. **3:** 71, 1955.)

scope reveals it as a continuous membrane of about 0.2 micron thickness, being organically connected to both the enamel matrix and the ameloblasts (Fig. 47).[79]

During the emergence of the tooth, the reduced enamel epithelium covering the crown produces a keratinous secondary cuticle on the surface of the erupting tooth. If a thin ground section of enamel is decalcified in acid celloidin,[10] the outer or secondary cuticle will resist acid and show marked birefringence in polarized light. This indicates a structurally oriented fibrous protein, presumably

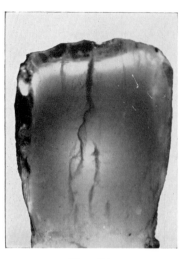

Fig. 49A   Fig. 49B

Fig. 49A. Decalcified incisor with moderately severe mottled enamel (from material obtained in Texas). Numerous lamellae can be observed. (×8.)

Fig. 49B. Maxillary first permanent molar of caries-free 2-year-old rhesus monkey. Numerous bands of organic matter, lamellae, can be seen after decalcification. (×8.) (From Sognnaes, R. F.: J. D. Res. **29:** 260, 1950.)

keratin.[14] In specimens stained with hematoxylin and eosin, the secondary cuticle stains bright yellowish red. It varies in thickness to a maximum of 10 microns, is homogenous in character, and seems to be brittle (see section on Structure of the Epithelial Attachment).

Mastication wears away the enamel cuticles on the incisal edges, occlusal surfaces, and contact areas of the teeth. On other exposed surfaces they may be worn off by other mechanical influences, e.g., brushing of teeth. In protected areas (proximal surfaces and gingival sulcus) they may remain intact throughout life.

Enamel lamellae. Enamel lamellae are thin, leaflike structures that extend from the enamel surface toward the dentinoenamel junction (Figs. 49A and 49B). They may extend to, and sometimes penetrate into, the dentin. They consist of organic material, with but little mineral content. In ground sections these structures may be confused with cracks caused by grinding of the specimen (Fig. 40). Careful decalcification of ground sections of enamel makes possible the distinction between cracks and enamel lamellae; the former disappear while the latter persist.

Lamellae develop in planes of tension. Where rods cross such a plane, a short segment of the rod may not fully calcify. If the disturbance is more severe, a crack may develop that is filled either by surrounding cells, if the crack occurred in the unerupted tooth, or by organic substances from the oral cavity, if the crack developed after eruption. Three types of lamellae can thus be differ-

A

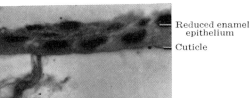

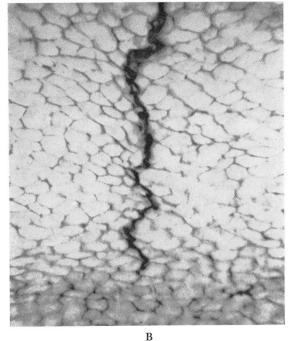

Reduced enamel
epithelium

Cuticle

Lamella

B

Fig. 50. A, Paraffin section through reduced enamel epithelium, enamel cuticle, and a lamella, isolated together by acid flotation from the surface of an unerupted human tooth. Note the intimate relationship between the three elements. (Hematoxylin and eosin stain; ×1,300.) **B,** Paraffin section of decalcified enamel of human molar showing the relation between a lamella and surrounding organic interprismatic substance. (Hematoxylin and eosin stain; ×1,000.) (**A,** From Ussing Marie J.: Acta odont. scandinav. **13:** 23, 1955; reprinted J. West. Soc. Periodont. **3:** 71, 1955; **B,** courtesy Dr. R. F. Sognnaes.)

entiated: Type A, lamellae composed of poorly calcified rod segments (Fig. 50, *B*); Type B, lamellae consisting of degenerated cells; Type C, lamellae arising in erupted teeth where the cracks are filled with organic matter, presumably originating from saliva.[72] This last type (Fig. 50, *A*) may be more common than

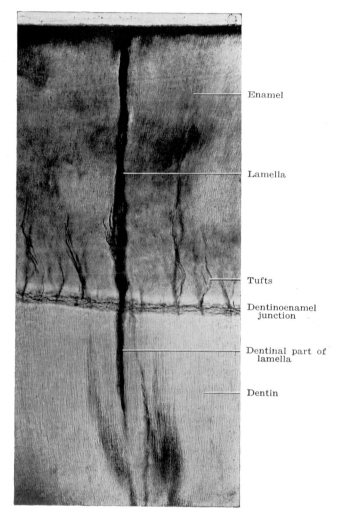

Enamel

Lamella

Tufts

Dentinoenamel
junction

Dentinal part of
lamella

Dentin

Fig. 51. Transverse ground section through a lamella reaching from the surface into the dentin.

formerly believed. While lamellae of Type A are restricted to the enamel, those of Types B and C may reach into the dentin. If cells from the enamel organ fill a crack in the enamel, those in the depth degenerate, whereas those close to the surface may remain vital for a time and produce a hornified secondary cuticle in the cleft.[24] In such cases the greater inner parts of the lamella consist of an organic cell detritus, the outer parts of a double layer of the secondary cuticle. If connective tissue invades a crack in the enamel, cementum may be formed. In such cases lamellae consist entirely or partly of cementum.[46]

Lamellae extend in the longitudinal and radial direction of the tooth, from the tip of the crown toward the cervical region (Figs. 49A and 49B). This arrangement explains why they can be observed better in horizontal sections. It has

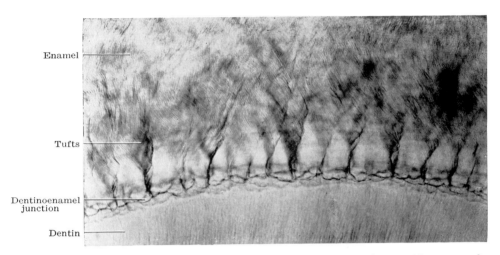

Enamel

Tufts

Dentinoenamel
junction

Dentin

Fig. 52. Transverse ground section through a tooth under low magnification. Numerous tufts extending from the dentinoenamel junction into the enamel.

been suggested that enamel lamellae may be a site of weakness in a tooth and may form a road of entry for bacteria that initiate caries.[10, 24]

Enamel tufts. Enamel tufts (Fig. 52) arise at the dentinoenamel junction and reach into the enamel to about one-fifth to one-third of its thickness. They were so termed because they resemble tufts of grass when viewed in ground sections. This picture is erroneous.[1, 32] An enamel tuft does not spring from a single small area but is a narrow, ribbonlike structure, the inner end of which arises at the dentin. The impression of a tuft of grass is created by examining such structures in thick sections under low magnification. Under these circumstances the imperfections, lying in different planes and curving in different directions (Fig. 36), are projected into one plane (Fig. 52).

Tufts consist of hypocalcified enamel rods and interprismatic substance. Like the lamellae they extend in the direction of the long axis of the crown; therefore, they are abundantly seen in horizontal, and rarely in longitudinal, sections. Their presence and their development are a consequence of, or an adaptation to, the spatial conditions in the enamel.

Dentinoenamel junction. The surface of the dentin at the dentinoenamel junction is pitted. Into the shallow depressions of the dentin fit rounded projections of the enamel. This relation assures the firm hold of the enamel cap on the dentin. In sections, therefore, the dentinoenamel junction appears not as a straight but as a scalloped line (Figs. 52 and 53). The convexities of the scallops are directed toward the dentin. The pitted dentinoenamel junction is already preformed in the arrangement of the ameloblasts and the basement membrane of the dental papilla, prior to the development of hard substances.

Odontoblastic processes and enamel spindles. Occasionally, odontoblastic processes pass across the dentinoenamel junction into the enamel. Since many

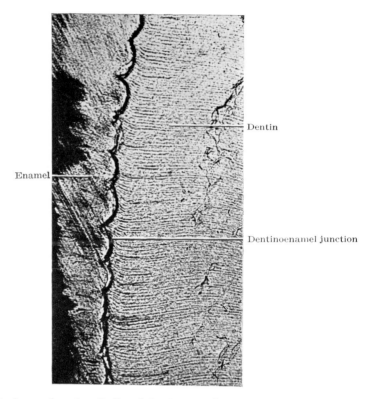

Fig. 53. Longitudinal ground section. Scalloped dentinoenamel junction.

Fig. 54. Ground section. Odontoblastic process extends into the enamel as enamel spindles.

are thickened at their end (Fig. 54), they have been termed enamel spindles. They seem to originate from processes of odontoblasts that extended into the enamel epithelium before hard substances were formed. The direction of the odontoblastic processes and spindles in the enamel corresponds to the original direction of the ameloblasts at right angles to the surface of the dentin. Since the enamel rods are formed at an angle to the axis of the ameloblasts, the direction of spindles and rods is divergent. In ground sections of dried teeth the organic contents of the spindles disintegrate and are replaced by air; then the spaces appear dark in transmitted light.

Age changes

The most apparent age change in enamel is attrition or wear of the occlusal surfaces and proximal contact points as a result of mastication. This is evidenced by a loss of vertical dimension of the crown and by a flattening of the proximal contour. In addition to these gross changes, the outer enamel surfaces themselves undergo posteruptive alterations in structure at the microscopic level. These result from environmental influences and occur with a regularity that can be related to age.[61] (Fig. 44.)

The surfaces of unerupted and recently erupted teeth are covered completely with pronounced rod ends, and perikymata at the points of highest contour of the surfaces begin to disappear. This is followed by a generalized loss of the rod ends and a much slower flattening of the perikymata. Finally, the perikymata disappear completely. The rate at which structure is lost depends on the location of the surface on the tooth and on the location of the tooth in the mouth. Facial and lingual surfaces lose their structure much more rapidly than do proximal surfaces, and anterior teeth lose their structure more rapidly than do posterior teeth.

Age changes within the enamel proper have been difficult to discern microscopically. The fact that alterations do occur has been brought out by chemical analyses, but the changes are not well understood. For example, the total amount of organic matrix is said by some to increase, by others to remain unchanged, and by still others to decrease.[19, 56] Localized increases of certain elements, such as nitrogen and fluorine, however, have been found in the superficial enamel layers of older teeth.[56, 74, 86] This suggests a continuous uptake, probably from the oral environment, during aging. As a result of age changes in the organic portion of enamel, presumably near the surface, the teeth may become darker, and their resistance to decay may be increased.[7, 8] Suggestive of an aging change is the greatly reduced permeability of older teeth to fluids.[68] There is insufficient evidence to show that enamel becomes harder with age.[53]

Clinical considerations

The course of the enamel rods is of importance in cavity preparations. The choice of instruments depends upon the location of the cavity in the tooth. Generally, the rods run at a right angle to the underlying dentin or tooth surface. Close to the cementoenamel junction the rods run in a more horizontal direction (Fig. 35, *B*). In preparing cavities it is important that unsupported enamel rods are not left at the cavity margins because they would soon break and produce a leakage. Bacteria would lodge in these spaces, inducing secondary dental caries. Enamel is brittle and does not withstand forces in thin layers or in areas where it is not supported by the underlying dentin. (Fig. 55A.)

Deep enamel fissures are predisposing to caries. Although these deep clefts between adjoining cusps cannot be regarded as pathologic, they afford areas for retention of caries-producing agents. Caries penetrates the floor of fissures rapidly because the enamel in these areas is very thin.[37] (Fig. 55B.) As the destructive process reaches the dentin, it spreads along the dentinoenamel junction, undermining the enamel. An extensive area of dentin becomes carious without giving any warning to the patient because the entrance to the cavity is minute. Careful examination is necessary to discover such cavities because most enamel fissures are more minute than a single toothbrush bristle and cannot be detected with the dental probe.

Enamel lamellae may also be predisposing locations for caries because they contain much organic material. Primarily from the standpoint of protection against caries, the structure and reactions of the outer enamel surface are subject to much current research. In vitro tests have shown that the acid solubility of enamel can be markedly reduced by treatment with various chemical agents, particularly fluoride compounds.[26, 67] Clinical trials based on these leads have demonstrated reductions of 40 per cent or more in the incidence of caries in children following topical applications of sodium or stannous fluoride.[44, 67] Incorporation of fluorides in dentifrices has also proved promising and is now being pursued further.[31, 43, 67]

The most effective means for mass control of dental caries to date has been adjustment of the fluoride level in communal water supplies to 1 part per million. Epidemiologic studies in areas where the drinking water contained natural fluoride revealed that the caries prevalence in both children and adults was about 65 per cent lower than in nonfluoride areas,[42, 67] and long-term studies have demonstrated that the same order of protection is afforded through water fluoridation programs.[1, 67] The mechanisms of action are thought to be primarily a combination of changes in enamel resistance, brought about by incorporation of fluoride during calcification, and alterations in the environment of the teeth, particularly with respect to the oral bacterial flora.[42, 67]

The surface of the enamel in the cervical region should be kept smooth and well polished by proper home care and by regular cleansing by the dentist. If the surface of the cervical enamel becomes decalcified, or otherwise roughened, food debris, bacterial plaques, etc., accumulate on this surface. The gingiva in contact with this roughened, debris-covered enamel surface undergoes inflamma-

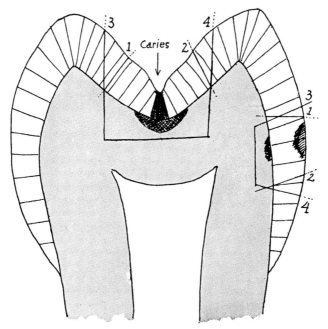

Fig. 55A. Diagrammatic illustration of the course of enamel rods in a molar in relation to cavity preparation. **1** and **2** indicate wrong preparation of cavity margins; **3** and **4** indicate correct preparation.

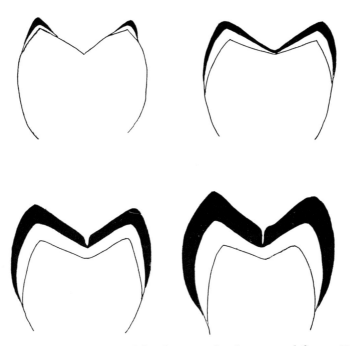

Fig. 55B. Diagrammatic illustration of development of a deep enamel fissure. Note the thin enamel layer forming the floor of the fissure. (From Kronfeld, R.: J. A. D. A. **22**: 1131, 1935.)

tory changes. The ensuing gingivitis, unless promptly treated, may lead to more serious periodontal disease.

DEVELOPMENT
Epithelial dental organ

The early development of the dental organ and its differentiation have been discussed in Chapter II. At the stage preceding the formation of hard structures, dentin and enamel, the dental organ, originating from the stratified epithelium of the primitive oral cavity, consists of four distinct layers: outer dental epithelium, stellate reticulum, stratum intermedium, and inner dental epithelium, ameloblastic layer (Fig. 56). The border line between the inner dental epithelium and the connective tissue of the dental papilla is the subsequent dentino-enamel junction; thus, its outline determines the pattern of the occlusal or incisal part of the crown. At the border of the wide basal opening of the dental organ,

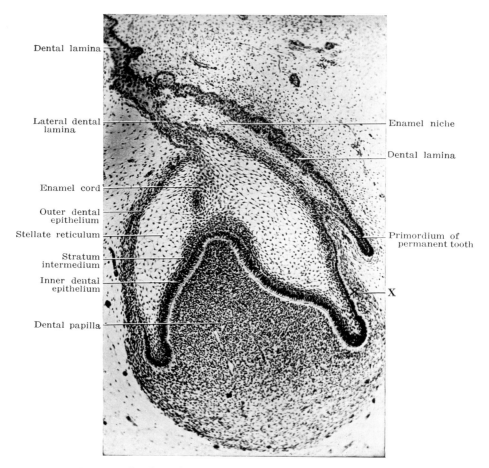

Fig. 56. Tooth germ (deciduous lower incisor) of human embryo (105 mm., fourth month). Four layers of the enamel organ. **X,** See Fig. 58.

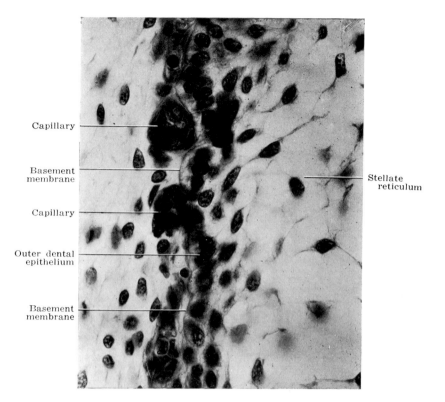

Capillary

Basement membrane

Capillary

Outer dental epithelium

Basement membrane

Stellate reticulum

Fig. 57. Capillaries in contact with the outer dental epithelium. Basement membrane separates outer dental epithelium from connective tissue.

the inner dental epithelium reflects into the outer dental epithelium; this is the cervical loop.[95] The inner and outer dental epithelia are separated from each other by a large mass of cells differentiated into two distinct layers. The layer that is close to the inner dental epithelium consists of two to three rows of flat polyhedral cells; it is the stratum intermedium; the other layer, which is more loosely arranged, constitutes the stellate reticulum.

The different layers of epithelial cells of the dental organ are named according to their morphology, function, or location. The stellate reticulum derives its term from the morphology of its cells; the outer dental epithelium and the stratum intermedium are so named because of their location; the inner dental epithelium is so named on the basis of its anatomic relation; on the basis of function it is called the ameloblastic layer.

Outer dental epithelium. In the early stages of development of the dental organ, the outer dental epithelium consists of a single layer of cuboidal cells, separated from the surrounding connective tissue of the dental sac by a delicate basement membrane (Fig. 57). Prior to the formation of hard structures, this regular arrangement of the outer dental epithelium is maintained only in the cervical parts of the dental organ. At the highest convexity of the organ (Fig.

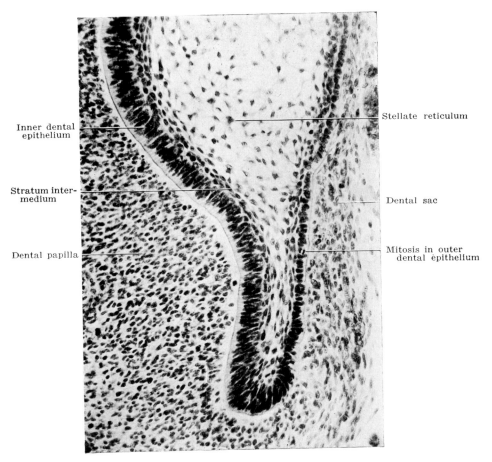

Inner dental epithelium

Stratum inter-medium

Dental papilla

Stellate reticulum

Dental sac

Mitosis in outer dental epithelium

Fig. 58. Region of the cervical loop (higher magnification of **X** in Fig. 56). Transition of the outer into the inner dental epithelium.

56), the cells of the outer dental epithelium become irregular in shape and cannot be distinguished easily from the outer portion of the stellate reticulum. The capillaries in the connective tissue surrounding the epithelial dental organ proliferate and protrude toward the dental organ (Fig. 57). Immediately before enamel formation commences, capillaries may even invade the stellate reticulum.[108] This increased vascularity ensures a rich metabolism when a plentiful supply of substances from the blood stream to the inner enamel epithelium is required.

Stellate reticulum. In the stellate reticulum, which forms the middle part of the dental organ, the neighboring cells are separated by wide intercellular spaces filled by a large amount of intercellular substance. The cells are star-shaped, with long processes reaching in all directions from a central body (Figs. 57 and 58). They are connected with each other and with the cells of the outer dental epithelium and the stratum intermedium by intercellular bridges (desmosomes).[121]

The structure of the stellate reticulum renders it resistant and elastic; therefore, it seems probable that it acts as a buffer against physical forces which might distort the conformation of the developing dentinoenamel junction, giving rise to gross morphologic changes. It seems to permit only a limited flow of nutritional elements from the outlying blood vessels to the formative cells. Indicative of this is the fact that the stellate reticulum is noticeably reduced in thickness when the first layers of dentin are laid down, and the inner dental epithelium is thereby cut off from the dental papilla, its original source of supply (Figs. 59A and 59B).

Stratum intermedium. The cells of the stratum intermedium are situated between the stellate reticulum and the inner dental epithelium. They are flat to cuboid in shape and are arranged in one to three layers. They are connected with

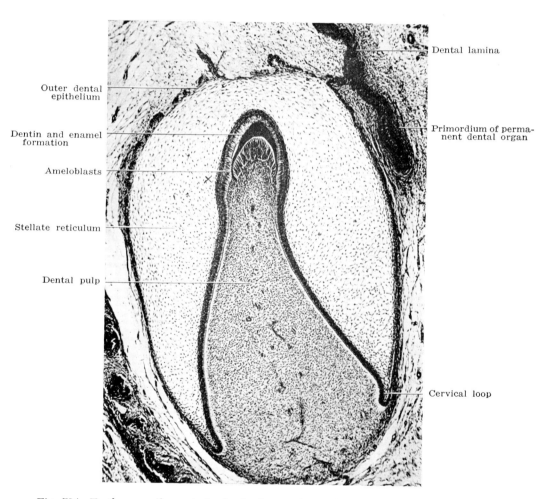

Fig. 59A. Tooth germ (lower incisor) of a human fetus (fifth month). Beginning of dentin and enamel formation. The stellate reticulum at the tip of the crown reduced in thickness. **X,** See Fig. 60.

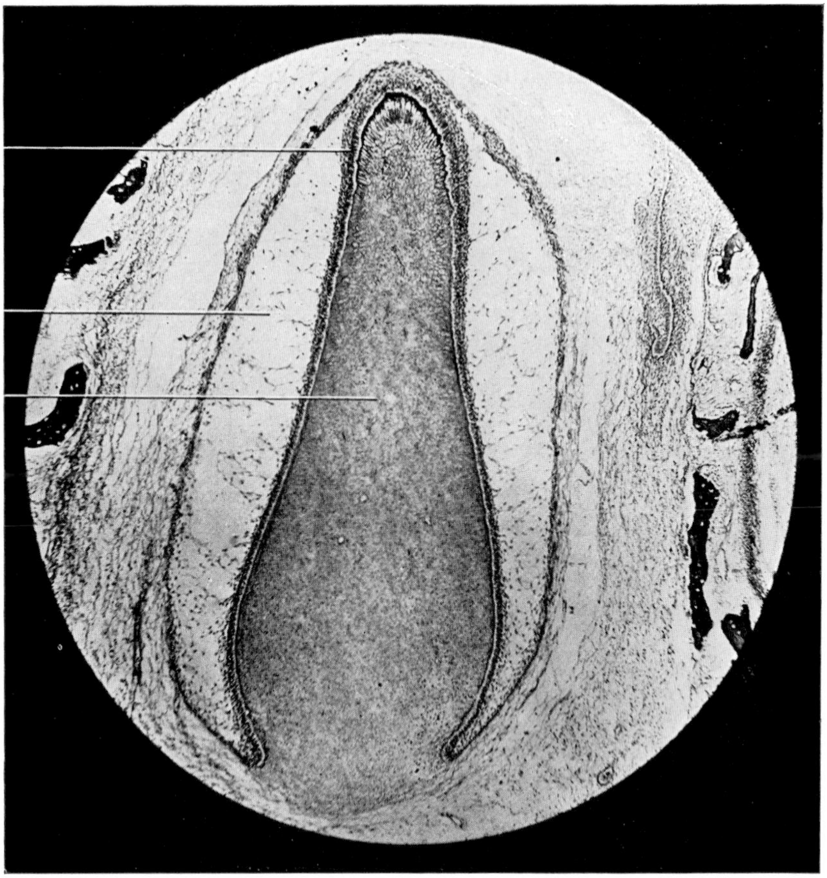

Fig. 59B. Tooth germ with beginning dentin formation. Silver impregnation. (Courtesy Dr. Gerrit Bevelander.)

each other and with the neighboring cells of the stellate reticulum and the inner dental epithelium by intercellular bridges. Tonofibrils, with an orientation parallel to the surface of the developing enamel, are found in the cytoplasm. The function of the stratum intermedium is not understood, but it is thought to play a role in production of the enamel itself, either through control of fluid diffusion into and out of the ameloblasts or by the actual contribution of necessary formative elements or enzymes.[96, 132, 135] The cells of the stratum intermedium show mitotic division even after the cells of the inner dental epithelium cease to divide.

Inner dental epithelium. The cells of the inner dental epithelium are derived from the basal cell layer of the oral epithelium. Before enamel formation begins, these cells assume a columnar form and differentiate into ameloblasts that produce the enamel matrix. The changes in shape and structure that the cells of the inner enamel epithelium undergo will be described in detail as the life cycle of the ameloblasts. It should be mentioned, however, that cell differentiation occurs earlier in the region of the incisal edge or cusps than in the area of the cervical loop. Thus, some or all stages of ameloblastic development and enamel formation can be observed in a single tooth germ.

Cervical loop. At the free border of the dental organ, the outer and inner dental epithelial layers are continuous and reflected into one another as the cervical loop (Figs. 56 and 58).[95] In this zone of transition between the outer dental epithelium and the inner dental epithelium, the cuboidal cells gradually gain in length. When the dental organ of the crown has been formed, the cells of this portion give rise to Hertwig's epithelial root sheath (see Chapter II).

Life cycle of the ameloblasts

According to their function, the life span of the cells of the inner dental epithelium can be divided into six stages: (1) morphogenetic, (2) organizing, (3) formative, (4) maturation, (5) protective, and (6) desmolytic. Since the differentiation of ameloblasts is most advanced in the region of the incisal edge or tips of the cusps and least advanced in the region of the cervical loop, all or some stages of the developing ameloblast can be observed in one tooth germ.

Morphogenetic stage. Before the ameloblasts are fully differentiated and produce the enamel, they play an important part in determining the shape of the crown, the later dentinoenamel junction (Figs. 59A and 59B). During this morphogenetic stage, the cells are short, columnar, with large oval nuclei that almost fill the cell body.

The Golgi apparatus and the centrioles are located in the proximal end of the cell,* whereas the mitochondria are evenly dispersed throughout the cytoplasm.[118] Terminal bars appear concomitantly with the mitochondria in the same region of the cell (Fig. 61, A). Both structures retain their basal position throughout the formative stage. (Figs. 64B and 65A.) The terminal bars represent points of close contact between cells. They were previously thought to consist of dense intercellular substance, but under the electron microscope it has been found that they comprise thickenings of the opposing cell membranes, associated with condensations of the underlying cytoplasm.[114]

The inner dental epithelium is separated from the connective tissue of the dental papilla by a delicate basement membrane. The adjacent pulpal layer is a cell-free, narrow, light zone containing fine argyrophil fibers and the cytoplasmic processes of the superficial cells of the pulp (Fig. 60).

Organizing stage. In the organizing stage of development, the inner dental epithelium exerts an influence upon the adjacent connective tissue cells that causes them to differentiate into odontoblasts. This stage is characterized by a change in the appearance of the cells of the inner dental epithelium; they become

---

*In modern usage, to conform with the terminology applied to other secretory cells, the dentinal end of the ameloblast, at which enamel is formed, is called *distal,* and the end facing the stratum intermedium is called *basal* or *proximal.*

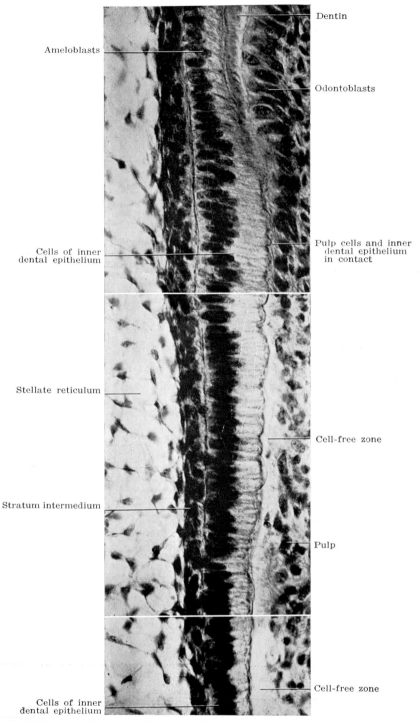

Dentin

Ameloblasts

Odontoblasts

Cells of inner
dental epithelium

Pulp cells and inner
dental epithelium
in contact

Stellate reticulum

Cell-free zone

Stratum intermedium

Pulp

Cell-free zone

Cells of inner
dental epithelium

Fig. 60. High magnification of the inner dental epithelium from X in Fig. 59A. In the cervical region the cells are short, and the outermost layer of the pulp is cell-free. Occlusally the cells are long, and the cell-free zone of the pulp has disappeared. The ameloblasts are again shorter where dentin formation has set in and enamel formation is imminent. (From Diamond, M., and Weinmann, J. P.: J. D. Res. **21:** 403, 1942.)

longer, and the nucleus-free zone at the basal end of the cells becomes almost as long as the proximal part containing the nucleus (Fig. 60). In preparation for this development, a reversal of the functional polarity of these cells takes place by the migration of the centrioles, the cell center,[125] and the Golgi apparatus[116, 125] from the periphery of the cell into the distal end (Fig. 61). Moreover, the cytoplasm shows differences in staining reaction proximally and distally to the nucleus. The narrow peripheral part stains red in hematoxylin-eosin preparations, the wide basal part slightly pink. Special staining methods reveal the presence of fine acidophil granules in the proximal part of the cell.[119]

Electron microscope studies[118, 123, 124, 136] have shown that these granules are actually the mitochondria, which have become concentrated in this part of the cell (Fig. 61, A). At the same time, the clear cell-free zone between the inner dental epithelium and the dental papilla disappears (Fig. 60), probably due to elongation of the epithelial cells toward the papilla. Thus the epithelial cells come into close contact with the connective tissue cells of the pulp, which are induced to differentiate into odontoblasts. During the terminal phase of the organizing stage, the formation of the dentin by the odontoblasts begins (Fig. 60).

The first appearance of dentin seems to be a critical phase in the life cycle of the inner dental epithelium. As long as it is in contact with the connective tissue of the dental papilla, it receives nutrient material from the blood vessels of this tissue. When dentin forms, however, it cuts off the ameloblasts from their original source of nourishment, and from then on they are supplied by the capillaries which surround and may even penetrate the outer dental epithelium. This reversal of nutritional source is characterized by proliferation of capillaries of the dental sac and by reduction and gradual disappearance of the stellate reticulum (Figs. 59A and 59B). Thus, the distance between the capillaries and the stratum intermedium and the ameloblast layer is shortened. Experiments with vital stains demonstrate this reversal of the nutritional stream.[134]

Formative stage. The ameloblasts enter their formative stage after the first layer of dentin has been formed. The presence of dentin seems to be necessary to induce the beginning of enamel matrix formation just as it was necessary for the epithelial cells to come into close contact with the connective tissue of the pulp to induce differentiation of the odontoblasts and the beginning of dentin formation. This mutual interaction between one group of cells and another is one of the fundamental laws of organogenesis and histodifferentiation.[101, 103]

During formation of the enamel matrix, the ameloblasts retain approximately the same length and arrangement. The changes in the cell bodies are related to the formation of enamel matrix.

Maturation stage. Enamel maturation occurs after most of the thickness of the enamel matrix has been formed in the occlusal or incisal area. In the cervical parts of the crown, enamel matrix formation is still progressing at this time. During enamel maturation, the ameloblasts are slightly reduced in length and are closely attached to the enamel matrix. The cells of the stratum intermedium

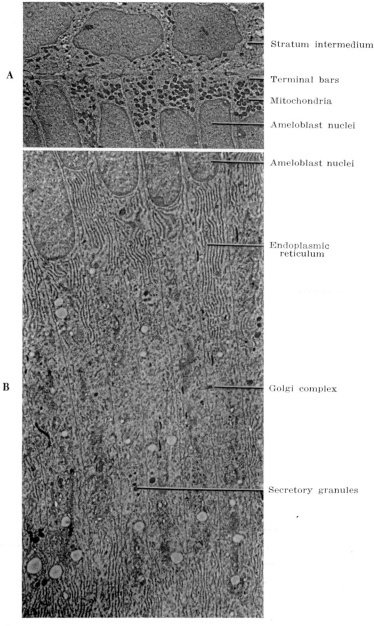

A — Stratum intermedium

Terminal bars

Mitochondria

Ameloblast nuclei

Ameloblast nuclei

Endoplasmic reticulum

B — Golgi complex

Secretory granules

Fig. 61. Portions of longitudinally sectioned fully differentiated ameloblasts as seen under the electron microscope. The basal ends of the cells are shown in **A** (×5,000), and the cell bodies distal to the nuclei are shown in **B** (×5,500). For the extreme distal ends of the ameloblasts, see Fig. 63. (From Nylen, M. U., and Scott, D. B.: J. Indiana State Dental Assoc. **39**: 406, 1960; and Scott, D. B., and Nylen, M. U.: Ann. New York Acad. Sc. **85**: 133, 1960.)

lose their cuboidal shape and regular arrangement and assume a spindle shape. It is certain that the ameloblasts also play a part in the maturation of the enamel; ultimately they produce the primary cuticle.

Protective stage. When the enamel has completely developed and has fully calcified, the ameloblasts cease to be arranged in a well-defined layer and can no longer be differentiated from the cells of the stratum intermedium and outer dental epithelium. These cell layers then form a stratified epithelial covering of the enamel, the so-called reduced enamel epithelium. The function of the reduced enamel epithelium is that of protecting the mature enamel by separating it from the connective tissue until the tooth erupts. If connective tissue comes in contact with the enamel, anomalies may develop. Under such conditions, the enamel may be either resorbed or covered by a layer of cementum.[110, 140]

Desmolytic stage. The reduced enamel epithelium seems also to induce atrophy of the connective tissue separating it from the oral epithelium, so that fusion of the two epithelia can occur, (see Chapter IX). It is probable that the epithelial cells elaborate enzymes that are able to destroy connective tissue fibers by desmolysis. Premature degeneration of the reduced enamel epithelium may prevent the eruption of a tooth.[140]

Amelogenesis

On the basis of ultimate structure and composition, two processes are involved in the development of enamel: organic matrix formation and mineralization. Though the inception of mineralization does not await the completion of matrix formation, the two processes will be treated separately.

FORMATION OF THE ENAMEL MATRIX

Dentinoenamel membrane. The ameloblasts (Fig. 61) begin their secretory activity when a small amount of dentin has been laid down. The first enamel matrix is deposited extracellularly by the ameloblasts in a thin layer along the dentin.[98, 107, 118, 137] (Fig. 62.) This has been termed the dentinoenamel membrane,[120, 127] and it is continuous with the interprismatic substance that forms subsequently. Its presence accounts for the fact that the distal ends of the enamel rods are not in direct contact with the dentin. (Fig. 63.)

Development of Tomes' processes. After formation of the dentinoenamel membrane, matrix is deposited between the distal ends of the ameloblasts. It completely surrounds the ends of the cells, delineating what have become known as Tomes' processes (Fig. 64A). In sections this matrix appears as a row of projections about 4 microns long, extending intercellularly from the last-formed matrix (Figs. 64B, 64C, and 65). The cytoplasm of Tomes' processes contains numerous granules but no organelles.[123, 137]

Distal terminal bars. At the time Tomes' processes begin to form, terminal bars appear at the distal ends of the ameloblasts, separating the Tomes' processes from the cell proper (Figs. 64B, 64C, 65A, and 65B). Structurally, they are localized condensations of cytoplasmic substance closely associated with the cell membranes.[124] They are observed only during the enamel-producing stage of the ameloblast,[113, 122] but their exact function is not known.

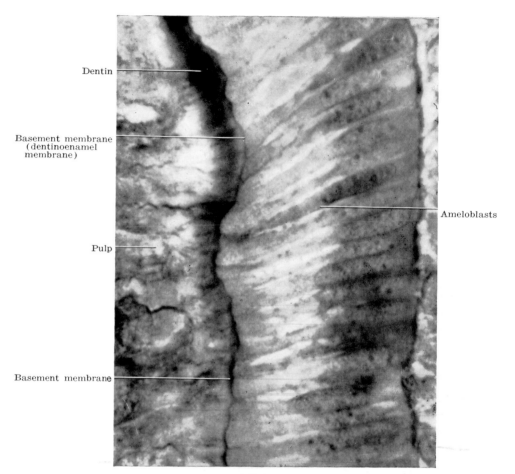

Dentin

Basement membrane
(dentinoenamel
membrane)

Pulp

Basement membrane

Ameloblasts

Fig. 62. Basement membrane of the dental papilla can be followed on the outer surface of the dentin, forming the dentinoenamel membrane. (From Orban, B., Sicher, H., and Weinmann, J. P.: J. Am. Coll. Dentists **10:** 13, 1943.)

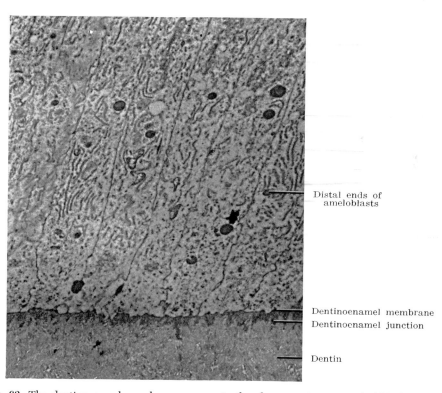

Distal ends of
ameloblasts

Dentinoenamel membrane
Dentinoenamel junction

Dentin

Fig. 63. The dentinoenamel membrane as seen in the electron microscope. (×5,500.)

Fig. 64A   Fig. 64B

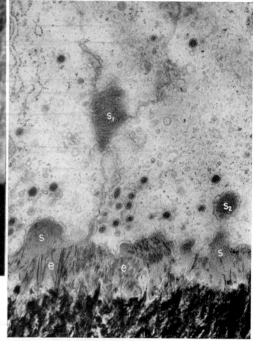

Fig. 64A. Formation of Tomes' processes and terminal bars, as the first step in enamel rod formation. Rat incisor. (From Orban, B., Sicher, H., and Weinmann, J. P.: J. Am. Coll. Dentists **10:** 13, 1943.)

Fig. 64B. Electron micrograph showing an early stage in the formation of enamel in the lower incisor of the rat. At this stage, dentin (at the bottom of the micrograph) is well developed. Enamel, **e,** appears as a less dense layer on the surface of the dentin and consists of thin, ribbon-shaped elements running more or less perpendicular to the dentinoenamel junction and masses of a less dense stippled material, s. Separating the enamel from the cytoplasm of the ameloblasts which occupies most of the upper part of the micrograph is the ameloblast plasma membrane. Parts of three ameloblasts are shown. In the middle of the micrograph in a region bounded by the membranes of the three ameloblasts lies another mass of stippled material, s_1, while a second mass, s_2, lies at the right surrounded by membrane, but within the bounds of the ameloblast. Numerous small, membrane-bound granules lie within the cytoplasm. The cotents of these have the same general consistency as the stippled material, but rather higher density. It is possible that these represent unsecreted granules of stippled material which in turn is a precursor of enamel matrix. (×24,000.) (From Watson, M. L.: J. Biophys. & Biochem. Cytol. **7:** 489, 1960.)

Fig. 64C

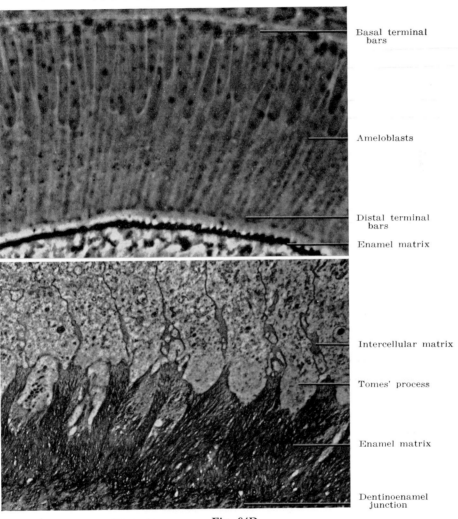

Basal terminal
bars

Ameloblasts

Distal terminal
bars

Enamel matrix

Intercellular matrix

Tomes' process

Enamel matrix

Dentinoenamel
junction

Fig. 64D

Fig. 64C. A phase-contrast micrograph showing the formation of Tomes' processes and terminal bars, the first step in enamel rod formation. Rodent incisor. (×1,000.)

Fig. 64D. An electron micrograph showing the Tomes' process region in more detail. (×8,000.) (From Nylen, M. U., and Scott, D. B.: J. Indiana State Dental Assoc. **39:** 406, 1960.)

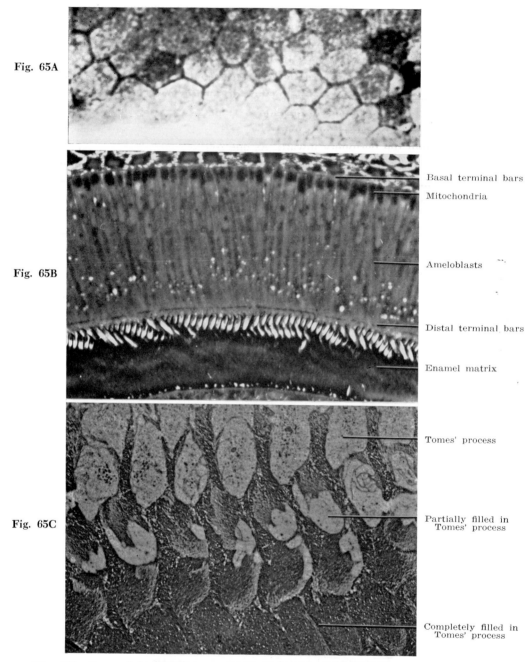

Fig. 65A

Fig. 65B

Fig. 65C

Basal terminal bars

Mitochondria

Ameloblasts

Distal terminal bars

Enamel matrix

Tomes' process

Partially filled in
Tomes' process

Completely filled in
Tomes' process

Fig. 65A. Terminal bar apparatus of the ameloblasts in surface view. (From Orban, B., Sicher, H., and Weinmann, J. P.: J. Am. Coll. Dentists **10:** 13, 1943.)
Fig. 65B. A phase-contrast micrograph showing the Tomes' processes and their transformation into enamel matrix. Rodent incisor. (×700.)
Fig. 65C. An electron micrograph showing the steps in conversion of the newly formed Tomes' processes (top) into matrix segments (bottom). (×7,000.) (From Nylen, M. U., and Scott, D. B.: J. Indiana State Dental Assoc. **39:** 406, 1960.)

Transformation of Tomes' processes. The next step in enamel matrix formation is the "filling in" of the distal ends of Tomes' processes with matrix material to form segments of enamel rods.[118, 130] Recent investigations on the development of rodent enamel show that Tomes' processes may actually become cut off from the parent cells by infolding of the lateral cell membranes prior to their change into rod substance.[118] Similar double membrane sheaths have been observed between individual rod segments in developing human enamel.[102] The transformation of the Tomes' processes into matrix substance secreted by the ameloblasts takes place from the periphery inward. As one row of processes is transformed, new processes are outlined basal to the preceding ones as a result of continued intercellular matrix deposition and reformation of the terminal bars. (Figs. 64, *D*, 65, *C*, and 66A.)

These two steps, e.g., formation of Tomes' processes and their change into matrix, are repeated again and again until the entire thickness of enamel is formed (Fig. 66B). The primary segmentation of the rods that results from this rhythmic deposition is considered the basis for the cross striations seen in mature rods as the length of the developmental segments (4 microns) corresponds to the distance between the striations. The ameloblasts generally are at an angle to the developing rod segments (Fig. 65A). They may bend first to one side, then to the other, which would explain the wavy course of the finished rods in certain regions. Each enamel rod, however, is derived from a single ameloblast.[89]

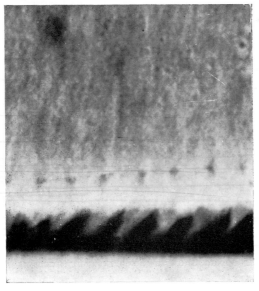

Fig. 66A. Homogenization of the dentinal ends of Tomes' processes and their transformation into pre-enamel matrix in a picket fence arrangement. The rods are at an angle to the ameloblasts and Tomes' processes. (From Orban, B., Sicher, H., and Weinmann, J. P.: J. Am. Coll. Dentists **10**: 13, 1943.)

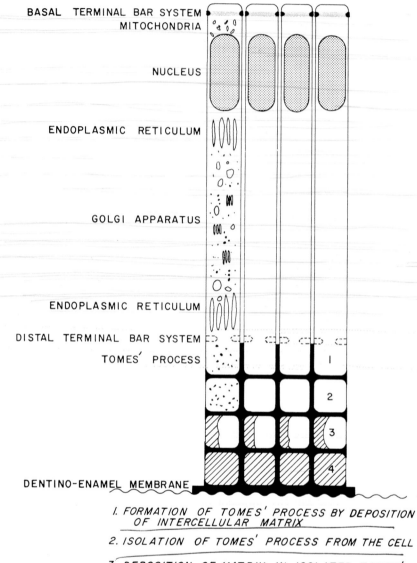

BASAL TERMINAL BAR SYSTEM
MITOCHONDRIA

NUCLEUS

ENDOPLASMIC RETICULUM

GOLGI APPARATUS

ENDOPLASMIC RETICULUM

DISTAL TERMINAL BAR SYSTEM

TOMES' PROCESS

DENTINO-ENAMEL MEMBRANE

*l. FORMATION OF TOMES' PROCESS BY DEPOSITION
OF INTERCELLULAR MATRIX*

2. ISOLATION OF TOMES' PROCESS FROM THE CELL

*3. DEPOSITION OF MATRIX IN ISOLATED TOMES'
PROCESS*

4. FULLY FORMED SEGMENT OF ENAMEL ROD

Fig. 66B. Diagrammatic illustration of enamel matrix formation. Ameloblast and enamel rod are shown in linear arrangement, although always at an angle to each other. (Courtesy Dr. D. B. Scott.)

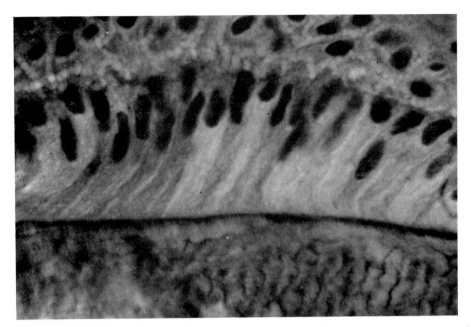

Fig. 67. A demineralized section showing the outer enamel layer of a recently completed human tooth. The enamel cuticle is interposed between the matrix and the shortened ameloblasts. (Hematoxylin and eosin stain; ×1,300.) (From Ussing, M. J.: Acta odont. scandinav. **13:** 123, 1955; reprinted J. West. Soc. Periodont. **3:** 71, 1955.)

The end product of the ameloblasts is the enamel cuticle, a thin organic membrane that covers the entire enamel surface (Fig. 67).

MINERALIZATION AND MATURATION OF THE ENAMEL MATRIX

Mineralization of the enamel matrix takes place in two stages, although the time interval between the two appears to be very small.[90, 91] In the first stage, an immediate partial mineralization occurs in the matrix segments and the interprismatic substance as they are laid down. Chemical analyses indicate that the initial influx may amount to 25 to 30 per cent of the eventual total mineral content.[138] It has been shown recently by electron microscopy and diffraction that this first mineral actually is in the form of crystalline apatite (Fig. 70, A).[99, 100, 118, 137]

The second stage, or *maturation*, is characterized by the gradual completion of mineralization. The process of maturation starts from the height of the crown and progresses cervically. (Fig. 68.) However, at each level, maturation seems to begin at the dentinal end of the rods.[87, 90, 104-106] Thus, there is an integration of two processes: each rod matures from the depth to the surface; the sequence of maturing rods is from cusp or incisal edge toward the cervical line.[138]

Maturation begins before the matrix has reached its full thickness. Thus, it is going on in the inner, first-formed matrix at the same time as initial mineraliza-

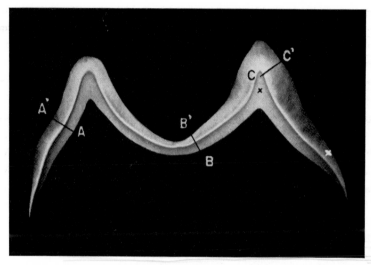

Fig. 68. Microradiograph of a ground section through a developing deciduous molar. From the gradation in radiopacity, maturation can be seen to progress from the dentinoenamel junction toward the enamel surface. Mineralization is more advanced occlusally than in the cervical region. The lines **A**, **B**, and **C** indicate planes in which actual microdensitometric tracings were made. (×15.) (From Hammarlund-Essler, E.: Tr. Royal Schools of Dentistry, Stockholm and Umea **4:** 15, 1958.)

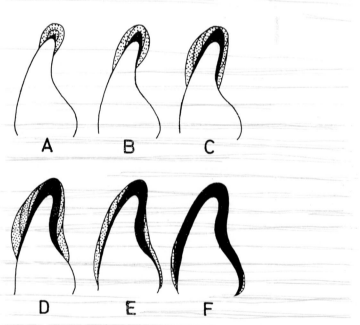

Fig. 69. Diagram showing the pattern of mineralization of an incisor tooth. The stippled zones represent consecutive layers of partly mineralized enamel matrix. The black areas indicate the advance of final mineralization during maturation (From Crabb, H. S. M.: Proc. Royal Soc. Med. **52:** 118, 1959; and Crabb, H. S. M., and Darling, A. I.: Arch. Oral Biol. **2:** 308, 1960.)

tion is taking place in the outer, recently formed matrix. The advancing front is at first parallel to the dentinoenamel junction and later to the outer enamel surface. Following this basic pattern, the incisal and occlusal regions reach maturity ahead of the cervical regions. (Fig. 69.)

At the ultrastructural level, maturation is characterized by growth and eventual fusion of the crystals seen in the primary phase. (Fig. 70).[99, 100, 128, 130] Concomitantly, the fibrils of the organic matrix gradually become thinner and more widely spaced to make room for the growing crystals.[131] It is likely, however, that some of the organic fibrils actually become embedded in the crystals.[99, 129] Chemical analysis shows that the loss in volume of the organic matter is due to withdrawal of some protein and mostly water from the matrix.[92, 93]

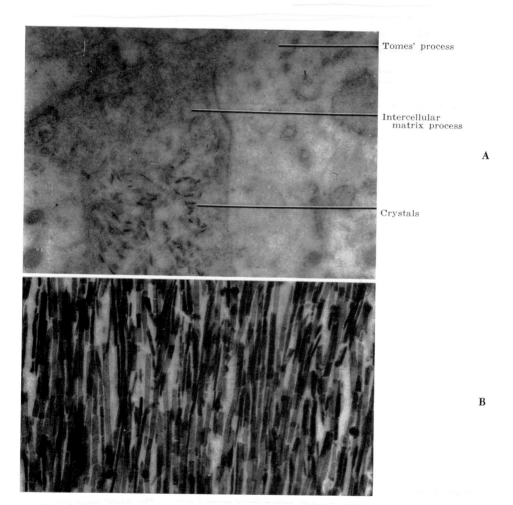

Tomes' process

Intercellular matrix process

A

Crystals

B

Fig. 70. Electron micrographs illustrating the difference between the short, needlelike crystals laid down in newly deposited enamel matrix, **A,** and the long, ribbonlike crystals seen in mature enamel, **B.** (×70,000.)

Clinical considerations

Clinical interest in amelogenesis is centered primarily on the perfection of enamel formation. While there is relatively little the dentist can do directly to alter the course of events in amelogenesis, it may be possible to minimize certain of the factors thought to be associated with the etiology of defective enamel structure. The principal expressions of pathologic amelogenesis are hypoplasia, which is manifested by pitting, furrowing, or even total absence of the enamel, and hypocalcification, in the form of opaque or chalky areas on normally contoured enamel surfaces. The causes of such defective enamel formation can be generally classified as systemic,[111, 126] local,[115] or genetic.[139-141] The most common systemic influences are nutritional deficiencies, endocrinopathies, febrile diseases, and certain chemical intoxications. It thus stands to reason that the dentist should exert his influence to insure sound nutritional practices and recommended immunization procedures during periods of gestation and postnatal amelogenesis. Chemical intoxication of the ameloblasts is not prevalent and is limited essentially to the ingestion of excessive amounts of water-borne fluoride. Where the drinking water contains naturally in excess of 1.5 parts per million fluoride, chronic endemic fluorosis may occur as a result of continuous use throughout the period of amelogenesis.[94] In such areas, it is important to urge substitution of a water with levels of fluoride (ca. 1 p.p.m.) well below the threshold for fluorosis, yet optimal with regard to protection against dental caries (see Clinical Considerations in section on Histology).

Since it has been realized that enamel development occurs in two phases, i.e., matrix formation and maturation, developmental disturbances of the enamel can be understood more fully. If matrix formation is affected, enamel hypoplasia will ensue; if maturation is lacking or incomplete, hypocalcification of the enamel results. In the case of hypoplasia a defect of the enamel is found; in the case of hypocalcification a deficiency in the mineral content of the enamel is found. In the latter case the enamel persists as enamel matrix and is, therefore, soft and acid-insoluble in routine preparation after formalin fixation.

Hypoplasia, as well as hypocalcification, may be caused by systemic, local, or hereditary factors. Hypoplasia of systemic origin is termed chronologic hypoplasia because the lesion is found in the areas of those teeth where the enamel was formed during the systemic (metabolic) disturbance. Since the formation of enamel extends over a longer period and the systemic disturbance is, in most cases, of short duration, the defect is limited to a circumscribed area of the affected teeth. A single narrow zone of hypoplasia (smooth or pitted) may be indicative of a disturbance of enamel formation during a short period in which only those ameloblasts were affected which at that time had just started enamel formation. Multiple hypoplasia develops if enamel formation is interrupted on more than one occasion.[126]

No specific etiology of chronologic hypoplasia has been established as yet. Recent investigations have demonstrated that exanthematous diseases are not so frequently a cause of enamel hypoplasia as was heretofore commonly believed.[126] The most frequent etiologic factors are said to be rickets and hypoparathyroidism, but hypoplasia cannot be predicted with any reliability even in the most severe forms of those diseases.[126]

The systemic influences causing enamel hypoplasia are in the majority of cases active during the first year of life. Therefore, the teeth most frequently affected are the incisors, canines, and first molars. The upper lateral incisor is sometimes found unaffected because its development starts later than that of the other teeth mentioned.

Local factors affect single teeth, in most cases only one tooth. If more than one tooth is affected by local hypoplasia, the location of the defects shows no relation to chronology of development. The cause of local hypoplasia may be an infection of the pulp with subsequent infection of the periapical tissues of a deciduous tooth if the irritation occurred during the period of enamel formation of the permanent successor.

The hereditary type of enamel hypoplasia is probably a generalized disturbance of the ameloblasts. Therefore, the entire enamel of all the teeth, deciduous as well as permanent, is affected rather than merely a beltlike zone of the enamel of a group of teeth, as in systemic cases. The anomaly is transmitted as a Mendelian dominant character. The enamel of such teeth is so thin that it cannot be noticed clinically or in radiographs. The crowns of the teeth of affected family members are yellow-brown, smooth, glossy, hard, and their shape resembles teeth prepared for jacket crowns.[139, 140]

An example of systemic hypocalcification of the enamel is the so-called mottled enamel. A high fluoride content in the water is the cause of the deficiency in calcification. Fluoride hypocalcification is endemic, that is, it is limited in its distribution to definite areas where the drinking water contains more than 1 part of fluoride per 1 million parts of water. It has been demonstrated that a small amount of fluoride (about 1 to 1.2 parts per million) reduces susceptibility to dental caries without causing mottling. For this reason, many communities are adding small quantities of fluoride to the community water supplies.

The same local causes that might affect the formation of the enamel can disturb maturation. If the injury occurs in the formative stage of enamel development, hypoplasia of the enamel will result; an injury during the maturation stage will cause a deficiency in calcification.

The hereditary type of hypocalcification is characterized by the formation of a normal amount of enamel matrix that, however, does not fully mature.[139, 140] Such teeth, if investigated before or shortly after eruption, show a normal shape. Their surfaces do not have the luster of normal enamel but appear dull. The enamel is opaque. The hypocalcified soft enamel matrix is soon discolored, abraded by mastication, or peeled off in layers. When parts of the soft enamel are lost, the teeth show an irregular, rough surface. When the enamel is altogether lost, the teeth are small and brown, and the exposed dentin is extremely sensitive.

References

Histology of enamel

1. Arnold, F. A., Jr.: Grand Rapids Fluoridation Study—Results Pertaining to the Eleventh Year of Fluoridation, Am. J. Pub. Health **47:** 539, 1957.
2. Bartelstone, H. J., Mandel, I. D., Oshry, E., and Seidlin, S. M.: Use of Radioactive Iodine as a Tracer in the Study of the Physiology of the Teeth, Science **106:** 132, 1947.
3. Battistone, G. D., and Burnett, G. W.: The Amino Acid Composition of Human Enamel Protein, J. D. Res. **35:** 260, 1956.
4. Baud, C. A., and Held, A. J.: Silberfärbung, Röntgenmikrographie und Mineralgehalt der Zahnhartgewebe (Silver Impregnation, Microradiography and Mineral Content of Calcified Tooth Structure), Deutsche zahnärztl. Z. **11:** 309, 1956.
5. Bergman, G., Hammerlund-Essler, E., and Lysell, L.: Studies on Mineralized Dental Tissues. XII. Microradiographic Study of Caries in Deciduous Teeth, Acta odont. scandinav. **16:** 113, 1958.
6. Beust, T.: Morphology and Biology of the Enamel Tufts With Remarks on Their Relation to Caries, J. A. D. A. **19:** 488, 1932.
7. Bhussry, B. R., and Bibby, B. G.: Surface Changes in Enamel, J. D. Res. **36:** 409, 1957.
8. Bibby, B. G., and Van Huysen, G.: Changes in the Enamel Surfaces; a Possible Defense Against Caries, J. A. D. A. **20:** 828, 1933.
9. Block, R. J., Horwitt, M. K., and Bolling, D.: Comparative Protein Chemistry. The Composition of the Proteins of Human Enamel and Fish Scales, J. D. Res. **28:** 518, 1949.
10. Bodecker, C. F.: Enamel of the Teeth Decalcified by the Celloidin Decalcifying Method and Examined by Ultraviolet Light, D. Rev. **20:** 317, 1906.
11. Bodecker, C. F.: The Color of the Teeth as an Index of Their Resistance to Decay, Internat. J. Orthodontia **19:** 386, 1933.
12. Brabant, H., and Klees, L.: Histological Contribution to the Study of Lamellae in Human Dental Enamel, Internat. D. J. **8:** 539, 1958.
13. Burgess, R. C., Nikiforuk, G., and Maclaren, C.: Chromatographic Studies of Carbohydrate Components in Enamel, Arch. Oral Biol. **1:** 8, 1960.
14. Cape, A. T., and Kitchin, P. C.: Histologic Phenomena of Tooth Tissue as Observed Under Polarized Light; With a Note on the Roentgen Ray Spectra of Enamel and Dentin, J. A. D. A. **17:** 193, 1930.
15. Chase, S. W.: The Number of Enamel Prisms in Human Teeth, J. A. D. A. **14:** 1921, 1927.
16. Eastoe, J. E.: Organic Matrix of Tooth Enamel, Nature **187:** 411, 1960.
17. Engel, M. B.: Glycogen and Carbohydrate-Protein Complex in Developing Teeth of the Rat, J. D. Res. **27:** 681, 1948.
18. Fish, E. W.: An Experimental Investigation of Enamel, Dentin and the Dental Pulp, London, 1932, John Bale Sons & Danielsson, Ltd.
19. Frank, R.: Études sur l'infrastructure microscopique de l'émail et sur la surface libre coronaire de la dent (Studies on the Submicroscopic Structure of the Enamel and the Free Coronal Surface of the Tooth), Schweiz. Monatschr. Zahnhk. **60:** 1109, 1950.
20. Frank, R. M., and Sognnaes, R. F.: Electron Microscopy of Matrix Formation and Calcification in Rat Enamel, Arch. Oral Biol. **1:** 339, 1960.
21. Frank, R. M., Sognnaes, R. F., and Kern, R.: In Sognnaes, R. F. (editor): Calcification in Biological Systems, Washington, D. C., 1960, American Association for the Advancement of Science.
22. Glas, J.-E., and Omnell, K.-A.: Studies on the Ultrastructure of Dental Enamel, J. Ultrastructure Res. **3:** 334, 1960.
23. Glimcher, M. J., Bonar, L. C., and Daniel, E. J.: The Molecular Structure of the Protein Matrix of Bovine Dental Enamel, J. Molecular Biol. **3:** 541, 1961.
24. Gottlieb, B.: Aetiologie und Prophylaxe der Zahnkaries (Etiology and Prophylaxis of Dental Caries), Ztschr. f. Stomatol. **19:** 129, 1921.
25. Gottlieb, B.: Dental Caries, Philadelphia, 1947, Lea & Febiger.

26. Gray, J. A., Schweizer, H. C., Rosevear, F. B., and Broge, R. W.: Electron Microscopic Observations of the Differences in the Effects of Stannous Fluoride and Sodium Fluoride on Dental Enamel, J. D. Res. **37**: 638, 1958.

27. Gustafson, G.: A Morphologic Investigation of Certain Variations in the Structure and Mineralization of Human Dental Enamel, Odont. Tskr. **67**: 361, 1959.

28. Gustafson, G.: The Structure of Human Dental Enamel, Odont. Tskr. **53**: (supp.), 1945.

29. Helmcke, Von J.-G.: Elektronenmikroskopische Strukturuntersuchungen an gesunden und kranken Zähnen (Investigations of Electron Microscopic Structure in Sound and Pathological Teeth), Deutsche zahnärztl. Z. **10**: 1461, 1955.

30. Hess, W. C., Lee, C. Y., and Neidig, B. A.: The Amino Acid Composition of Enamel Protein, J. D. Res. **32**: 585, 1953.

31. Hill, T. J.: Fluoride Dentifrices, J. A. D. A. **59**: 1121, 1959.

32. Hodson, J. J.: An Investigation Into the Microscopic Structure of the Common Forms of Enamel Lamellae With Special Reference to Their Origin and Contents, Oral Surg., Oral Med. & Oral Path. **6**: 305, 383, 495, 1953.

33. Hollander, F., Bodecker, C. F., Applebaum, E., and Saper, E.: A Study of the Bands of Schreger by Histological and Grenz-Ray Methods, D. Cosmos **77**: 12, 1935.

34. Jansen, M. T., and Visser, J. B.: Permeable Structures in Normal Enamel, J. D. Res. **29**: 622, 1950.

35. Klees, L.: Les lamelles, les buissons, et le développement de la carie dans l'émail dentaire humain (Lamellae, Tufts and the Development of Caries in Human Dental Enamel), Bull. du Group Int. pour la Recher. Scient. en Stomatol. **1**: 1, 1961.

36. Klees, L., and Klees, K.: Ueber die Regenerationsfähigkeit des Schmelzoberhäutchens (The Regenerative Capacity of the Enamel Cuticle), Stoma **2**: 58, 1958.

37. Kronfeld, R.: First Permanent Molar. Its Condition at Birth and Its Postnatal Development, J. A. D. A. **22**: 1131, 1935.

38. Lefkowitz, W., and Bodecker, C. F.: Concerning the "Vitality" of the Calcified Dental Tissue. II. Permeability of the Enamel, J. D. Res. **17**: 453, 1938.

39. Losee, F. L., Jennings, W. H., Lawson, M. E., and Forziati, A. F.: Microstructure of the Human Tooth, J. D. Res. **36**: 911, 1957.

40. Lyon, D. G., and Darling, A. I.: Orientation of the Crystallites in Human Dental Enamel, Brit. D. J. **102**: 483, 1957.

41. Manly, R. S.: A Structureless Recurrent Deposit on Teeth, J. D. Res. **22**: 479, 1943.

42. Moulton, F. R.: Dental Caries and Fluorine, Washington, D. C., 1946, American Association for the Advancement of Science.

43. Muhler, J. C., and Radike, A. W.: Effect of a Dentifrice Containing Stannous Fluoride on Adults. II. Results at the End of Two Years of Unsupervised Use, J. A. D. A. **55**: 196, 1957.

44. Muhler, J. C.: Present Status of Topical Fluoride Therapy, J. Dent. Child. **26**: 173, 1959.

45. Nasmyth, A.: Researches on the Development, Structures and Diseases of the Teeth, London, 1839, John Churchill.

46. Orban, B.: Histology of Enamel Lamellae and Tufts, J. A. D. A. **15**: 305, 1928.

47. Pautard, F. G. E.: An X-ray Diffraction Pattern From Human Enamel Matrix, Arch. Oral Biol. **3**: 217, 1961.

48. Pickerill, H. P.: The Prevention of Dental Caries and Oral Sepsis, New York, 1924, Paul B. Hoeber, Inc.

49. Piez, K. A.: The Nature of the Protein Matrix of Human Enamel, J. D. Res. **39**: 712, 1960.

50. Piez, K. A., and Likins, R. C.: The Nature of Collagen. II. Vertebrate Collagens. In Sognnaes, R. F. (editor): Calcification in Biological Systems, Washington, D. C., 1960, American Association for the Advancement of Science, p. 411.

51. Posner, A. S., and Stephenson, S. R.: Isomorphous Substitution in Enamel Apatite, J. A. D. A. **46**: 257, 1953.

52. Retzius, A.: Microscopic Investigation of the Structure of the Teeth, Arch. Anat. & Physiol., p. 486, 1837.

53. Robinson, H. B. G., Boling, L. R., and Lischer, B.: In Cowdry, E. V. (editor): Problems of Ageing, ed. 2, Baltimore, 1942, Williams & Wilkins Co.

54. Rushton, M. A.: On the Fine Contour Lines of the Enamel of Milk Teeth, D. Rec. **53**: 170, 1933.

55. Rushton, M. A.: The Birefringence of Deciduous Tooth Enamel Formed Before and After Birth, Brit. D. J. **67**: 1, 1939.

56. Savory, A., and Brudevold, F.: The Distribution of Nitrogen in Human Enamel, J. D. Res. **38:** 436, 1959.

57. Schmidt, W. J., and Keil, A.: Die gesunden und die erkrankten Zahngewebe des Menschen und der Wirbeltiere im Polarisationsmikroskop (Normal and Pathological Tooth Structure of Humans and Vertebrates in the Polarization Microscope), München, 1958, Carl Hanser Verlag.

58. Schour, I.: The Neonatal Line in the Enamel and Dentin of the Human Deciduous Teeth and First Permanent Molar, J. A. D. A. **23:** 1946, 1936.

59. Schour, I., and Hoffman, M. M.: Studies in Tooth Development. I. The 16 Microns Rhythm in the Enamel and Dentin From Fish to Man, J. D. Res. **18:** 91, 1939.

60. Scott, D. B., and Wyckoff, R. W. G.: Typical Structures on Replicas of Apparently Intact Tooth Surfaces, Pub. Health Rep. **61:** 1397, 1946.

61. Scott, D. B., Kaplan, H., and Wyckoff, R. W. G.: Replica Studies of Changes in Tooth Surfaces With Age, J. D. Res. **28:** 31, 1949.

62. Scott, D. B., and Wyckoff, R. W. G.: Studies of Tooth Surface Structure by Optical and Electron Microscopy, J. A. D. A. **39:** 275, 1949.

63. Scott, D. B., Ussing, M. J., Sognnaes, R. F., and Wyckoff, R. W. G.: Electron Microscopy of Mature Human Enamel, J. D. Res. **31:** 74, 1952.

64. Scott, D. B.: The Electron Microscopy of Enamel and Dentin, J. New York Acad. Sc. **60:** 575, 1955.

65. Scott, D. B.: Studies of the Crystal Structure of Enamel by Electron Microscopy and Electron Diffraction, Proc. 25th Year Celebration University of Rochester D. Res. Fell. Program, 175, 1957.

66. Scott, D. B.: The Crystalline Component of Dental Enamel, Fourth International Conference on Electron Microscopy, Berlin, 1960, Springer-Verlag.

67. Shaw, J. H.: Fluoridation as a Public Health Measure, Washington, D. C., 1954, American Association for the Advancement of Science.

68. Skillen, W. C.: The Permeability of Enamel in Relation to Stain, J. A. D. A. **11:** 402, 1924.

69. Smreker, E.: Ueber die Form der Schmelzprismen menschlicher Zähne und die Kittsubstanz des Schmelzes (On the Form of Enamel Prisms of Human Teeth, and the Cement Substance of the Enamel), Arch. f. mikr. Anat. **66:** 312, 1905.

70. Sognnaes, R. F.: The Organic Elements of the Enamel. III. The Pattern of the Organic Framework in the Region of the Neonatal and Other Incremental Lines of the Enamel, J. D. Res. **29:** 260, 1950.

71. Sognnaes, R. F.: The Organic Elements of the Enamel. IV. The Gross Morphology and the Histological Relationship of the Lamellae to the Organic Framework of the Enamel, J. D. Res. **29:** 260, 1950.

72. Sognnaes, R. F.: Microstructure and Histochemical Characteristics of the Mineralized Tissues, J. New York Acad. Sc. **60:** 545, 1955.

73. Sognnaes, R. F., Shaw, J. H., and Bogoroch, R.: Radiotracer Studies of Bone, Cementum, Dentin and Enamel of Rhesus Monkeys, Am. J. Physiol. **180:** 408, 1955.

74. Spiers, R. L.: The Nature of Surface Enamel, Brit. D. J. **107:** 209, 1959.

75. Stack, M. V.: Organic Constituents of Enamel, J. A. D. A. **48:** 297, 1954.

76. Thewlis, J.: The Structure of Teeth as Shown by X-ray Examination, Medical Research Council, Special Report Series No. 238, London, 1940, Her Majesty's Stationery Office.

77. Trautz, O. R., Klein, E., Fessenden, E., and Addelston, H. K.: The Interpretation of the X-ray Diffractograms Obtained From Human Dental Enamel, J. D. Res. **32:** 420, 1953.

78. Turner, E. P.: The Integument of the Enamel Surface of the Human Tooth, D. Practitioner & D. Record **8:** 341, 1958.

79. Ussing, Marie J.: The Development of the Epithelial Attachment, Acta odont. scandinav. **13:** 123, 1955; reprinted J. West. Soc. Periodont. **3:** 71, 1955.

80. Vallotton, C. F.: An Acquired Pigmented Pellicle of the Enamel Surface, J. D. Res. **24:** 161, 1945.

81. Wainwright, W. W., and Lemoine, F. A.: Rapid Diffuse Penetration of Intact Enamel and Dentin by Carbon[14]-labeled urea, J. A. D. A. **41:** 135, 1950.

82. Watson, M. L.: The Extracellular Nature of Enamel in the Rat, J. Biophys. & Biochem. Cytol. **7:** 489, 1960.

83. Wislocki, G. B., and Sognnaes, R. F.: Histochemical Reactions of Normal Teeth, Am. J. Anat. **87:** 239, 1950.

84. Wolf, J.: Plastische Histologie der Zahngewebe (Plastic Histology of Dental Tissues), Deutsche Zahn-, Mund- u. Kieferheilk. **7**: 265, 1940.
85. Wolf, J.: Reparative Vorgänge an der Oberflache naturlicher und kunstlich hervorgerufener Schmelzdefekte (Reparative Processes on the Surface of Natural and Artificially Created Enamel Defects), Deutsche Zahn-, Mund- u. Kieferheilk. **8**: 222, 1941.
86. Yoon, S. H., Brudwold, F., Gardner, D. E., and Smith, F. A.: Distribution of Fluoride in Teeth From Areas With Different Levels of Fluoride in the Water Supply, J. D. Res. **39**: 845, 1960.

Development of enamel

87. Allan, J. H.: Investigations Into the Mineralization Pattern of Human Dental Enamel, J. D. Res. **38**: 1096, 1959.
88. Beams, H. W., and King, R. L.: The Golgi Apparatus in the Developing Tooth With Special Reference to Polarity, Anat. Rec. **57**: 29, 1933.
89. Chase, S. W.: The Development, Histology and Physiology of Enamel and Dentin, J. D. Res. **27**: 87, 1948.
90. Crabb, H. S. M.: The Pattern of Mineralization of Human Dental Enamel, Proc. Royal Soc. Med. **52**: 118, 1959.
91. Crabb, H. S. M., and Darling, A. I.: The Gradient of Mineralization in Developing Enamel, Arch. Oral Biol. **2**: 308, 1960.
92. Deakins, M.: Changes in the Ash, Water, and Organic Content of Pig Enamel During Calcification, J. D. Res. **21**: 429, 1942.
93. Deakins, M., and Burt, R. L.: The Deposition of Calcium, Phosphorus, and Carbon Dioxide in Calcifying Dental Enamel, J. Biol. Chem. **156**: 77, 1944.
94. Dean, H. T.: Chronic Endemic Dental Fluorosis, J. A. M. A. **107**: 1269, 1936.
95. Diamond, M., and Applebaum, E.: The Epithelial Sheath: Histogenesis and Function, J. D. Res. **21**: 403, 1942.
96. Engel, M. B., and Furuta, W.: Histochemical Studies of Phosphates: Distribution in Developing Teeth of Albino Rat, Proc. Soc. Exper. Biol. & Med. **50**: 5, 1942.
97. Engel, M. B.: Some Changes in the Connective Tissue Ground Substance Associated With the Eruption of the Teeth, J. D. Res. **30**: 322, 1951.
98. Fearnhead, R. W.: Mineralization of Rat Enamel, Nature **189**: 509, 1960.
99. Frank, R. M., Sognnaes, R. F., and Kern, R.: Calcification of Dental Tissue With Special Reference to Enamel Ultrastructure. In Sognnaes, R. F. (editor): Calcification in Biological Systems, Washington, D. C., 1960, American Association for the Advancement of Science.
100. Frank, R. M., and Sognnaes, R. F.: Electron Microscopy of Matrix Formation and Calcification in Rat Enamel, Arch. Oral Biol. **1**: 339, 1960.
101. Glasstone, S.: Development of Tooth Germs in Vitro, J. Anat. **70**: 260, 1936.
102. Gustafson, A.-G.: A Morphologic Investigation of Certain Variations in the Structure and Mineralization of Human Dental Enamel, Odont. Tskr. **67**: 361, 1959.
103. Hahn, W. E.: The Capacity of Developing Tooth Germ Elements for Self-Differentiation When Transplanted, J. D. Res. **20**: 5, 1941.
104. Hals, E.: Fluorescence Microscopy of Developing and Adult Teeth, Oslo, 1953, Norwegian Academic Press.
105. Hammarlund-Essler, E.: A Microradiographic, Microphotometric and X-ray Diffraction Study of Human Developing Enamel, Transactions Royal Schools of Dentistry, Stockholm and Umea **4**: 15, 1958.
106. Harders-Steinhäuser, M.: Die Erhärtung des Zahnschmelzes nach polarisationsoptischen Untersuchungen (Mineralization of the Enamel Studied With the Polarization Microscope), Z. f. zellforsch. u. mikroskop. Anat. **28**: 274, 1938.
107. Held, H.: Ueber die Bildung des Schmelzgewebes (On the Formation of Enamel), Ztschr. f. mikr.-anat. Forsch. **5**: 668, 1926.
108. Jump, E. B.: Vascularity of the Human Enamel Organ, J. D. Res. **17**: 505, 1938.
109. Kérébel, B., and Grimbert, L.: Histogénèse de l'émail (Histogenesis of the Enamel), Rev. Franc. d'Odonto-Stomatol. **7**: 1, 1958.
110. Kotanyi, E.: Histologische Befunde an retinierten Zähnen (Histologic Findings on Embedded Teeth), Ztschr. f. Stomatol. **22**: 747, 1924.
111. Kreshover, S. J., and Hancock, J. A., Jr.: The Pathogenesis of Abnormal Enamel Formation in Rabbits Inoculated With Vaccinia, J. D. Res. **35**: 685, 1936.

112. Lenz, V. H.: Elektronenmikroskopische Untersuchungen der Schmelzgenese (Electron Microscopic Studies of Enamel Formation), Deutsche zahnärztl. Z. **13:** 991, 1958.
113. Marsland, E. A.: A Histological Investigation of Amelogenesis in Rats, Brit. D. J. **91:** 252, 1951; **92:** 109, 1952.
114. Maximow, A. A., and Bloom, W.: A Textbook of Histology, ed. 7, Philadelphia, 1957, W. B. Saunders Co.
115. Morningstar, C. H.: Effect of Infection of the Deciduous Molar on the Permanent Tooth Germ, J. A. D. A. **24:** 786, 1937.
116. Nuckolls, J., Leicester, H. M., and Dienstein, B.: Amelogenesis, J. Am. Coll. Dentists **14:** 118, 1947.
117. Nylen, M. U., and Scott, D. B.: An Electron Microscopic Study of the Early Stages of Dentinogenesis, Pub. 613, U. S. Public Health Service, Washington, D. C., 1958, U. S. Government Printing Office.
118. Nylen, M. U., and Scott, D. B.: Electron Microscopic Studies of Odontogenesis, J. Indiana State Dental Assoc. **39:** 406, 1960.
119. Orban, B.: Zur Histologie des Schmelzes und der Schmelzdentingrenze (Histology of Enamel and Dentino-Enamel Junction), Vrtljschr. f. Zahnheilk. **42:** 336, 1926.
120. Orban, B., Sicher, H., and Weinmann, J. P.: Amelogenesis (a Critique and a New Concept), J. Am. Coll. Dentists **10:** 13, 1943.
121. Pannese, E.: Observations on the Ultrastructure of the Enamel Organ. I. Stellate Reticulum and Stratum Intermedium, J. Ultrastructure Res. **4:** 372, 1960.
122. Pindborg, J. J., and Weinmann, J. P.: Morphologic and Functional Correlations in the Enamel Organ of the Rat Incisor During Amelogenesis, Acta anat. **36:** 367, 1959.
123. Quigley, M. B.: Electron Microscopy of Developing Enamel Matrix in the Syrian Hamster, J. D. Res. **38:** 180, 1959.
124. Reith, E. J.: The Ultrastructure of Ameloblasts From the Growing End of Rat Incisors, Arch. Oral Biol. **2:** 253, 1960.
125. de Renyi, G. S.: Central Bodies in the Cells of the Inner Enamel Epithelium, Am. J. Anat. **53:** 413, 1933.
126. Sarnat, B. G., and Schour, I.: Enamel Hypoplasia (Chronologic Enamel Aplasia) in Relation to Systemic Disease, J. A. D. A. **28:** 1989, 1941; **29:** 67, 1942.
127. Saunders, J. B. De C. M., Nuckolls, J., and Frisbie, H. E.: Amelogenesis, J. Am. Coll. Dentists **9:** 107, 1942.
128. Scott, D. B., Nylen, M. U., and Takuma, S.: Electron Microscopy of Developing and Mature Calcified Tissues, Rev. Belge de Sci. Dent. **14:** 329, 1959.
129. Scott, D. B.: The Crystalline Component of Dental Enamel, Fourth International Conference on Electron Microscopy, Berlin, 1960, Springer-Verlag.
130. Scott, D. B., and Nylen, M. U.: Changing Concepts in Dental Histology, Ann. New York Acad. Sc. **85:** 133, 1960.
131. Sognnaes, R. F., Scott, D. B., Ussing, M. J., and Wyckoff, R. W. G.: Electron Microscopy of the Enamel of Teeth in Various Stages of Development, J. D. Res. **31:** 85, 1952.
132. Suga, S.: Amelogenesis—Some Histological and Histochemical Observations, Internat. D. J. **9:** 394, 1959.
133. Ussing, M. J.: The Development of the Epithelial Attachment, Acta odont. scandinav. **13:** 123, 1955; reprinted J. West. Soc. Periodont. **3:** 71, 1955.
134. Wasserman, F.: Enamel Formation Under Normal and Experimental Conditions, J. D. Res. **20:** 254, 1941.
135. Wasserman, F.: Analysis of the Enamel Formation in the Continuously Growing Teeth of Normal and Vitamin C Deficient Guinea Pigs, J. D. Res. **23:** 463, 1944.
136. Watson, M. L., and Avery, J. K.: The Development of the Hamster Lower Incisor as Observed by Electron Microscopy, Am. J. Anat. **95:** 109, 1954.
137. Watson, M. L.: The Extracellular Nature of Enamel in the Rat, J. Biophys. & Biochem. Cytol. **7:** 489, 1960.
138. Weinmann, J. P., Wessinger, G. D., and Reed, G.: Correlation of Chemical and Histological Investigations on Developing Enamel, J. D. Res. **21:** 171, 1942.
139. Weinmann, J. P.: Developmental Disturbances of the Enamel, Bur **43:** 20, 1943.
140. Weinmann, J. P., Svoboda, J. F., and Woods, R. W.: Hereditary Disturbances of Enamel Formation and Calcification, J. A. D. A. **32:** 397, 1945.
141. Witkop, C. J., Jr.: Dental Genetics 1959, J. A. D. A. **60:** 564, 1960.

Chapter IV • DENTIN*

The dentin constitutes the bulk of the tooth. As a living tissue it consists of specialized cells, the odontoblasts, and an intercellular substance. Though the bodies of the odontoblasts are arranged on the pulpal surface of the dentin, the entire cell biologically and morphologically has to be considered the cell of the dentin. A simple calculation will show that the odontoblastic process is at least four times the volume of the nucleus-containing body, perikaryon, of the odontoblast. In its physical and chemical qualities, the dentin closely resembles bone. The main morphologic difference between bone and dentin is that some of the osteoblasts forming the bone are enclosed in the intercellular substance as osteocytes, whereas the dentin contains only cytoplasmic processes of the odontoblasts.

PHYSICAL PROPERTIES

In teeth of young individuals the dentin usually is light yellowish in color. Unlike enamel, which is very hard and brittle, dentin is subject to slight deformation and is highly elastic. It is somewhat harder than bone but is considerably softer than enamel. The smaller content of mineral salts in dentin renders it more radiolucent than enamel.

Under polarized light dentin exhibits a slight positive birefringence. Actually, the organic matrix fibrils are optically positive, and the inorganic crystals are optically negative. The observed birefringence represents a net effect.[20, 48]

CHEMICAL COMPOSITION

Dentin consists of 30 per cent organic matter and water and 70 per cent inorganic material (see Table 2, Chapter III). The organic substance consists of collagenous fibrils and a ground substance of mucopolysaccharides.[27, 37] The

---

*First draft submitted by Gerrit Bevelander; revised by D. B. Scott and Marie U. Nylen.

inorganic component has been shown by roentgen ray diffraction to consist of hydroxyapatite, as in bone, cementum, and enamel. Organic and inorganic substances can be separated by decalcification or incineration. In the process of decalcification the organic constituents can be retained and maintain the shape of the dentin. Incineration removes the organic constituents; the inorganic substances shrink but retain the shape of the organ and become very brittle and porous.

STRUCTURE

As indicated earlier, the bodies of the odontoblasts are arranged in a layer on the pulpal surface of the dentin, and only their cytoplasmic processes are embedded in the mineralized matrix. Each cell gives rise to one process, which traverses the entire thickness of the dentin in a narrow channel called the dentinal tubule. Inasmuch as the inner surface of the dentin is lined completely with odontoblasts, tubules are found throughout.

Dentinal tubules. The course of the dentinal tubules is somewhat curved,

Fig. 71. Ground section of human incisor. Observe course of dentinal tubules.

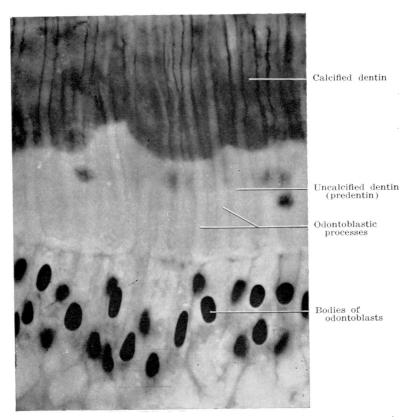

Calcified dentin

Uncalcified dentin
(predentin)

Odontoblastic
processes

Bodies of
odontoblasts

Fig. 72. Odontoblastic processes (Tomes' fibers) lying in dentinal tubules, extend from the perikaryon of the odontoblasts into the dentin.

resembling an S in shape (Fig. 71). Starting at right angles from the pulpal surface, the first convexity of this doubly curved course is directed toward the apex of the tooth. In the root and in the area of incisal edges and cusps, the tubules are almost straight. Over their entire lengths the tubules exhibit minute, relatively regular secondary curvatures that are sinusoid in shape.

The ratio between surface areas at the outside and inside of the dentin is about 5 to 1. Accordingly, the tubules are farther apart in the peripheral layers and are more closely packed near the pulp. In addition, they are wider near the pulpal cavity (2 to 3 microns) and become narrower at their outer ends (1 micron). The ratio between the numbers of tubules per unit area on the pulpal and outer surfaces of the dentin is about 4 to 1. Near the pulpal surface of the dentin, the number per square millimeter is said to vary between 30,000 and 75,000.[35] There are more tubules per unit area in the crown than in the root.

Odontoblastic processes. The odontoblastic processes, which run inside the tubules, are thin-walled tubes (Figs. 72 and 77, *C* and *D*) filled with cytoplasm that is continuous with that of the cell bodies. The walls themselves are elongations of the cell membranes of the odontoblasts. The processes are thickest near

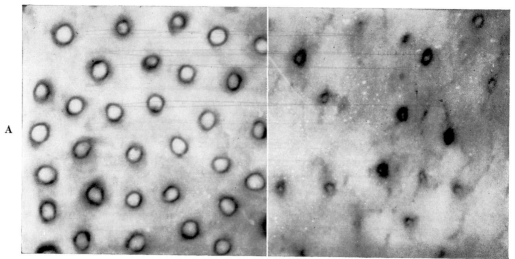

Fig. 73. Well-fixed decalcified section of dentin. **A,** Close to the pulp. **B,** Close to the outer surface. No shrinkage between dentinal fibers and dentinal tubules. The entire tubule is filled by the fiber. Note size and number of dentinal tubules in **A** and **B.** (×2,000.)

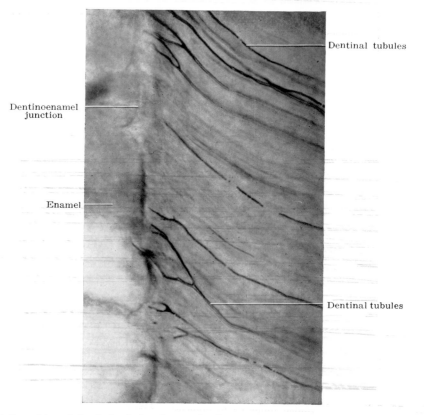

Fig. 74. Branching of dentinal tubules close to the dentinoenamel junction.

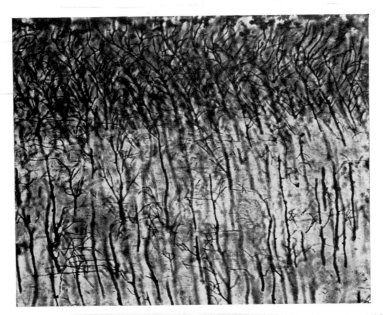

Fig. 75. Secondary branches of dentinal tubules anastomosing with those of neighboring as well as distant tubules. (Courtesy Dr. Gerrit Bevelander.)

Fig. 76. Splitting of dentinal tubules into branches. (Courtesy Dr. Gerrit Bevelander.)

2o3/1

the cell bodies, tapering toward the outer surface of the dentin (Fig. 73). They divide near their ends into several terminal branches. (Fig. 74.) Along their course they send out thin secondary processes, enclosed in fine tubules, which seem to unite with similar lateral extensions from neighboring odontoblastic processes (Fig. 75). These may be compared to the anastomosing processes of osteocytes. Some terminal branches of the odontoblastic processes extend into the

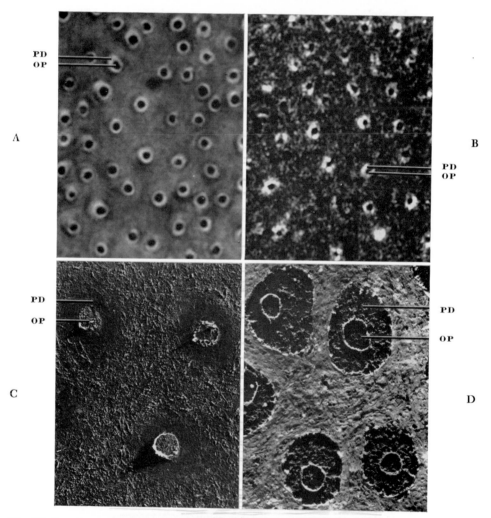

Fig. 77. Four types of microscopic preparations, illustrating the peritubular dentin. **OP,** Odontoblastic process; **PD,** peritubular dentin. **A,** An undemineralized ground section, photographed by transmitted light. The peritubular zone appears translucent. (×1,000.) **B,** A contact roentgen ray micrograph of an undemineralized ground section. The high degree of mineralization in the peritubular zone is evident from its radiopacity. (×1,000.) **C,** An electron micrograph of a surface replica from an undemineralized ground section. The peritubular zone appears solid. (×5,000.) **D,** An electron micrograph of a demineralized section. The organic matrix in the peritubular zone is comparatively sparse. (×5,000.)

enamel (see Chapter III). Occasionally a process splits into two almost equally thick branches; this division can occur at any distance from the pulp. (Fig. 76.) In reality, all of these divisions and anastomoses are the result of splitting and fusion of the cell extensions during dentinogenesis, as the odontoblasts recede from the dentinoenamel or dentinocemental junction.

Peritubular dentin. The structural interrelations in dentin are visualized best in cross sections. When undemineralized ground sections are observed by transmitted light, a ring-shaped transparent zone surrounding the odontoblastic process can be differentiated from the remaining darker matrix (Fig. 77, A).[16] This transparent zone, which forms the wall of the dentinal tubule, has been termed peritubular dentin[22] and the regions external to it, intertubular dentin. Studies with soft roentgen rays[5, 8, 13, 40] and with the electron micro-

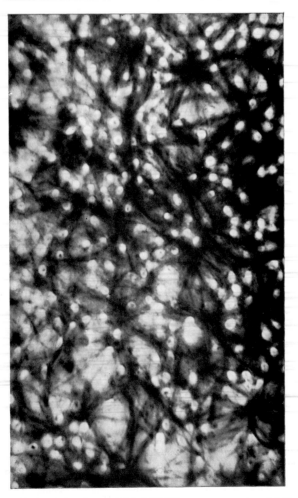

Fig. 78. Collagenous fibrils of the dentin (decalcified transverse section; Mallory-Azan). (From Orban, B.: J. A. D. A. **16:** 1547, 1929.)

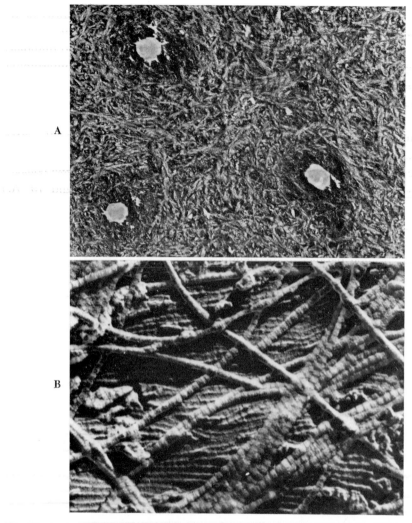

Fig. 79. A, A cross section of undecalcified human dentin, showing the crisscross arrangement of the collagenous matrix fibrils. Also note the densely calcified peritubular dentin. (Electron micrograph, ×9,000.) **B,** Fibrils of the intertubular matrix at higher magnification showing the typical crossbanding of collagen. (Electron micrograph, ×40,000.)

scope[22, 26, 58, 59, 65] have shown convincingly that the peritubular dentin is more highly mineralized than the intertubular dentin (Fig. 77, B). A very delicate organic matrix has been demonstrated in the peritubular dentin[22, 25, 56, 57, 65] (Fig. 77, C and D), but this usually is lost in demineralized sections, and then the odontoblastic process appears to be surrounded by an empty space.

The interface between the peritubular and the intertubular dentin stands out very clearly in ground sections (Fig. 77, A), and in earlier years it was thought that this sharply defined boundary was due to a special structure known as the sheath of Neumann. Electron microscopic studies have so far failed to confirm the presence of such a sheath.[54, 55] On the contrary, the organic fibrils of the peritubular dentin appear to intermix with the fibrils of the intertubular dentin.[17, 25, 65] It is possible that the optical effect is due to the marked difference in the degree of mineralization between the peritubular and the intertubular dentin. Differences in staining reactions between the boundary area and the dentin on either side indicate, however, that this boundary area does have special properties, although its true nature is not understood.[39]

Intertubular dentin. The main body of the dentin is constituted by the intertubular dentin. Although it is highly mineralized, over half of its volume is taken up by the organic matrix. This matrix consists of large numbers of fine collagen fibrils enveloped in an amorphous ground substance. (Figs. 78 and 79, A.) The fibrils are from 0.05 to 0.2 micron in diameter, and they show the cross-banding at 640Å intervals, which is typical of collagen. (Fig. 79, B).[53, 54] They are quite densely packed together, often in the form of bundles, and they run in crisscross fashion parallel to the dentin surface, at right or oblique angles to the tubules (Figs. 78 and 79, A). The external, first-formed portions of the dentin beneath both the enamel and the cementum contain variable amounts of coarse fibril bundles, which are arranged at right angles to the dentinal surface and give the layer a different microscopic appearance.[33] This is called mantle dentin[73] in distinction from the subsequently formed main portion, which is known as circumpulpal dentin.

Mineral component. Roentgen ray diffraction studies have shown that the

Fig. 80. Incremental lines in the dentin. Imbrication or incremental lines of von Ebner. Ground section.

apatite crystals that comprise the mineral component of dentin have average lengths of about 0.04 micron.[66] Due to their minuteness and to the masking effect of the organic elements, crystals have been very difficult to discern microscopically in mature dentin.[26] When they have been observed under the electron microscope, they have appeared as flat platelets, up to 0.1 micron long.[29]

Polarized light studies have shown that the mineralization of dentin is largely the result of crystallization around and between the collagen fibrils,[21, 48] although electron microscopic investigations have indicated that the fibrils themselves may mineralize.[64, 72] Within and around individual collagen fibrils, the crystals appear to be oriented with their long axes paralleling the fibril direction.[48, 64] Since the fibrils form a network, the over-all distribution pattern of the crystals in dentin is far more complex than in enamel.

Incremental lines. The imbrication or incremental lines of von Ebner appear as fine lines, which in cross sections run at right angles to the dentinal tubules (Fig. 80). They correspond to the Retzius lines in the enamel and likewise

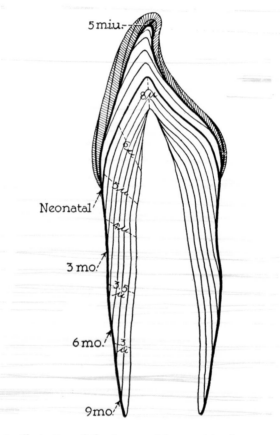

Fig. 81. Diagrammatic illustration of the incremental, appositional pattern (upper deciduous central incisor). **5 m.i.u.,** 5 months in utero. (From Schour, I., and Massler, M.: J. A. D. A. **23:** 1946, 1936.)

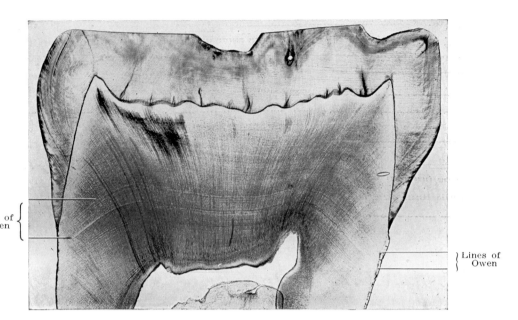

Lines of Owen }

} Lines of Owen

Fig. 82. Accentuated incremental lines in the dentin: contour lines of Owen.

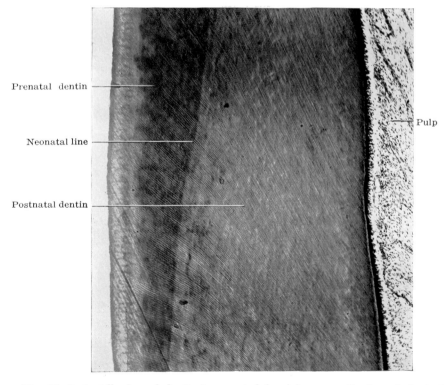

Prenatal dentin

Pulp

Neonatal line

Postnatal dentin

Fig. 83. Postnatally formed dentin is separated from the prenatally formed dentin by an accentuated incremental line, the neonatal line. (From Schour, I., and Poncher, H. G.: **Am. J.** Dis. Child. **54:** 757, 1937.)

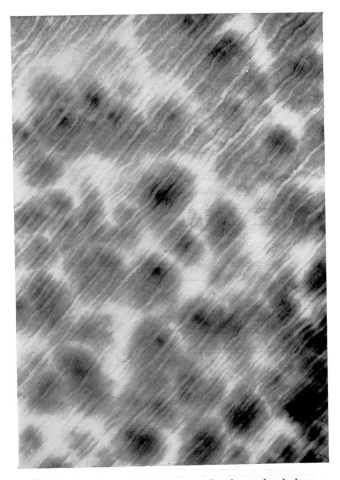

Fig. 84. Interglobular dentin (decalcified section). The dentinal tubules pass uninterrupted through the uncalcified and hypocalcified areas.

reflect variations in structure and mineralization during formation of the dentin. The course of the lines indicates the growth pattern of the dentin. The distance between the lines corresponds to the daily rate of apposition, which in the crown varies from 4 to 8 microns[51, 52] and becomes decreasingly less as root formation progresses[50] (Fig. 81.)

Occasionally, some of the incremental lines are accentuated due to disturbances in the mineralization process. Such lines, readily demonstrated in ground sections, are known as the contour lines of Owen. (Fig. 82.) Studies with soft roentgen rays have shown that these lines represent hypocalcified bands.[1, 2, 7]

In the deciduous teeth and in the first permanent molars, where the dentin is formed partly before and partly after birth, the prenatal and postnatal dentin are separated by an accentuated contour line, the so-called neonatal line (Fig. 83).[49] This line is the result of incomplete calcification, due to metabolic disturbances at the time of adjustment of the newborn to the abrupt changes in environment and nutrition.

Interglobular dentin. Mineralization of the dentin sometimes begins in small globular areas that normally fuse to form a uniformly calcified dentin layer (see section on Dentinogenesis). If fusion does not take place, unmineralized or hypomineralized regions remain between the globules; these are termed interglobular dentin. The dentinal tubules pass uninterrupted through the uncalcified areas (Fig. 84). Interglobular dentin is found chiefly in the crown,

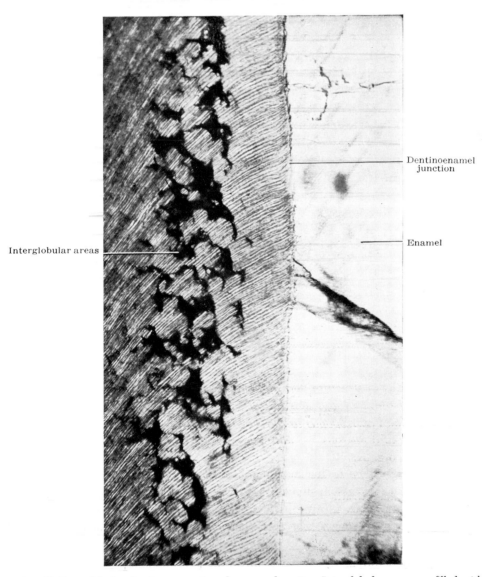

Dentinoenamel junction

Enamel

Interglobular areas

Fig. 85. Interglobular dentin as seen in a dry ground section. Interglobular areas are filled with air and appear black in transmitted light. (Courtesy Dr. Gerrit Bevelander.)

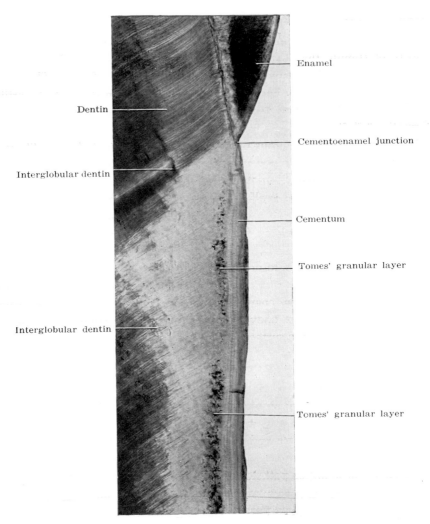

Fig. 86. Tomes' granular layer lies in the peripheral zone of the root dentin. Ground section.

near the dentinoenamel junction, and it follows the incremental pattern of the tooth.

In dry ground sections the interglobular dentin is largely lost and replaced by air. Then the interglobular "spaces" appear black (Fig. 85).

Tomes' granular layer. In the ground sections, a thin layer of dentin adjacent to the cementum almost invariably appears granular (Fig. 86). This is known as Tomes' granular layer, and it is thought to be made up of minute areas of interglobular dentin. The configuration is found only in the root, and it does not follow the incremental pattern. It is thought to represent an interference with mineralization of the entire surface layer of the root dentin prior to the beginning of cementum formation.

INNERVATION

Despite the obvious clinical observation that dentin is highly sensitive to a diversity of stimuli, the anatomic basis for this sensitivity is still controversial. The literature contains many accounts of the presence of nerve fibers in the dentinal tubules, but these findings have repeatedly been shown to be artifacts. The difficulties of histologic technique are the cause for the lack of definitive information.[9, 35, 71]

The pulp contains numerous unmyelinated and myelinated nerve fibers. The former end on the pulpal blood vessels, whereas the latter can be followed into the subodontoblastic layer. Here they lose their myelin sheath and can be followed into the odontoblastic layer itself. In this layer most of the fibers apparently end in contact with the cell body or perikaryon of the odontoblasts. Occasionally, part of a nerve fiber seems to be embedded in the predentin or the dentin, curving back into the odontoblastic layer or, more rarely, ending in the dentin. Intratubular nerve fibers could not be established.[47]

The sensitivity of the dentin can be explained by changes in the odontoblastic processes, possibly causing changes of surface tension and surface electrical charges on the odontoblast body that in turn provide a stimulus for the nerve endings in contact with the surface of the cell body.

AGE AND FUNCTIONAL CHANGES

Vitality of dentin. Since the odontoblasts, the perikaryon, as well as the process, must be considered an integral part of the dentin, there is no question of dentin being a vital tissue. Also, if vitality is understood to be the capacity of the tissue to react to physiologic and pathologic stimuli, dentin must be considered a vital tissue.

The effects of aging or pathologic influences are expressed by the deposition of new layers of dentin (secondary or reparative dentin) and through alteration of the original dentin (transparent or sclerotic dentin). While the renewed formation of dentin is explained easily on the basis of dentinogenetic activity of the odontoblasts, the mechanisms by which the primary dentin is modified are not well understood. It is generally thought, however, that the permeation of chemical substances into mature dentin occurs by intracellular transport within the odontoblastic processes and by diffusion in the calcified matrix.[61] Since the entire dentin is in a moderate state of hydration (see Table 2, Chapter III), diffusion is most likely mediated by the fluid component. The latter probably is present simply as an integral constituent of the odontoblastic cytoplasm, the collagenous matrix fibrils, the organic ground substance, and even the inorganic crystals. The term "dental lymph" has been applied by some to this component,[14, 15, 23, 24] but the consequent implication that it is a circulating medium has seemed unwarranted. The dentin owes to this tissue fluid its turgor that plays an important role in securing the connection between dentin and enamel.

Secondary dentin. Under normal conditions, formation of dentin may con-

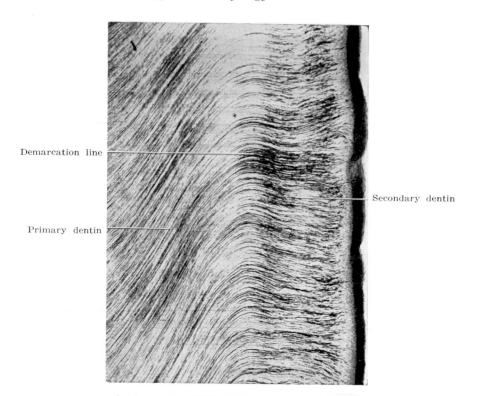

Fig. 87. The dentinal tubules bend sharply as they pass from the primary into the secondary dentin. Dentinal tubules are somewhat irregular in the secondary dentin. Ground section. Pulpal surface at the right.

tinue throughout life. Frequently, the dentin formed in later years of life is separated from that previously formed by a darkly stained line. In such cases the dentinal tubules bend more or less sharply at this line (Fig. 87). In other cases the newly formed dentin shows irregularities of varying degree; the tubules are often wavy and less numerous for a unit area of the dentin. The dentin, forming pulpward of the line of demarcation, is called secondary dentin. This dentin is deposited on the entire pulpal surface of the dentin. However, its formation does not proceed at an even rate in all areas. This is observed best in premolars and molars, where more secondary dentin is produced on the floor and on the roof of the pulpal chamber than on the side walls (see Chapter V).

The change in the structure from primary to secondary dentin may be caused by the progressive crowding of the odontoblasts, which finally leads to the elimination of some and to the rearrangement of the remaining odontoblasts.[60]

Reparative dentin. If, by extensive wear, erosion, caries, or operative procedures, odontoblastic processes are exposed or cut, the entire cell is more or less severely damaged. Such damaged odontoblasts may either continue to form a hard substance or may degenerate, and then they are replaced by migration to

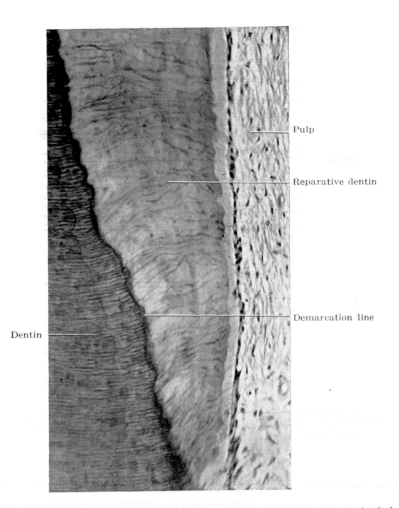

Pulp

Reparative dentin

Demarcation line

Dentin

Fig. 88. Reparative dentin stimulated by penetration of caries into the dentin. Dentinal tubules are irregular and less numerous than in regular dentin. Decalcified section.

the dentinal surface of undifferentiated cells from the deeper layers of the pulp. Damaged or newly differentiated odontoblasts are stimulated to a defense reaction in which hard tissue seals off the area of injury. This hard tissue is best called reparative dentin.[74] Here, the course of the tubules is frequently twisted, and their number is greatly reduced (Fig. 88). Some areas of reparative dentin contain few or no tubules. Dentin-forming cells are often included in the rapidly produced intercellular substance; such cells degenerate and vacate the spaces that they formerly occupied. Frequently, reparative dentin is separated from primary or secondary dentin by a deeply staining line.

Transparent (sclerotic) dentin. Stimuli of different nature not only induce additional formation of reparative dentin but also lead to changes in the dentin itself. Calcium salts may be deposited in or around degenerating odontoblastic

Fig. 89. Root transparency in a tooth from a middle-aged individual. Note the glasslike character of the apical dentin, which permits almost unobstructed visualization of the underlying grid. (Courtesy Dr. A. E. W. Miles.)

processes and may obliterate the tubules. The refractive indices of dentin in which the tubules are occluded are equalized, and such areas become transparent. Transparent dentin can be observed in teeth of old people, especially in their roots (Fig. 89). On the other hand, zones of transparent dentin develop around the dentinal part of enamel lamellae of Type B (Fig. 51) and under slowly progressing caries (Fig. 90). In such cases the blocking of the tubules may be considered as a defensive reaction of the dentin. Roentgen ray absorption tests[68] and permeability studies[12] have shown that such areas are denser, and hardness tests[28] have demonstrated that they are harder than normal dentin.[68, 69]

Transparent dentin can be demonstrated only in ground sections. It appears light in transmitted (Fig. 90, *A*) and dark in reflected light (Fig. 90, *B*) because the light passes through the transparent dentin but is reflected from the normal dentin. Dentin, decalcified by caries, normal dentin, and transparent dentin can be differentiated by the examination of ground section with soft roentgen rays, grenz rays.[2]

Fig. 90. Transparent dentin under a carious area viewed by **A,** transmitted light, **B,** reflected light, and **C,** grenz rays. Normal dentinal tubules are filled with air in dried ground sections and appear dark in transmitted light, **A,** and white in reflected light, **B.** Transparent dentin shows the opposite behavior because the tubules are filled with calcium salts. In a grenz-ray picture, **C,** transparent dentin appears more white because of its higher degree of radiopacity. (Grenz-ray picture courtesy Dr. E. Applebaum, Columbia University.)

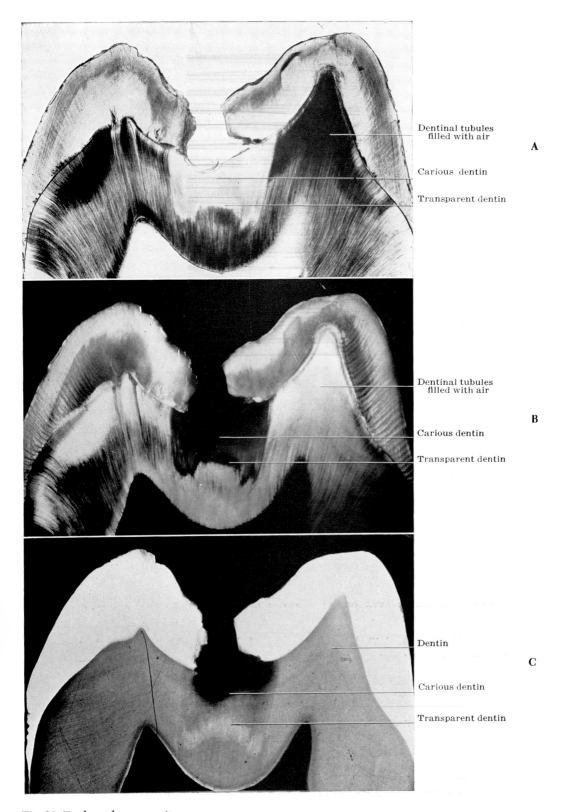

Dentinal tubules
filled with air

Carious dentin

Transparent dentin

A

Dentinal tubules
filled with air

Carious dentin

Transparent dentin

B

Dentin

Carious dentin

Transparent dentin

C

Fig. 90. For legend see opposite page.

The composition of dentin does not change with age though an increase of specific gravity of dentin with advancing age and reduction of its strength was reported.

Dead tracts. In dried ground sections of normal dentin the odontoblastic processes disintegrate, and the empty tubules are filled with air. They appear black in transmitted and white in reflected light (Fig. 90, *A* and *B*). Disintegration of odontoblastic processes may also occur in living teeth as a result of the injury of caries, attrition, abrasion, cavity preparation, or erosion (Figs. 91 and 92). Degeneration of odontoblasts is observed frequently in the narrow pulpal horns (Fig. 92) due to crowding of odontoblasts. Reparative dentin seals these tubules at their pulpal end. In all these cases dentinal tubules in vital teeth are filled with gaseous substances; in ground sections such groups of tubules appear black in transmitted and white in reflected light. Dentin areas characterized by degenerated odontoblastic processes have been called dead tracts.[24] They are areas of decreased sensitivity.[24, 67]

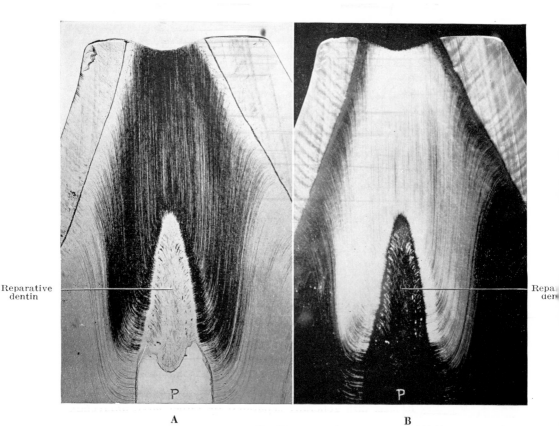

Reparative
dentin

Repa.
der

A   B

Fig. 91. Dead tracts in the dentin of a vital tooth, due to attrition and exposure of a group of dentinal tubules. Corresponding to the dead tract reparative dentin formation. **P,** Pulp. Dead tracts appear dark in transmitted light, **A,** and white in reflected light, **B.**

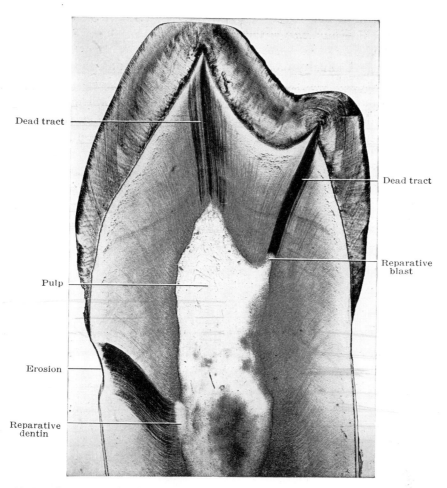

Fig. 92. Dead tracts in the dentin of a vital tooth, due to crowding and degeneration of odontoblasts in narrow pulpal horns and exposure of dentinal tubules in erosion. Well-fixed ground section (not dry!).

DEVELOPMENT

Life cycle of odontoblasts. The odontoblasts, which have been described in the preceding sections of this chapter as integral parts of mature dentin structure, are highly specialized connective tissue cells that differentiate from the peripheral cellular layer of the dental papilla. Prior to differentiation of the odontoblasts, the inner dental epithelium is separated from the dental papilla by a very thin, continuous basement membrane.[36, 57] The cells of the papilla are spindle-shaped, relatively uniform in size, and generally separated by rather large intercellular spaces. Some of the cells, however, come in contact with each other and with the basement membrane. At the beginning of differentiation, which takes place only in the presence of the inner dental epithelium, the peripheral cells of the dental papilla assume a short columnar shape and become aligned in a single layer along the basement membrane. The nuclei are already basally placed at this early stage in odontoblast formation, and they remain in this position permanently. The distal ends of the cells are villose, and several projections from each cell extend to the basement membrane. As differentiation progresses, the cells grow to several times their original length, whereas their width remains quite constant. Concomitantly, pronounced changes occur in the cytoplasm of the odontoblasts. These take the form of marked increases in the concentration of organelles, granular components, and globular elements.[36, 43, 72] (Fig. 93.) It is currently thought that

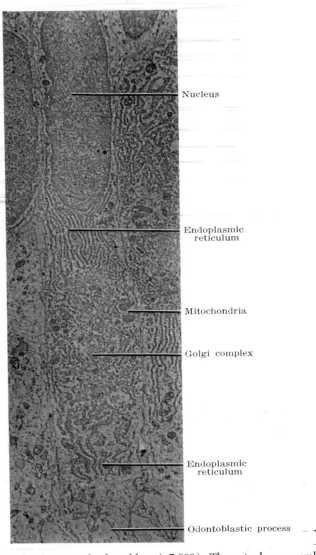

Nucleus

Endoplasmic reticulum

Mitochondria

Golgi complex

Endoplasmic reticulum

Odontoblastic process

Fig. 93. An electron micrograph of a typical odontoblast (×7,000). The cytoplasm resembles that of the ameloblasts, except that the mitochondria are scattered throughout the cell and there are less granules and vacuoles. Compare with Fig. 61.

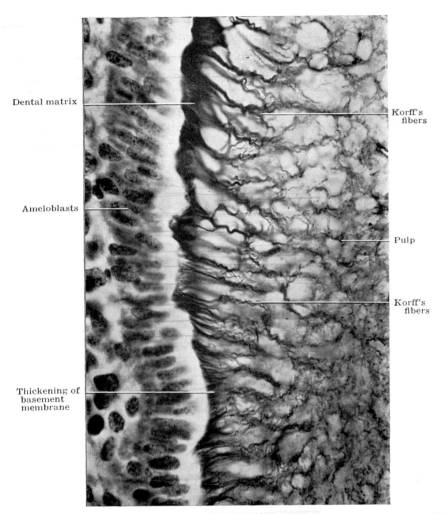

Dental matrix

Ameloblasts

Thickening of
basement
membrane

Korff's
fibers

Pulp

Korff's
fibers

Fig. 94. Thickening of the basement membrane between pulp and inner dental epithelium. Development of Korff's fibers. (Courtesy Dr. Gerrit Bevelander.)

such cytoplasmic alterations reflect a rise in cellular activity. This is taken as evidence that the odontoblasts participate actively in the formation of the dentinal matrix, a concept which has found additional support in histochemical studies.[30, 62]

The odontoblasts begin to recede from the basement membrane with the formation of the first dentin layer, and their distal ends become funnel-shaped. As more dentin is laid down, the cells continue to draw back, so that they are always located in a layer along the pulpal surface of the most recently formed predentin. As the cells recede they leave behind single extensions, the odontoblastic processes, which become embedded in the matrix.

The fully differentiated odontoblasts decrease in size during further dentin formation but otherwise retain their structural characteristics until dentin matrix formation is completed. At this point the odontoblasts enter a quiescent state. Unless they are stimulated by external influences to produce reparative dentin, their activity is restricted to an ordinarily very slow formation of secondary dentin.

Dentinogenesis. Dentinogenesis takes place in a two-phase sequence, the first of which is the elaboration of an uncalcified organic matrix called predentin. The second phase, mineralization, does not begin until a fairly wide band of predentin has been laid down. Mineralization proceeds at a rate which roughly parallels that of matrix formation. Thus, until the matrix is completed, the width of the predentin layer remains relatively constant.

The formation and calcification of dentin begin at the tips of the cusps or incisal edges and proceed inward by a rhythmic apposition of conic layers, one within the other. When the dentin of the crown has been laid down, the apical layers assume the shape of elongated, truncated cones (Fig. 81).[49] With completion of the root dentin, primary dentin formation comes to an end.

Predentin formation. The first sign of predentin development is the appearance of bundles of fibrils between the differentiating odontoblasts (Fig. 94). Near the basement membrane, where the cells are now funnel-shaped, the fibrils diverge in a fanlike arrangement (Figs. 94 and 95). These fibrillar bundles are known as Korff's fibers, and their origin and role in dentinogenesis have been the subject of much discussion.[11, 31, 32, 43, 45] Because they stain black with silver (argyrophil reaction), it was concluded that they are precollagenous, but more

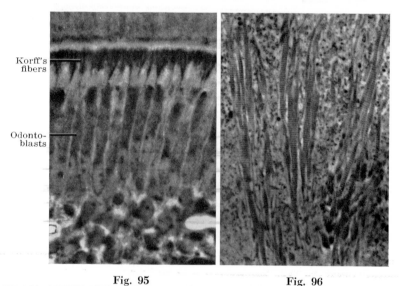

Fig. 95

Fig. 96

Fig. 95. Fanlike arrangement of Korff's fibers in mantle predentin.
Fig. 96. An electron micrograph showing at higher magnification the fibrils making up the Korff's fibers. Note the cross-bandings which identify these fibrils as collagen. (×10,000.)

recent studies with the electron microscope have revealed that at their first appearance the fibrils already demonstrate all the structural characteristics of collagen itself.[43] (Fig. 96.)

The Korff's fibers are a major constituent of the first-formed matrix, due to the fanlike arrangement of the fibrils near the basement membrane. This relatively narrow layer comprises the mantle predentin. In addition to the Korff's fibers, with fibrils from 0.1 to 0.2 micron in diameter, the remainder of the mantle pre-

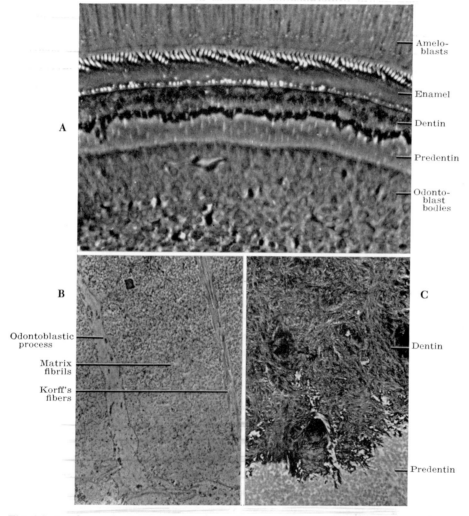

Fig. 97. **A,** The predentin and dentin layers in a developing rodent tooth, as seen by phase contrast. Observe the relations of all the layers of the odontogenic complex, from ameloblasts to odontoblasts. (×350.) **B,** The circumpulpal predentin layer, as seen under the electron microscope. Note the odontoblastic process, the compact Korff's fiber bundles, and the network of fine matrix fibrils. (×6,000.) **C,** The dentin layer, as seen under the electron microscope. Note the increased density in contrast to the predentin as a result of mineralization. (×6,000.)

dentin is made up of smaller collagen fibrils, around 0.05 micron in diameter. The latter fibrils, which form a network, predominate throughout all of the succeeding circumpulpal predentin layers, whereas the Korff's fibers, now compact bundles of parallel fibrils, become a minor component. (Fig. 97, B).

Electron microscope studies have shown that the smaller collagen fibrils of the predentin are formed in the immediate vicinity of the distal ends of the odontoblasts.[36, 43, 72] This finding is in agreement with the general concept that collagen fibril synthesis in connective tissues takes place through the extracellular aggregation of molecules secreted by fibril-forming cells.

Mineralization. After several microns of predentin have been laid down, mineralization of the layers closest to the dentinoenamel junction begins in small islands that subsequently fuse and form a continuous, calcified layer.[64] With further predentin formation, mineralization usually advances pulpward as a linear front roughly paralleling the odontoblastic layer. (Fig. 97, A and C.) Sometimes

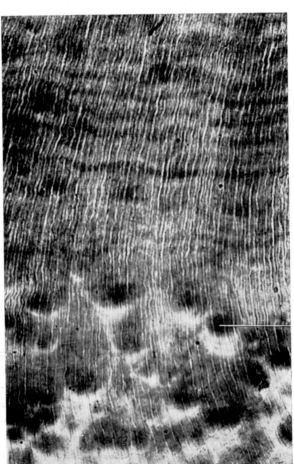

Linear
calcification

Globular
calcification

Fig. 98. Linear and globular calcification of dentin.

advancing mineralization occurs, however, in globular areas that subsequently fuse. On occasion, both globular and linear calcification are seen in combination (Fig. 98.)

Inception and advance of mineralization are accompanied by a number of changes in the ground substance of the organic matrix. Histochemical and radio-autographic investigation show that a mucopolysaccharide is deposited into the matrix and that it becomes especially prominent in the peritubular areas.[34, 75]

The phenomena actually involved in mineralization within collagenous matrices are still under investigation. There seems to be little doubt that the mucopolysaccharide ground substance plays a most important part in mineralization, but it has not yet been determined if it serves to initiate or promote the process, or rather to regulate it. It is likewise quite evident that the molecular configurations of the collagen fibrils influence the geometric distribution of the crystals that are laid down.[44]

The basic mineralization sequence in dentin appears to be as follows. The earliest crystal deposition is in the form of very fine plates of hydroxyapatite on the surfaces of the collagen fibrils and in the ground substance (Fig. 99, *A*). Subsequently, crystals seem to be laid down within the fibrils themselves.[64, 72] The crystals associated with the collagen fibrils are arranged in an orderly fashion, with their long axes paralleling the fibril axes, and in rows conforming to the 640Å striation pattern. Within the globular islands of mineralization, crystal deposition appears to take place radially from common centers, in a so-called spherulite form.[20, 48]

The general calcification process is gradual, but the peritubular region becomes highly mineralized at a very early stage (Fig. 99, *A*).[64] While there is obviously some crystal growth as dentin matures, the ultimate crystal size remains very small, the greatest length being on the order of 0.1 micron (Fig. 99, *B*).[29]

The collagens of the exposed dentin should not be insulted by strong drugs, undue operative trauma, unnecessary thermal changes, or irritating filling materials. Contact of exposed dentin with saliva should be avoided. It should be borne in mind that, by exposing 1 square millimeter of dentin, about 30,000 odontoblastic processes are exposed and thus 30,000 living cells are damaged. The surface may be treated with adstringent drugs, such as phenol or silver nitrate,[41, 76] to coagulate the protoplasm of the exposed odontoblastic processes. It is advisable to cover the exposed dentin surface by a nonirritating insulating substance.

The rapid penetration and spreading of caries in the dentin are due to the high content of organic substances in the dentin matrix. The enamel may be undermined at the dentinoenamel junction, even when caries in the enamel is confined to a small area. The dentinal tubules form a passage for invading bacteria that may thus reach the pulp through a thick dentinal layer.

The sensitivity of the dentin varies considerably in different layers. In most cases, it is greater close to the outer surface of the dentin and diminishes in the deeper layers. The sensitivity of the dentin, therefore, is not a warning signal

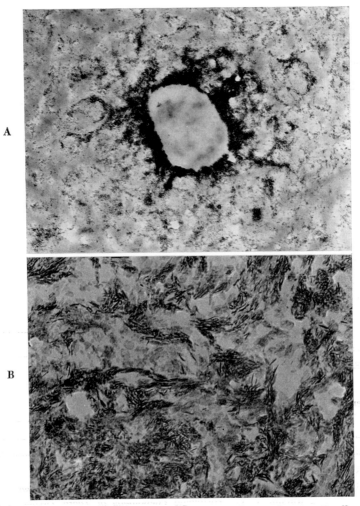

Fig. 99. A, A section of human dentin in an early stage of mineralization. Small crystals can be seen scattered in the intertubular matrix, whereas they are more densely packed in the peritubular region. (Electron micrograph, ×35,000.) **B,** The crystals in the intertubular matrix at a later stage in mineralization. (Electron micrograph, ×70,000.) Nearly maximal crystal size has been attained. Compare the dimensions of these crystals to those of the enamel crystals shown in Fig. 70.

to avoid exposure of the pulp. The operations in the dentin can be rendered less painful by avoiding heat and pressure by the use of cooling and of sharp instruments. The sensitivity of the dentin has been explained by the hypothesis that any injury or alteration of the odontoblast leads to changes in the surface charges of the cell body and that these changes stimulate the nerve endings on these cells (page 121). If this hypothesis is correct, then the greater sensitivity of the dentin near the dentinoenamel junction could be related to the branching of the odontoblastic processes in this zone, and, therefore, to the larger surface area of exposed cytoplasm of each cell.

References
Dentin

1. Amprino, R., and Camanni, F.: Historadiographic and Autoradiographic Researches on Hard Dental Tissues, Acta Anat. **28:** 217, 1956.
2. Applebaum, E., Hollander, F., and Bodecker, C. F.: Normal and Pathological Variations in Calcification of Teeth as Shown by the Use of Soft X-rays, D. Cosmos **75:** 1097, 1933.
3. Arwill, T.: Innervation of the Teeth, Stockholm, 1958, Ivar Haeggströms Boktryckeri AB.
4. Battistone, G. C., and Burnett, G. W.: The Amino Acid Composition of Human Dentinal Protein, J. D. Res. **35:** 255, 1956.
5. Baud, C. A., and Held, A. J.: Silberfärbung, Röntgenmikrographie und Mineralgehalt der Zahnhartgewebe (Silver Impregnation, Microradiography and Mineral Content of Calcified Tooth Structure), Deutsche zahnärztl. Z. **11:** 309, 1956.
6. Berggren, H.: Experimental Studies on the Permeability of Enamel and Dentine, Swed. D. J. **40** (No. 1B): 1, 1947.
7. Bergman, G., and Engfeldt, B.: Studies on Mineralized Dental Tissues. II. Microradiography as a Method for Studying Dental Tissue and Its Application to the Study of Caries, Acta odont. scandinav. **12:** 99, 1954.
8. Bergman, G., and Engfeldt, B.: Studies on Mineralized Dental Tissues. VI. The Distribution of Mineral Salts in the Dentine With Special Reference to the Dentinal Tubules, Acta odont. scandinav. **13:** 1, 1955.
9. Berkelbach van der Sprenkel, H.: Zur Neurologie des Zahnes (The Neurology of the Tooth), Ztschr. f. mikr.-anat. Forsch. **38:** 1, 1935.
10. Bernick, S.: Innervation of the Human Tooth, Anat. Rec. **101:** 81, 1948.
11. Bevelander, G.: The Development and Structure of the Fiber System of Dentin, Anat. Rec. **81:** 79, 1941.
12. Bevelander, G., and Amler, M. H.: Radioactive Phosphate Absorption by Dentin and Enamel, J. D. Res. **24:** 45, 1944.
13. Blake, G. C.: The Peritubular Translucent Zones in Human Dentine, Brit. D. J. **104:** 57, 1958.
14. Bodecker, C. F., and Lefkowitz, W.: Concerning the "Vitality" of Calcified Dental Tissues, J. D. Res. **16:** 463, 1937.
15. Bodecker, C. F., and Gies, Wm. J.: Concerning the Character of the Age Changes in Enamel and Dentin and Their Relation to the Vital Dental Pulp, J. Am. Coll. Dentists **9:** 381, 1942.
16. Bradford, E. W.: Interpretation of Ground Sections of Dentine, Brit. D. J. **90:** 303, 1951.
17. Bradford, E. W.: The Interpretation of Decalcified Sections of Human Dentin, Brit. D. J. **98:** 153, 1955.
18. Bradford, E. W.: The Maturation of the Dentine, Brit. D. J. **105:** 212, 1958.
19. Bradford, E. W.: The Dentine, A Barrier to Caries, Brit. D. J. **109:** 387, 1960.
20. Cape, A. T., and Kitchin, P. C.: Histologic Phenomena of Tooth Tissues as Observed Under Polarized Light, J. A. D. A. **17:** 193, 1930.
21. Ebner, V. v.: Ueber die Entwicklung der leimgebenden Fibrillen im Zahnbein (Development of Collagenous Fibrils in the Dentin), Sitzungsb. d. k. Akad. d. Wissensch. Vienna **115:** 281, 1906; and Anat. Anz. **29:** 137, 1906.
22. Fearnhead, R. W.: Histological Evidence for the Innervation of Human Dentine, J. Anat. **91:** 267, 1957.
23. Fish, E. W.: The Circulation of Lymph in Dentin and Enamel, J. A. D. A. **14:** 1, 1927.
24. Fish, E. W.: An Experimental Investigation of Enamel, Dentin and the Dental Pulp, London, 1932, John Bale Sons & Danielsson, Ltd.
25. Frank, R. M.: Contributions a l'étude au microscope electronique des tissus calcifiés normaux et pathologiques (Contributions to the Electron Microscope Study of Normal and Pathologic Calcified Tissues), Strasbourg, 1957, Sutter Waerth.
26. Frank, R. M.: Electron Microscopy of Undecalcified Sections of Human Adult Dentine, Arch. Oral Biol. **1:** 29, 1959.
27. Hess, W. C., Leo, D. Y., and Peckham, S. C.: The Lipid Content of Enamel and Dentin, J. D. Res. **35:** 273, 1956.
28. Hodge, H. C.: Microhardness Studies of Transparent Dentine, Brit. D. J. **63:** 181, 1937.
29. Johansen, E., and Parks, H. F.: Electron Microscopic Observations on the Three Dimensional Morphology of Apatite Crystallites of Human Dentine and Bone, J. Biophys. & Biochem. Cytol. **7:** 743, 1960.

30. Kerébel, B., and Grimbert, L.: Rôle des odontoblastes (Role of the Odontoblasts), Rev. Mensuelle Suisse d'Odontologie **68**: 729, 1958.
31. Korff, K. v.: Die Entwicklung der Zahnbein Grundsubstanz der Saugetiere (The Development of the Dentin Matrix in Mammals), Arch. f. mikr. Anat. **67**: 1, 1905.
32. Korff, K. v.: Wachstum der Dentingrundsubstanz verschiedener Wirbeltiere (Growth of the Dentin Matrix of Different Vertebrates), Ztschr. f. mikr.-anat. Forsch. **22**: 445, 1930.
33. Kramer, I. R. H.: The Distribution of Collagen Fibrils in the Dentine Matrix, Brit. D. J. **91**: 1, 1951.
34. Leblond, C. P., Bélanger, L. F., and Greulich, R. C.: Formation of Bones and Teeth as Visualized by Radioautography, Ann. New York Acad. Sc. **60**: 629, 1955.
35. Lehner, J., and Plenk, H.: Die Zähne (The Teeth). In von Möllendorff, W. (editor): Handbuch der Mikroskopischen Anatomie des Menschen, vol. 5, pt. 3, Berlin, 1936, Julius Springer, p. 449.
36. Lenz, H.: Elektronenmikroskopische Untersuchungen der Dentinentwicklung (Electron Microscopic Studies of Dentin Development), Deutsche Zahn- Mund- u. Kieferheilk. **30**: 367, 1959.
37. Losee, F. L., Leopold, R. F., and Hess, W. C.: Dentinal Protein, J. D. Res. **30**: 565, 1951.
38. Manley, E. B.: Traumatic Effect of the Drill During Cavity Preparation, Brit. D. J. **70**: 329, 1941.
39. Martens, P. J., Bradford, E. W., and Frank, R. M.: Tissue Changes in Dentine, Internat. D. J. **9**: 330, 1959.
40. Miller, J.: The Micro-Radiographic Appearance of Dentine, Brit. D. J. **97**: 7, 1954.
41. Muntz, J. A., Dorfman, A., and Stephan, R. M.: In Vitro Studies on Sterilization of Carious Dentin, J. A. D. A. **30**: 1893, 1943.
42. Nalbandian, J., Gonzales, F., and Sognnaes, R. F.: Sclerotic Age Changes in Root Dentin of Human Teeth as Observed by Optical, Electron, and X-ray Microscopy, J. D. Res. **39**: 598, 1960.
43. Nylen, M. U., and Scott, D. B.: An Electron Microscopic Study of the Early Stages of Dentinogenesis, Pub. 613, U. S. Public Health Service, Washington, D. C., 1958, U. S. Government Printing Office.
44. Nylen, M. U., and Scott, D. B.: Basic Studies in Calcification, J. D. Med. **15**: 80, 1960.
45. Orban, B.: The Development of the Dentin, J. A. D. A. **16**: 1547, 1929.
46. Piez, K. A., and Likins, R. C.: The Nature of Collagen; II. Vertebrate Collagens. In Sognnaes, R. F. (editor): Calcification in Biological Systems, Washington, D. C., 1960, American Association for the Advancement of Science.
47. Powers, M. M.: The Staining of Nerve Fibers in Teeth, J. D. Res. **31**: 383, 1952.
48. Schmidt, W. J., and Keil, A.: Die gesunden und die erkrankten Zahngewebe des Menschen und der Wirbeltiere im Polarisationsmikroskop (Normal and Pathological Tooth Structure of Humans and Vertebrates in the Polarization Microscope), München, 1958, Carl Hanser Verlag.
49. Schour, I., and Massler, M.: The Neonatal Line in Enamel and Dentin of the Human Deciduous Teeth and First Permanent Molar, J. A. D. A. **23**: 1946, 1936.
50. Schour, I., and Poncher, H. G.: The Rate of Apposition of Human Enamel and Dentin as Measured by the Effects of Acute Fluorosis, Am. J. Dis. Child. **54**: 757, 1937.
51. Schour, I., and Hoffman, M. M.: The Rate of Apposition of Enamel and Dentin in Man and Other Animals, J. D. Res. **18**: 161, 1939.
52. Schour, I., and Massler, M.: Studies in Tooth Development: The Growth Pattern of the Human Teeth, J. A. D. A. **27**: 1778, 1918, 1940.
53. Scott, D. B., and Wyckoff, R. W. G.: Electron Microscopy of Human Dentin, J. D. Res. **29**: 556, 1950.
54. Scott, D. B.: Recent Contributions in Dental Histology by the Use of the Electron Microscope, Internat. D. J. **4**: 64, 1953.
55. Scott, D. B.: The Electron Microscopy of Enamel and Dentin, J. New York Acad. Sc. **60**: 575, 1955.
56. Scott, D. B., Nylen, M. U., and Takuma, S.: Electron Microscopy of Developing and Mature Calcified Tissues, Rev. Belge de Sci. Dent. **14**: 329, 1959.
57. Scott, D. B., and Nylen, M. U.: Changing Concepts in Dental Histology, Ann. New York Acad. Sc. **85**: 133, 1960.
58. Shroff, F. R., Williamson, K. I., and Bertaud, W. S.: Electron Microscope Studies of Dentin, Oral Surg., Oral Med., & Oral Path. **7**: 662, 1954.

59. Shroff, F. R.: Further Electron Microscope Studies on Dentin: The Nature of the Odontoblast Process, Oral Surg., Oral Med., & Oral Path. **9**: 432, 1956.
60. Sicher, H.: The Biology of Dentin, Bur **46**: 121, 1946.
61. Sognnaes, R. F., Shaw, J. H., and Bogoroch, R.: Radiotracer Studies on Bone, Cementum, Dentin and Enamel of Rhesus Monkeys, Am. J. Physiol. **180**: 408, 1955.
62. Sognnaes, R. F.: Microstructure and Histochemical Characteristics of the Mineralized Tissues, J. New York Acad. Sc. **60**: 545, 1955.
63. Stanley, H. R., Jr., and Swerdlow, H.: Reaction of the Human Pulp to Cavity Preparation: Results Produced by Eight Different Grinding Techniques, J. A. D. A. **58**: 49, 1959.
64. Takuma, S.: Preliminary Report on the Mineralization of Human Dentin, J. D. Res. **39**: 964, 1960.
65. Takuma, S.: Electron Microscopy of the Structure Around the Dentinal Tubule, J. D. Res. **39**: 973, 1960.
66. Thewlis, J.: The Structure of Teeth as Shown by X-ray Examination, Medical Research Council, Special Report Series No. 238, London, 1940, Her Majesty's Stationery Office.
67. Thomas, B. O. A.: Protective Metamorphosis of the Dentin: Its Relationship to Pain, J. A. D. A. **31**: 459, 1944.
68. Van Huysen, G., Hodge, H. C., Warren, S. L., and Bishop, F. W.: Quantitative Roentgen-Ray Study of Certain Pathological Changes in Dentin, D. Cosmos **75**: 729, 1933.
69. Van Huysen, G., Bale, W. F., and Hodge, H. C.: Comparative Study of the Roentgen-Ray Absorption Properties of Normal and Pathological Dentin, D. Cosmos **77**: 146, 1935.
70. Van Huysen, G., and Gurley, W. B.: Histologic Changes in the Teeth of Dogs Following Preparation of Cavities at Various Depths, J. A. D. A. **26**: 87, 1939.
71. Wasserman, F.: The Innervation of Teeth, J. A. D. A. **26**: 1097, 1939.
72. Watson, M. L., and Avery, J. K.: The Development of the Hamster Lower Incisor as Observed by Electron Microscopy, Am. J. Anat. **95**: 109, 1954.
73. Weidenreich, F.: Ueber den Bau und die Entwicklung des Zahnbeines in der Reihe der Wirbeltiere (Structure and Development of the Dentin of the Vertebrates), Ztschr. f. Anat. u. Entwcklngsgesch. **76**: 218, 1925.
74. Weider, F. R., Schour, I., and Mohamed, C. I.: Reparative Dentin Following Cavity Preparation and Fillings in the Rat Molars, Oral Surg., Oral Med., & Oral Path. **9**: 221, 1956.
75. Wislocki, G. B., and Sognnaes, R. E.: Histochemical Reactions of Normal Teeth, Am. J. Anat. **87**: 239, 1950.
76. Zander, H. A., and Burrill, D.: Penetration of Silver Nitrate Solution Into Dentin, J. D. Res. **22**: 85, 1943.

Chapter V • PULP*

FUNCTION

Formative. The dental pulp is of mesodermal origin and contains most of the cellular and fibrous elements that are present in loose connective tissue. The primary function of the dental pulp is the production of dentin.

Nutritive. The pulp furnishes nourishment through the odontoblasts with their odontoblastic processes, to the dentin. The nutritional elements are contained in the tissue fluid.

Sensory. The nerves of the pulp contain both sensory and motor fibers. The sensory fibers, responsible for the sensitivity of pulp and dentin, mediate the sensation of pain and pain only. However, their main function seems to be the initiation of reflexes for the control of the circulation in the pulp. The motor leg of the reflex arch is provided by the visceral motor fibers that end on the muscles of the pulpal blood vessels.

Defensive. The pulp is well protected against external injuries as long as it is surrounded by an intact wall of dentin. However, if exposed to irritation, whether it is of mechanical, thermal, chemical, or bacterial nature, it can produce an effective defense reaction. The defensive reaction may be expressed in the formation of reparative dentin (see Chapter IV), if the irritation is mild, or as an inflammatory reaction, in cases of more severe irritation. While the rigid dentinal wall has to be considered as a protection to the pulp, it also endangers its existence under certain conditions. During inflammation of the pulp, the hyperemia and the exudate cause increasing pressure which, by occlusion of the blood vessels, may lead to pulpal necrosis—self-strangulation of the pulp.

---

*First draft submitted by Balint J. Orban.

ANATOMY

Pulp chamber. The dental pulp occupies the pulp cavity, which consists of the coronal pulp chamber and the root canals. The pulp is continuous with the periapical tissues through the apical foramen or foramina. In young individuals the shape of the pulp chamber follows, roughly, the outline of the tooth. The extensions into the cusps of the tooth are called pulpal horns. At the time of eruption the pulp chamber is large, but it becomes smaller with advancing age, due to continuous deposition of dentin[15] (Fig. 100). The decrease in the size of the pulp cavity in molars does not occur at the same rate on all walls of the pulp chamber. Formation of dentin progresses fastest on the floor* of the pulp chamber; some is formed at the occlusal wall or roof and less is formed on the side walls of the pulp chamber, so that the pulp dimension is reduced mainly in an occlusal direction. The chamber may be narrowed further and its shape may become irregular by formation of reparative dentin. The formation of pulpstones (Fig. 100, *B*) may also reduce the size and change the shape of the formerly wide pulp cavity, occasionally even occluding it.

Root canal. Advancing age induces similar changes in the root canals. During root formation the apical root end is a wide opening, limited by the epithelial diaphragm (Fig. 101, *A*). The dentinal walls taper, and the shape of the pulp canal is like a wide, open tube. As growth proceeds more dentin is formed, so that when the root of the tooth has matured, the root canal is considerably narrower. In the course of root formation, Hertwig's epithelial root sheath breaks up into epithelial rests, and cementum is laid down on the dentin surface (Fig. 101, *B*). The cementum will influence the size and shape of the apical foramen in the fully formed tooth. Root canals are not always straight and single but vary by the occurrence of accessory canals, as seen in corrosion specimens[12] or after filling of the root canals with India ink and clearing (Fig. 102).

At any distance from the apex of the tooth (Fig. 103*A*), side branches of the root canal may be present. In multirooted teeth these are observed at, or close to, the floor of the pulp chamber (Figs. 103*B* and 103*C*). A possible explanation for the development of all side branches of the pulp canals may be a defect in Hertwig's epithelial root sheath during development of the root at the site of a larger supernumerary blood vessel.

Apical foramen. There are variations in shape, size, and location of the apical foramen.[8] A regular, straight apical opening is rare (Fig. 101, *B*); occasionally the cementum can be traced from the outer surface of the dentin into the pulpal canal. Sometimes the apical opening is found on the lateral side of the apex (Fig. 104, *B*) although the root itself is not curved. Frequently there are two or more distinct apical foramina separated by a band of dentin and cementum, or cementum only.

---

*Regardless of the position of a tooth in the maxilla or the mandible, the occlusal wall is called the roof, the cervical wall, the floor.

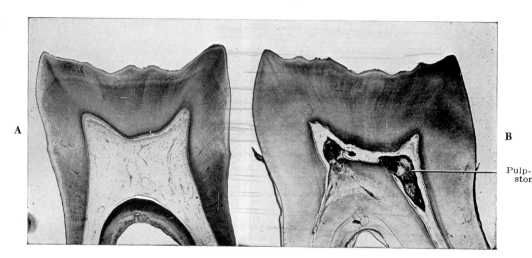

Pulp-
stone

Fig. 100A and B. Age changes in the pulp chamber of the first permanent molar. Decalcified sections. Enamel lost. **A,** From an individual 8 years of age. **B,** From an individual 55 years of age. Reduction of the pulp chamber in height is greater than in mesiodistal diameter. Pulpstones narrowing the entrance into the root canals in **B.** (From Kronfeld, R.: Dental Histology and Comparative Dental Anatomy, Philadelphia, 1937, Lea & Febiger.)

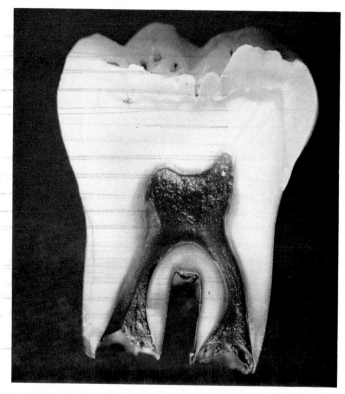

Fig. 100C. Mandibular third molar. Pulp exposed by grinding away the lingual wall. Note the shape of the dentin at the end of the incompletely formed roots. (Courtesy D. Permar.)

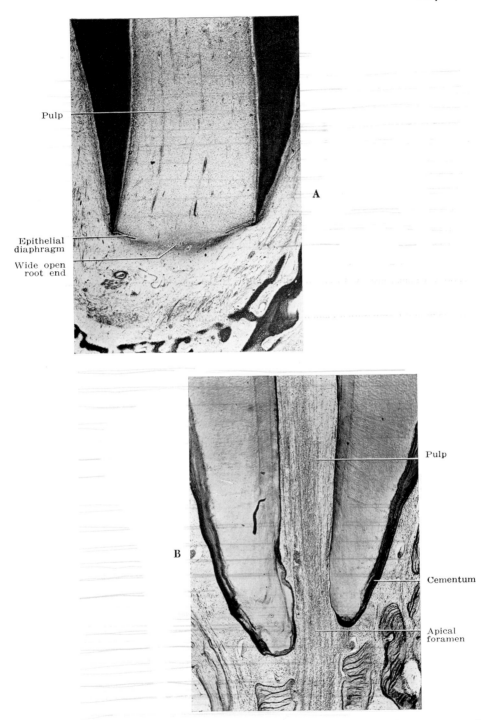

Pulp

Epithelial
diaphragm

Wide open
root end

A

B

Pulp

Cementum

Apical
foramen

Fig. 101. Development of the apical foramen. **A,** Undeveloped root end. Wide opening at end of the root, partly limited by epithelial diaphragm. **B,** Apical foramen fully formed. Root canal straight. Apical foramen surrounded by cementum. (From Coolidge, E. D.: J. A. D. A. **16:** 1456, 1929.)

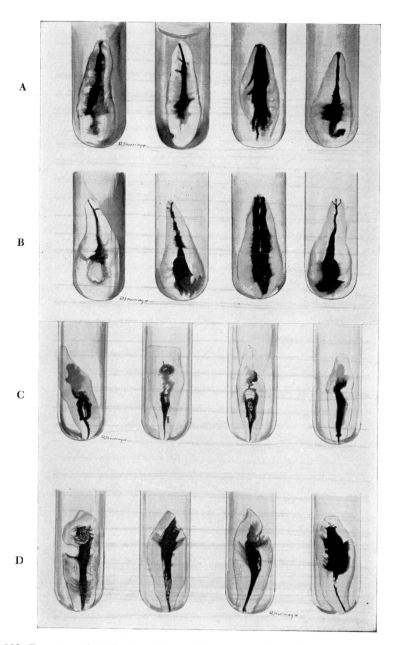

Fig. 102. Drawings of teeth after filling of the root canals with India ink and clearing. **A,** Upper incisors. **B,** Upper canines. **C,** Lower incisors. **D,** Lower canines. (From Aprile, E. C. de, and Aprile, H.: Rev. Odontologia **35:** 686, 1947.)

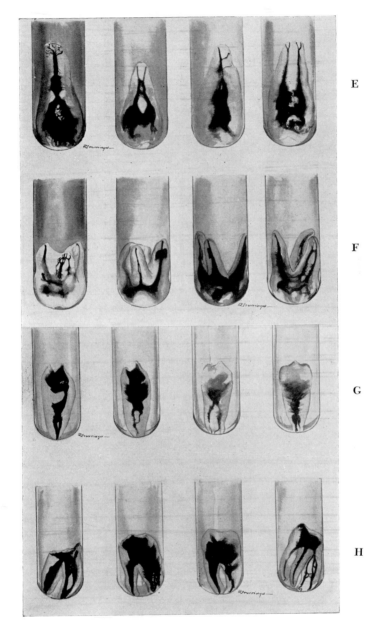

Fig. 102 (cont'd). **E,** Upper premolars. **F,** Upper molars. **G,** Lower premolars. **H,** Lower molars. (From Aprile, E. C. de, and Aprile, H.: Rev. Odontologica **35:** 686, 1947.)

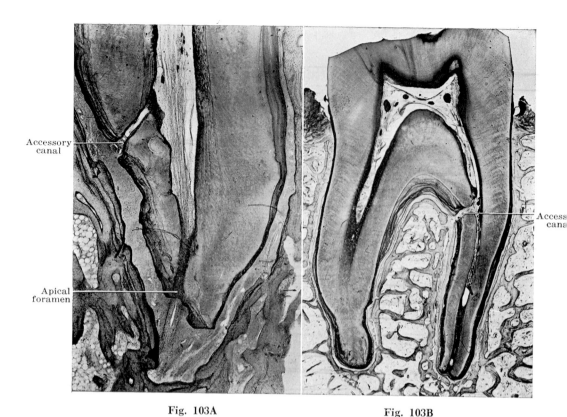

Accessory
canal

Apical
foramen

Access
cana

Fig. 103A   Fig. 103B

Fig. 103A. Sections through teeth with accessory canals. Close to the apex.
Fig. 103B. Sections through teeth with accessory canals. Close to the bifurcation.

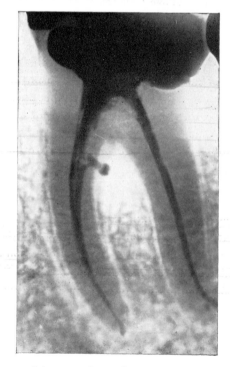

Fig. 103C. Roentgenogram of lower molar with accessory canal filled. (From Johnston, H.
B., and Orban, B.: J. Endodontia 3: 21, 1948.)

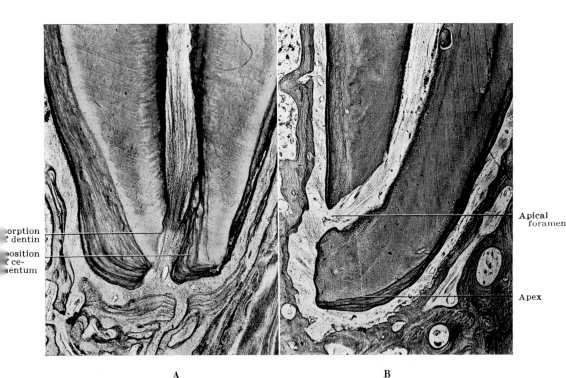

orption
dentin
osition
ce-
entum

Apical
foramen

Apex

A   B

Fig. 104. Variations of the apical foramen. **A,** Shift of the apical foramen by resorption of dentin and cementum on one surface and apposition of cementum on the other. **B,** Apical foramen on the side of the apex. (From Coolidge, E. D.: J. A. D. A. **16:** 1456, 1929.)

The location and the shape of the apical foramen may also undergo changes, due to functional influences upon the teeth.[21] A tooth may be tipped due to horizontal pressure, or it may migrate mesially, causing the apex to deviate in the opposite direction. Under these conditions, the tissues entering the pulp through the apical foramen exert pressure on one wall of the foramen, causing resorption. At the same time, cementum is laid down on the opposite side of the apical root canal, resulting in a change in the relative position of the original opening (Fig. 104, A).

DEVELOPMENT

The development of the dental pulp begins at a very early stage of embryonic life (in the eighth week) in the region of the incisors; in the other teeth, its development begins later. The first indication is a proliferation and condensation of mesenchymal elements, known as the dental papilla, at the basal end of the dental organ. (Fig. 105.) Due to the rapid proliferation of the epithelial elements, the tooth germ changes into a bell-shaped organ, and the future pulp is well defined in its outline. In a silver-impregnated section, the arrangement of the fibers in the embryonic dental papilla is clearly visible. (Fig. 105.) In the

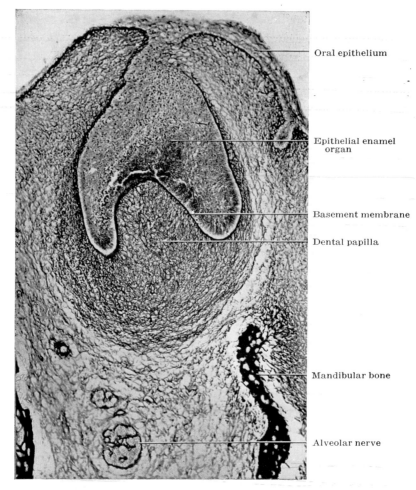

Oral epithelium

Epithelial enamel
organ

Basement membrane

Dental papilla

Mandibular bone

Alveolar nerve

Fig. 105. Development of the pulp. Dental papilla of a 2½-month embryo. The papilla contains a rich network of fine argyrophil fibers. Basement membrane between mesenchyme and epithelium. Silver impregnation. (Courtesy Dr. P. Gruenwald.)

future pulp area, the fibers are fine and arranged irregularly and much more densely than in the surrounding tissue.

The fibers in the embryonic pulp are argyrophil. There are no mature collagenous fibers in the embryonic pulp except where the fibers follow the course of the blood vessels.[9, 10, 17] As the development of the tooth germ progresses, the pulp becomes increasingly vascular, and the cells develop into star-shaped connective tissue cells, fibroblasts. (Fig. 106, A.) The cells are more numerous in the periphery of the pulp. Between the epithelium and the pulp cells is a cell-free layer. This contains numerous fibers, forming the basement or limiting membrane (see Chapter IV, section on Development).

Little is known about the time and mode of penetration of the pulp by nerve fibers.

STRUCTURAL ELEMENTS

The pulp is a specialized loose connective tissue. It consists of cells, fibroblasts, and an intercellular substance. The latter, in turn, consists of fibers and a ground substance. In addition, defense cells and the bodies of the cells of the dentin, the odontoblasts, are part of the dental pulp. The fibroblasts of the pulp and the defense cells are identical to those found elsewhere in loose connective tissue. The

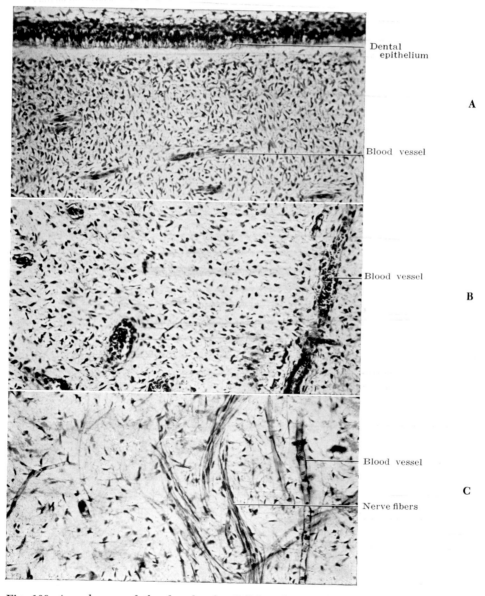

Dental epithelium

A

Blood vessel

Blood vessel

B

Blood vessel

C

Nerve fibers

Fig. 106. Age changes of the dental pulp. Cellular elements decrease, fibrous intercellular substance increases with advancing age. **A,** Newborn infant. **B,** Nine months of age. **C,** Adult.

fibers of the pulp are in part argyrophil, in part mature collagenous fibers. Elastic fibers are absent. The ground substance of the pulp seems to be of a much higher consistency than that in the loose connective tissue outside the pulp.

Fibroblasts and fibers. In the course of development the relative number of cellular elements in the dental pulp decreases, whereas the intercellular substance increases (Fig. 106, *B*). With advancing age there is a progressive reduction in the number of fibroblasts, accompanied by an increase in the number of fibers (Fig. 106, *C*). In the embryonic and immature pulp the cellular elements are predominant; in the mature tooth the fibrous constituents are predominant. In a fully developed tooth the cellular elements decrease in number toward the apical region, and the fibrous elements become more numerous (Fig. 109).

A microscopic specimen of a mature pulp, stained with hematoxylin and eosin,

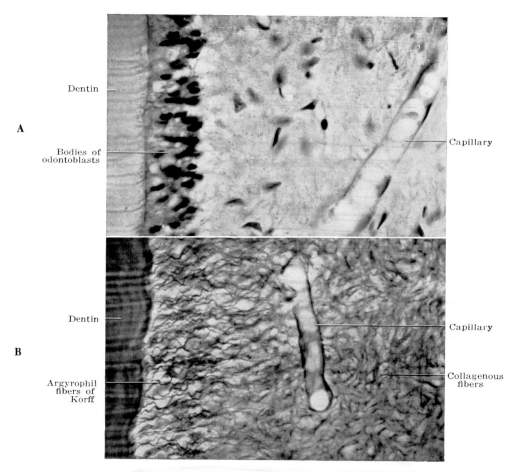

Fig. 107. Cellular and fibrous elements in the pulp. **A,** Cellular elements stained with hematoxylin and eosin. **B,** Fibrous elements stained by silver impregnation. Both specimens are from the same tooth.

does not present a complete picture of the structure of the pulp because not all of the fibrous elements are stained by means of this method (Fig. 107, A). A great abundance of fibers is revealed by silver impregnation (Fig. 107, B), especially the so-called Korff's fibers between the odontoblasts.

The Korff's fibers originate from among the pulp cells as thin fibers, thickening at the periphery of the pulp to form relatively thick bundles that pass between the odontoblasts and attach to the predentin. They stain black with silver, hence the term argyrophil fibers. The remaining part of the pulp contains a dense, irregular network of collagenous fibers.

Odontoblasts. The most significant change in the dental pulp during development is the differentiation of the connective tissue cells adjacent to the dental epithelium into odontoblasts. Dentin development begins in approximately the fifth embryonic month soon after the odontoblasts have differentiated. The

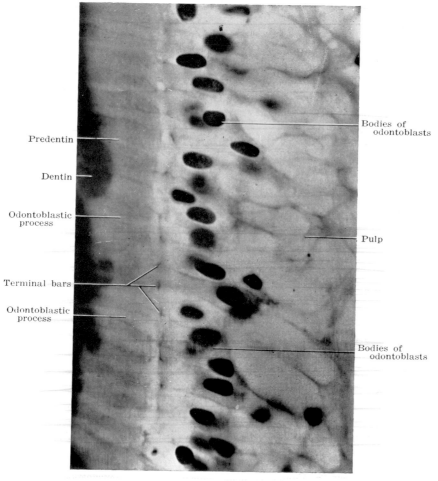

Fig. 108. Bodies of odontoblasts.

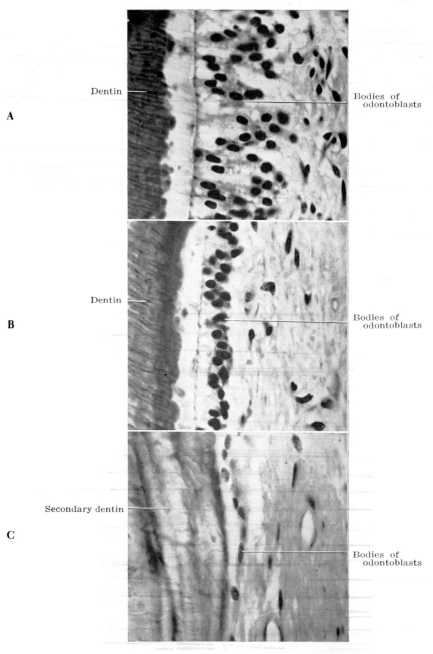

Dentin

Bodies of
odontoblasts

A

Dentin

Bodies of
odontoblasts

B

Secondary dentin

Bodies of
odontoblasts

C

Fig. 109. Variation of odontoblasts in different regions of one tooth. **A,** High columnar odontoblasts in the pulp chamber. **B,** Low columnar odontoblasts in the root canal. **C,** Flat odontoblasts in the apical region.

development of odontoblasts starts at the highest point in the pulpal horn and progresses apically.

Odontoblasts are highly differentiated connective tissue cells. Their body is columnar in shape, with an oval nucleus (Fig. 108). Each cell extends as a cytoplasmic process into a tubule in the dentin. At the dentinal surface the cell bodies of the odontoblasts are separated from each other by condensations, the so-called terminal bars. In a section the terminal bars appear as fine dots or lines. The odontoblasts are connected with each other and with the adjacent cells of the pulp by intercellular bridges. The cell bodies of some odontoblasts are long, others short, the nuclei being irregularly placed.

The form and arrangement of the bodies of the odontoblasts are not uniform throughout the pulp. They are more cylindrical and longer in the crown (Fig. 109, A) and become cuboid in the middle of the root (Fig. 109, B). Close to the apex of an adult tooth the odontoblasts are flat and spindle-shaped and can be recognized as odontoblasts only by their extensions into the dentin. In areas close to the apical foramen the dentin is irregular (Fig. 109, C).

The odontoblasts are responsible for the formation of the dentin and mediate its nutrition. Histogenetically and biologically they have to be regarded as

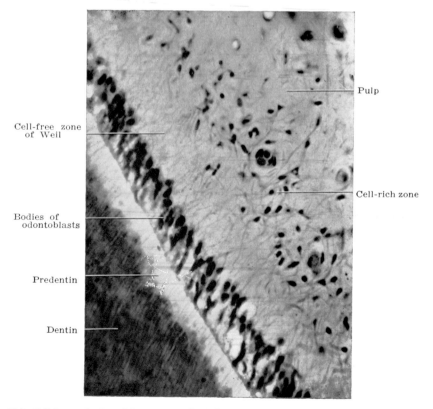

Fig. 110. Cell-free subodontoblastic zone of Weil.

the cells of the dentin. They play a part in the sensitivity of the dentin (see Chapter IV).

In the crown of the pulp a cell-free layer can be found just inside the layer of odontoblasts (Fig. 110). This layer is known as the zone of Weil or subodontoblastic layer, and it contains a network of nerve fibers, the subodontoblastic plexus. Most unmyelinated nerve fibers are a continuation of the myelinated fibers of the deeper layers and continue to their terminal arborization in the odontoblastic layer. The zone of Weil can be found but rarely in young teeth.

Defense cells. In addition to fibroblasts and odontoblasts there are other cellular elements in the human pulp, usually associated with small blood vessels and capillaries. They are important for the defense activity of the pulp, especially in inflammatory reaction.[26] In the normal pulp these cells are in a resting state.

One group of these cells is that of the histiocytes or adventitial cells or, according to Maximow's nomenclature,[19, 20] the "resting wandering cells." These cells generally are located along the capillaries. Their cytoplasm has a notched, irregular, branching appearance; the nuclei are dark and oval. They may have diverse forms in the human pulp but usually can be recognized easily. (Fig. 111.) Intravital staining methods have revealed that histiocytes are able to store dyes. During an inflammatory process the histiocytes withdraw their cytoplasmic branches, assume a rounded shape, migrate to the site of inflammation, and develop into macrophages.

Another cell type, the reserve cell of the loose connective tissue, was described by Maximow as undifferentiated mesenchymal cell (Fig. 111). These cells are also associated with capillaries, have oval, elongated nuclei, similar to those of fibroblasts or endothelial cells, and long, faintly visible cytoplasmic bodies. They are in close proximity to the capillary wall. These cells can be differentiated from endothelial cells only by their location outside the capillary wall. They are pluripotential; i.e., they can, under the proper stimulus, develop into any type of connective tissue element. In an inflammatory reaction they may form macrophages or plasma cells. After loss of odontoblasts they migrate to the dentinal wall through the zone of Weil and differentiate into cells that produce the reparative (irregular) dentin.

A third type of cell that plays an important part in defense reactions is the ameboid wandering cell or the lymphoid wandering cell (Fig. 111, *C*). These cells are migrating elements that probably escape from the blood stream. Their cytoplasm is sparse and shows fine extensions, pseudopodia, suggesting a migratory character. The dark nucleus fills almost the entire cell and is often slightly indented. In chronic inflammatory reactions they migrate to the site of injury; the function of these cells is not as yet fully known.

Blood vessels. The blood supply of the pulp is abundant. The blood vessels of the dental pulp enter through the apical foramen. Usually one artery and one or two veins are found at the foramen. The artery, carrying the blood into the pulp, branches out into a rich network of blood vessels soon after entering the root canal. The veins gather blood from the capillary network and carry it back through the apical foramen into larger vessels. (Fig. 112.) The arteries are clearly identified by their straight course and thicker walls, whereas the thin-walled veins are wider and frequently have an irregular outline. The capillaries form loops

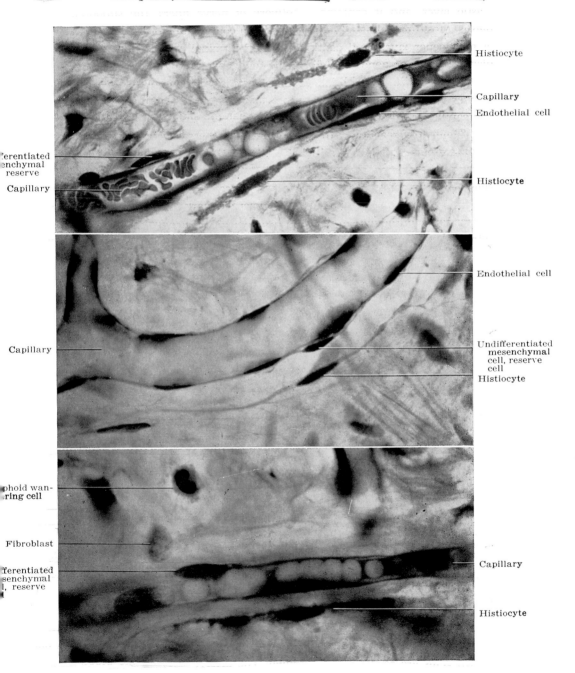

Fig. 111. Defense cells in the pulp.

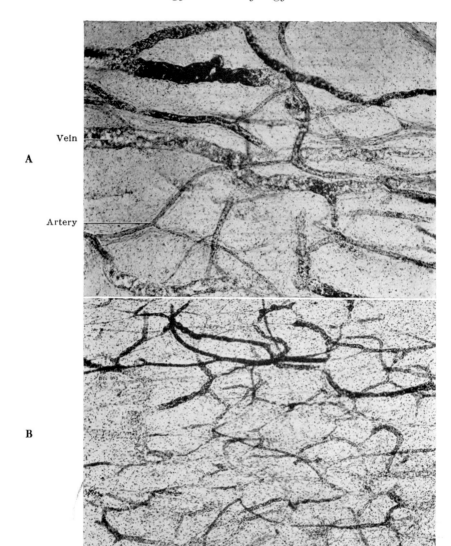

A

Vein

Artery

B

Fig. 112. Blood vessels of the pulp. **A,** Larger vessels in the center of the pulp. **B,** Dense capillary network in the periphery of the pulp. Arteries narrow, with thick walls and even outline. Veins wide with thin walls and irregular outline.

close to the odontoblasts, near the surface of the pulp, and may even reach into the odontoblastic layer.

The larger vessels in the pulp, especially the arteries, have a typical circular muscular coating (Fig. 113). These muscular elements can be traced to the finer branches. Along the capillaries are found branching cells, the pericytes (Rouget's cells). It has been claimed that they are modified muscular elements.[20]

Occasionally it is difficult to differentiate between pericytes and undifferenti-

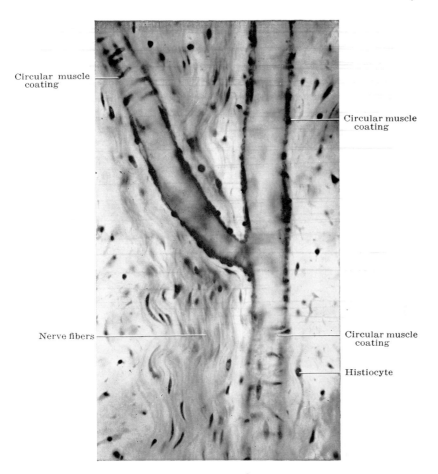

Circular muscle coating

Circular muscle coating

Nerve fibers

Circular muscle coating

Histiocyte

Fig. 113. Branching artery in the pulp. Circular muscle coating.

ated mesenchymal cells. However, some sections show both types of cells, thus making it possible to distinguish between the two (Fig. 114). The nuclei of the pericytes can be distinguished as round or slightly oval bodies outside the endothelial wall of the capillary. A very thin cytoplasm can be seen between the nuclei and the endothelium. The endothelial cells can be recognized because they lie in the wall of the capillary. The undifferentiated reserve cells lie outside the pericytes and have fingerlike projections. If no pericytes are present, the undifferentiated mesenchymal reserve cells are in close proximity to the endothelial wall. (Fig. 111.)

Lymph vessels. Lymph vessels are present in the dental pulp. Special methods are required to render them visible; the common histologic technique does not reveal them. The presence of lymph vessels has been demonstrated by the application into the pulp of dyes that are carried into the regional lymph nodes.[11, 23, 24] Injection methods have also been tried successfully.[22, 30]

Nerves. The nerve supply of the dental pulp is abundant. Thick nerve bundles

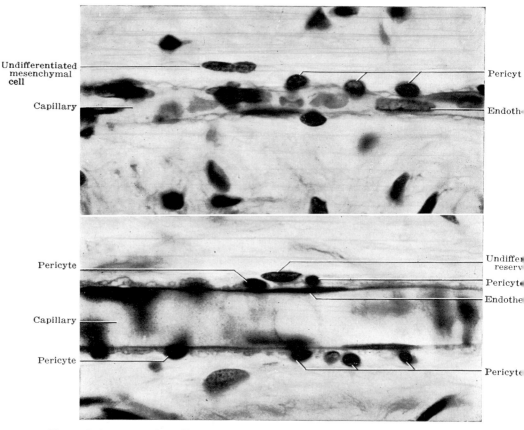

Fig. 114. Pericytes of capillaries in the pulp. Note the differences in location and nuclear shape between endothelial cells, pericytes, and undifferentiated reserve cells.

enter the apical foramen and pass into the crown portion of the pulp, where they split into numerous fiber groups and ultimately into single fibers and their branches (Fig. 115). Usually the nerve bundles follow the blood vessels, and the finer branches can be seen along the smaller vessels and capillaries.

Most nerve fibers that enter the pulp are myelinated; they mediate the sensation of pain. The unmyelinated nerve fibers belong to the sympathetic nervous system and are the nerves of the blood vessels, reflectorily regulating their lumen.

The bundles of myelinated fibers follow closely the arteries, dividing coronally into smaller and smaller branches. Individual fibers form a network beneath the subodontoblastic zone of Weil, the parietal plexus. From there the individual fibers pass through the subodontoblastic zone and, losing their myelin sheath, begin to branch. Their terminal arborization occurs in the odontoblastic layer (see Chapter IV).

It is a peculiar feature that whatever stimulus reaches the pulp it will always elicit only pain sensation. There is no possibility in the pulp to differentiate be-

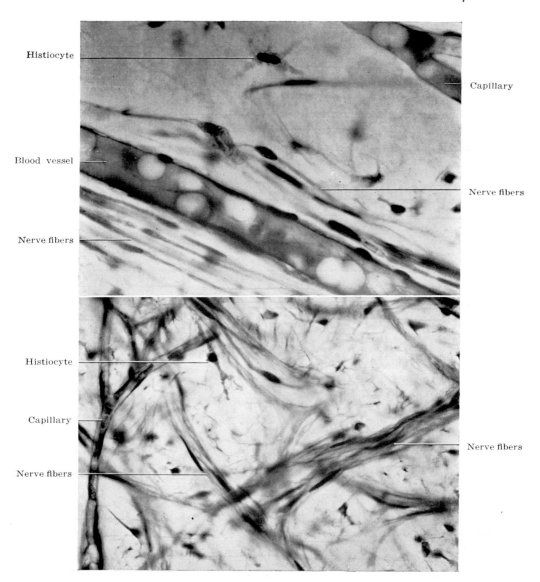

Fig. 115. Nerve fibers in the pulp.

tween heat, cold, touch, pressure, or chemicals—the result is always pain. The cause of this behavior is the fact that only one type of nerve endings, free nerve endings, are found in the pulp. The free nerve endings are specific for the reception of pain. Pulpal pain is as a rule not localized to the diseased tooth. This is in strong contrast to the sharp localization of periodontal pain.

REGRESSIVE CHANGES

Pulpstones. Certain formations in the dental pulp, such as pulpstones or denticles, are' on the borderline of pathologic changes. Their discussion' in this chapter is justified, however, because of their frequent occurrence. Pulpstones are often found in teeth which appear to be quite normal in all other respects. They have been found not only in functioning teeth but also in embedded teeth.

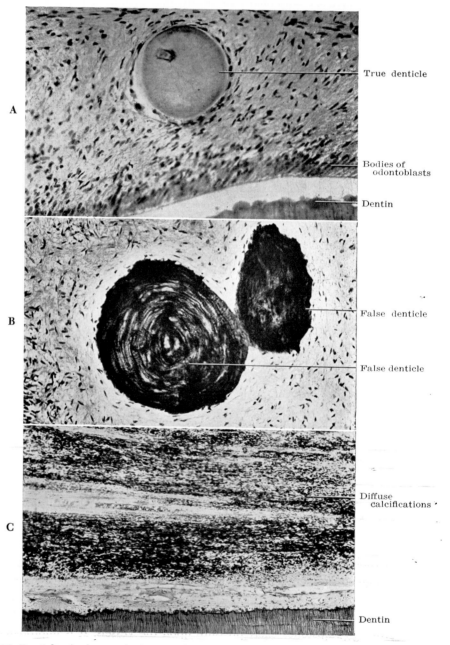

Fig. 116. Denticles (pulpstones). **A,** True denticle. **B,** False denticle. **C,** Diffuse calcifications.

Pulpstones are classified, according to their structure, as true denticles, false denticles, and diffuse calcifications (Fig. 116). True denticles consist of dentin, showing traces of dentinal tubuli and odontoblasts (Fig. 116, *A*). They are comparatively rare and usually are found close to the apical foramen. A theory has been advanced[27] that the development of this type of pulpstones is caused by remnants of Hertwig's epithelial root sheath that invade or become enclosed in the pulp because of some local disturbance during development. These epithelial remnants may induce cells of the pulp to form true denticles. It is an accepted fact that cells of the dental epithelium are necessary for the differentiation of odontoblasts and the onset of dentin formation.[7]

False denticles do not show the structure of true dentin. They consist, instead, of concentric layers of calcified tissue (Fig. 116, *B*). In the center of these concentric calcified structures there usually are remnants of necrotic and calcified cells. Calcification of thrombi in blood vessels, phleboliths, may also be the nidus for false denticles. Once calcification has begun, more layers of calcium phosphate are laid down on the surface of the pulpstones, thereby increasing their size. The surrounding pulp tissue may be quite normal (Fig. 116, *B*); no pathologic changes can be detected in the cells or intercellular fibrous matrix. Sometimes pulpstones of this character fill the pulp chamber almost completely. They increase in number and size with advancing age. Overdoses of vitamin D may cause formation of numerous denticles.[1]

Calcifications. Diffuse calcifications (Fig. 116, *C*) are irregular calcific deposits in the pulp tissue, usually following collagenous fiber bundles or blood vessels. Sometimes they develop into large bodies; at other times they persist as fine spicules. They are amorphous, having no specific structure, and usually are the final outcome of a hyalin degeneration of the pulp tissue. The pulp, in its coronal portion, may be quite normal without any sign of inflammation or other pathologic changes. These diffuse calcifications usually are located in the root canal, seldom in the pulp chamber; advancing age favors their development.

Pulpstones are classified not only according to their structure, but also according to their location in relation to the dentinal wall. Free, attached, and embedded denticles can be distinguished (Fig. 117). The free denticles are entirely surrounded by pulp tissue; attached denticles are partly fused with the dentin; embedded denticles are entirely surrounded by dentin. All are formed free in the pulp, and some become attached or embedded as formation of the dentin progresses.

Pulpstones are frequently found close to nerve bundles, as shown in Fig. 118. Occasionally this may bring about a disturbance if the pulpstones come close enough to the nerves to exert pressure. This may entail pain in the jaw in which the affected tooth is located, rendering a satisfactory diagnosis difficult. The close proximity of pulpstones to blood vessels may cause atrophy of the pulp if the growing pulpstones exert pressure upon the vessels. It is improbable that the pulsation of the blood in the arteries, close to pulpstones, causes sufficient

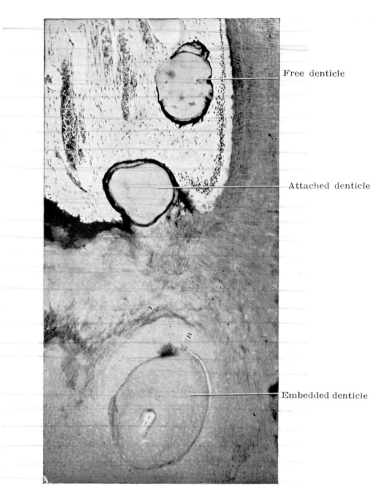

Free denticle

Attached denticle

Embedded denticle

Fig. 117. Free, attached, and embedded denticles.

movement of the stone to irritate nerves and cause pain. Pulp calcifications are more common in older teeth. Diffuse calcium deposits may be found in and around the pulpal vessels or close to nerves, especially in the roots of older teeth. Well-outlined calcified bodies are more frequently found in the coronal portion of the pulp. In 29 teeth from individuals between 10 and 30 years of age, Hill[13] found pulp calcifications in 66 per cent; in 62 teeth from individuals between 30 and 50 years of age, 80 to 82.5 per cent showed calcification in the pulp; and in 31 teeth from individuals over 50 years of age, 90 per cent had pulp calcification.

Fibrosis. It has been pointed out that with advancing age the cellular elements of the pulp decrease in number, whereas the fibrous components increase. In older individuals this shift in tissue elements can be considerable, and fibrosis may thus develop in the pulp.

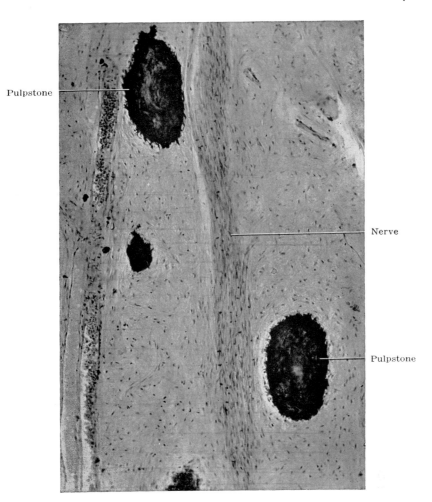

Pulpstone

Nerve

Pulpstone

Fig. 118. Pulpstones in close proximity to a nerve.

CLINICAL CONSIDERATIONS

For all operative procedures it is important to bear in mind the shape of the pulp chamber and its extensions into the cusps, the pulpal horns. The wide pulp chamber in the tooth of a young person will make a deep cavity preparation hazardous, and it should, if possible, be avoided. In some rare instances the pulpal horns project high into the cusps, and this may in some cases explain the exposure of a pulp when it is least anticipated.[28] (Fig. 119.) Sometimes a roentgenogram will help to determine the size of a pulp chamber and the extent of the pulpal horns.

If it becomes necessary to open a pulp chamber for treatment, its size and variation in shape must be taken into consideration. With advancing age the pulp chamber becomes smaller and, due to excessive dentin formation at the roof and floor of the chamber, it is sometimes difficult to locate the root canals. In such

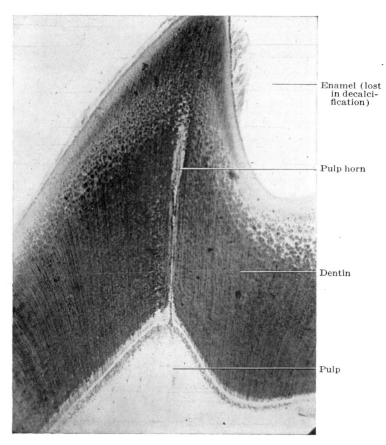

Fig. 119. Pulp horn reaching far into the cusp of a molar. (From Orban, B.: J. A. D. A. 28: 1069, 1941.)

cases it is advisable, when opening the pulp chamber, to advance toward the distal root in the lower molar and toward the lingual root in the upper molar; in this region one is most likely to find the opening of the pulp canal without risk of perforating the floor of the pulp chamber. In the anterior teeth the coronal part of the pulp chamber may be filled with secondary dentin, making it difficult to locate the root canal. Pulpstones lying at the opening of the root canal may cause considerable difficulty when an attempt is made to locate the canals. (Fig. 100, *B.*)

The shape of the apical foramen and its location may play an important part in the treatment of root canals, especially in root canal filling. When the apical foramen is narrowed by cementum, it is more readily located because further progress of the broach will be stopped at the foramen. If the apical opening is at the side of the apex, as shown in Fig. 104, *A,* not even the roentgenograms will reveal the true length of the root canal, and this may lead to misjudging the length of the canal and the root canal filling.

The problem of accessory canals in root canal work plays an important part in making the outcome of the root canal treatment questionable. Side branches of the pulp are rarely seen in the roentgenograms and usually are overlooked in the treatment and filling of the root canal.

There is another condition in which accessory canals may play an important part, especially if they are located in the bifurcation, or high up near the cementoenamel junction (Fig. 103, *B*). In periodontal diseases, e.g., where pocket formation progresses, accessory canals may be exposed, and infection of the pulp may follow. This may account for some causes of pulp necrosis in periodontal diseases, not only in molars but also in single-rooted teeth.

For a long time it was believed that an exposed pulp meant a lost pulp. The fact that defense cells have been recognized in the pulp has changed this concept.[26] Extensive experimental work has shown that exposed pulps can be preserved if proper pulp capping or pulp amputation procedures are applied.[29, 32] This is especially so in noninfected, accidentally exposed pulps in young individuals. In many instances dentin is formed at the site of the exposure, forming a dentin barrier or bridge, and the pulp may remain vital. Pulp capping of primary teeth has been shown to be remarkably successful.

References

1. Aprile, E. C. de, and Aprile, H.: Topografia de los conductos radiculares, Rev. Odontologia **35:** 686, 1947.
2. Becks, Hermann: Dangerous Effects of Vitamin D Overdosage on Dental and Paradental Structures, J. A. D. A. **29:** 1947, 1942.
3. Bodecker, C. F.: The Soft Fiber of Tomes, J. Nat. D. A. **9:** 281, 1922.
4. Bodecker, C. F., and Applebaum, E.: Metabolism of the Dentin, D. Cosmos **73:** 995, 1931.
5. Bodecker, C. F., and Lefkowitz, W.: Concerning the "Vitality" of the Calcified Dental Tissues, J. D. Res. **16:** 463, 1937.
6. Boling, L. R.: Blood Supply of Dental Pulp, J. D. Res. **20:** 247, 1941.
7. Brunn, A. v.: Die Ausdehnung des Schmelzorganes und seine Bedeutung für die Zahnbildung (The Extension of the Enamel Organ and Its Significance in the Formation of Teeth), Anat. Anz. **1:** 259, 1886.
8. Coolidge, E. D.: Anatomy of Root Apex in Relation to Treatment Problems, J. A. D. A. **16:** 1456, 1929.
9. Ebner, V. v.: Ueber die Entwicklung der leimgebenden Fibrillen im Zahnbein (The Development of Collagenous Fibrils in Dentin), Anat. Anz. **29:** 137, 1906.
10. Ebner, V. v.: Histologie der Zähne (Histology of the Teeth, Scheff's Handbook of Dentistry), ed. 4, Vienna, 1922, A. Hoelder.
11. Fish, E. W.: An Experimental Investigation of Enamel, Dentin and the Dental Pulp, London, 1932, John Bale Sons & Danielsson, Ltd.
12. Hess, W., and Zurcher, E.: The Anatomy of the Root Canals, London, 1925, John Bale Sons & Danielsson, Ltd.
13. Hill, T. J.: Pathology of the Dental Pulp, J. A. D. A. **21:** 820, 1934.
14. Johnston, H. B., and Orban, B.: Interradicular Pathology as Related to Accessory Root Canals, J. Endodontia **3:** 21, 1948.
15. Kronfeld, R.: Dental Histology and Comparative Dental Anatomy, Philadelphia, 1937, Lea & Febiger.
16. Langeland, K.: Effect of Various Procedures on the Human Dental Pulp, Oral Surg., Oral Med. & Oral Path. **14:** 210, 1961.
17. Lehner, J., and Plenk, H.: Die Zähne (The Teeth). In von Möllendorff, W. (editor): Handbuch der mikroskopischen Anatomie des Menschen, vol. 5, pt. 3, Berlin, 1936, Julius Springer, p. 449.

18. Magnus, G.: Ueber den Nachweis der Lymphgefässe in der Zahnpulpa (Demonstration of Lymph Vessels in the Dental Pulp), Deutsche Monatschr. f. Zahnh. **40:** 661, 1922.
19. Maximow, A. A.: Morphology of the Mesenchymal Reactions, Arch. Path. & Lab. Med. **4:** 557, 1927.
20. Maximow, A. A., and Bloom, W.: Textbook of Histology, ed. 4, Philadelphia, 1942, W. B. Saunders Co.
21. Meyer, W.: Ist das Foramen apicale stationär? (Is the Apical Foramen Stationary?) Deutsche Monatschr. f. Zahnh. **45:** 1016, 1927.
22. Noyes, F. B., and Dewey, K.: Lymphatics of the Dental Region, J. A. M. A. **71:** 1179, 1918.
23. Noyes, F. B.: Review of the Work of Lymphatics of Dental Origin, J. A. D. A. **14:** 714, 1927.
24. Noyes, F. B., and Ladd, R. L.: The Lymphatics of the Dental Region, D. Cosmos **71:** 1041, 1929.
25. Okumura, T.: Anatomy of the Root Canals, J. A. D. A. **14:** 632, 1927.
26. Orban, B.: Contribution to the Histology of the Dental Pulp, J. A. D. A. **16:** 965, 1929.
27. Orban, B.: Epithelial Rests in the Teeth, Proc. Am. Assoc. D. Schools, 5th Annual Meeting, Washington, D. C., 1929, p. 121.
28. Orban, B.: Biologic Considerations in Restorative Dentistry, J. A. D. A. **28:** 1069, 1941.
29. Restarski, J. S.: Preserving Vitality of Pulps Exposed by Caries in Young Children, Illinois D. J. **9:** 2, 1940.
30. Schweizer, G.: Die Lymphgefässe des Zahnfleisches und der Zähne (Lymph Vessels of the Gingiva and Teeth), Arch. f. mikr. Anat. **69:** 807, 1907; **74:** 927, 1909.
31. Wassermann, F.: The Innervation of Teeth, J. A. D. A. **26:** 1097, 1939.
32. Zander, H. A.: Reaction of the Pulp to Calcium Hydroxide, J. D. Res. **18:** 373, 1939.

Chapter VI • CEMENTUM*

INTRODUCTION

Cementum is the hard dental tissue covering the anatomic roots of the human teeth. It was first demonstrated microscopically in 1835 by two pupils of Purkinje.[5] It begins at the cervical portion of the tooth at the cementoenamel junction and continues to the apex. Cementum furnishes a medium for the attachment of the fibers that bind the tooth to the surrounding structures. It can be defined as a specialized, calcified tissue of mesodermal origin, a modified type of bone covering the anatomic root of the teeth.

PHYSICAL CHARACTERISTICS

The hardness of adult or fully formed cementum is less than that of dentin.[11, 24] It is light yellowish in color and is easily distinguished from the enamel by its lack of luster and its darker hue; it is somewhat lighter in color than dentin. By means of vital staining and other experiments, the cementum has been proved to be permeable.[25]

CHEMICAL COMPOSITION

Adult cementum consists of about 45 to 50 per cent inorganic substances and 50 to 55 per cent organic material and water (see Table 2, Chapter III). The inorganic substances consist mainly of calcium phosphates. The molecular structure is hydroxyl apatite, as in enamel, dentin, and bone. The chief constituents of the organic material are collagen and mucopolysaccharides.

CEMENTOGENESIS

When the dentin of the root has begun to form under the organizing influence of the epithelium of the root sheath, it is separated by this epithelium from the

---

*First draft submitted by Emmerich Kotanyi.

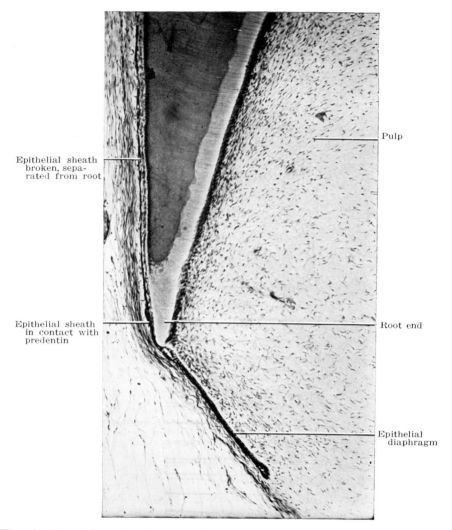

Epithelial sheath
broken, sepa-
rated from root

Pulp

Epithelial sheath
in contact with
predentin

Root end

Epithelial
diaphragm

Fig. 120. Hertwig's epithelial root sheath at end of forming root. At the side of the root the sheath is broken up, and cementum formation begins. (From Gottlieb, B.: J. Periodont. **13:** 13, 1942.)

surrounding connective tissue. However, the continuity of the epithelium of the root sheath soon is broken either by partial degeneration of the epithelium or by active proliferation of the connective tissue. Thus, contact of the connective tissue with the surface of the dentin is established (Fig. 120). The epithelial sheath persists as a network of epithelial strands that lie fairly close to the root surface. The remnants of the epithelial sheath are known as epithelial rests of Malassez[15] (see Chapter VII). When the separation of the epithelium from the surface of the root dentin has been accomplished, cells of the periodontal connective tissue, now in contact with the root surface, form cementum.

Cementoblasts. Before cementum is formed, cells of the loose connective tissue that are in contact with the root surface differentiate into cuboidal cells, the cementoblasts (Fig. 121). These cells produce the cementum in two consecutive phases. In the first phase, uncalcified cementoid tissue is laid down. In the second phase, the cementoid tissue is transformed into calcified cementum. This is similar to the process of bone and dentin formation.

In elaborating the cementoid tissue, the cementoblasts use the collagen material of the argyrophil connective tissue fibers (Figs. 122 and 123) to integrate the collagen material into the cementoid substance as collagen fibrils. At the same time, the mucopolysaccharides of the connective tissue are changed chemically and polymerized into the ground substance.

The second phase is characterized by a change in the molecular structure of the ground substance in the sense of depolymerization and its combination with calcium phosphates that are deposited as apatite crystals along the fibrils.[26]

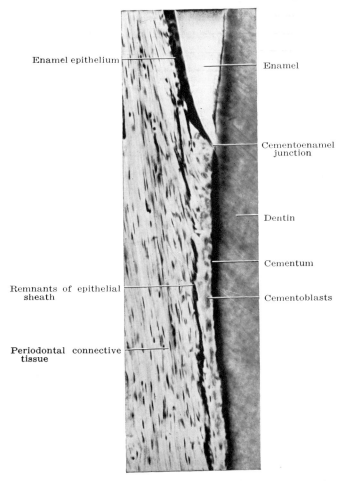

Enamel epithelium

Enamel

Cementoenamel junction

Dentin

Cementum

Remnants of epithelial sheath

Cementoblasts

Periodontal connective tissue

Fig. 121. Epithelial sheath is broken and separated from root surface by connective tissue.

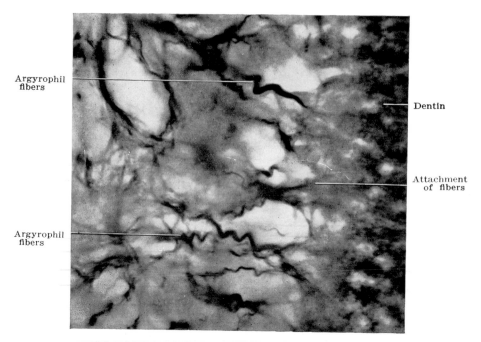

Fig. 122. Argyrophil collagenous fibers of the periodontal connective tissue attached to the dentin (silver impregnation).

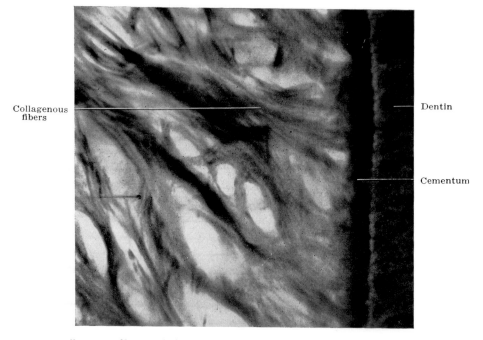

Fig. 123. Collagenous fibers and the mucopolysaccharides of the periodontal connective tissue are utilized in the formation of cementum.

The changes of the ground substance that occur in the second phase of cementogenesis are in all probability responsible for the different behavior of cementoid tissue and cementum. Cementoid tissue, like osteoid tissue and predentin, is highly resistant to destruction by osteoclastic activity, whereas cementum, bone, and dentin are readily resorbable.

Cementoid tissue. Since growth of the cementum is a continuous process under normal conditions, a thin layer of cementoid tissue is always seen on the surface of the cementum (Figs. 124 and 125). This cementoid tissue is lined by cementoblasts. Connective tissue fibers from the periodontal ligament pass between the cementoblasts into the cementum. These fibers are embedded in the

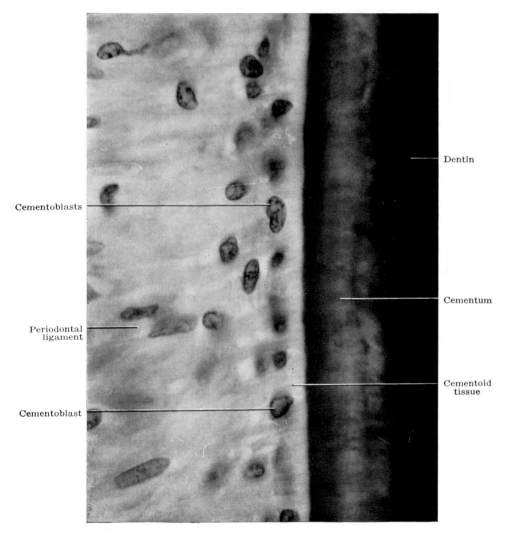

Dentin

Cementoblasts

Cementum

Periodontal ligament

Cementoid tissue

Cementoblast

Fig. 124. Cementoid tissue on the surface of calcified cementum. Cementoblasts between fibers.

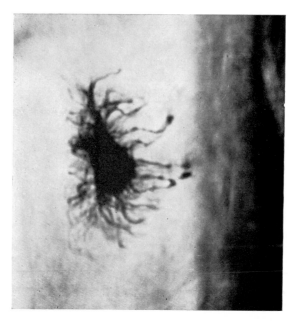

Fig. 125. Cementum lacuna and canaliculi filled with air (ground section).

cementum and serve as an attachment for the tooth to the surrounding bone. Their embedded portions are known as Sharpey's fibers. These were described accurately by G. V. Black,[2] in 1887, as an essential part of the suspensory apparatus.

STRUCTURE

From a morphologic standpoint two kinds of cementum can be differentiated: (1) acellular and (2) cellular. Functionally, however, there is no difference between the two.

Acellular cementum. Acellular cementum may cover the root dentin from the cementoenamel junction to the apex, but it is often missing on the apical third of the root. Here the cementum may be entirely of the cellular type. The acellular cementum is thinnest at the cementoenamel junction (20 to 50 microns) and thickest toward the apex (150 to 200 microns). The apical foramen is surrounded by cementum. Sometimes the cementum extends to the inner wall of the dentin for a short distance, forming a lining of the root canal.

Acellular cementum consists only of the calcified intercellular substance and contains the embedded Sharpey's fibers. The intercellular substance is composed of two elements, the collagenous fibrils and the calcified ground substance. The fibrils in the matrix are perpendicular to the embedded Sharpey's fibers and parallel to the cementum surface. The fibrils are less numerous than in lamellated bone and about as numerous as those of bundle bone. Due to identical optical qualities, i.e., the same refractive index, the fibrils are masked by the interfibrillar ground substance and can be made visible only by special staining methods, for instance, by means of silver impregnation. In dried ground sections Sharpey's fibers are disintegrated; the spaces and channels that they occupied formerly are filled with air and appear as dark lines.

Cellular cementum. The cells in cellular cementum, cementocytes, are similar to osteocytes. They lie in spaces designated as lacunae. Frequently the cell body has the shape of a plum stone, with numerous long processes radiating from the cell body. These processes may branch, and they frequently anastomose with those of a neighboring cell. Most of the processes are directed toward the periodontal surface of the cementum.

The cells are irregularly distributed throughout the thickness of the cellular cementum. The cavities can be observed best in ground sections of dried teeth, where they appear as dark, spiderlike figures (Fig. 125). The dark ap-

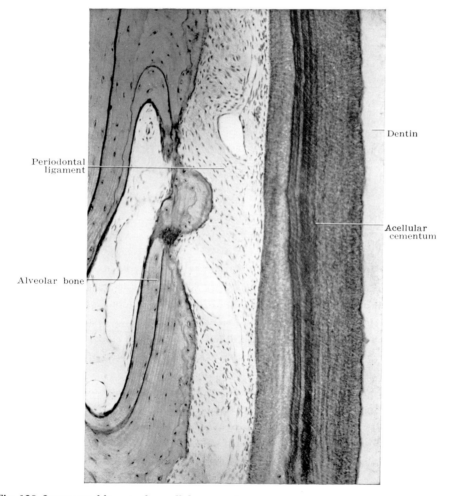

Fig. 126. Incremental lines in the acellular cementum.

pearance is due to the fact that the spaces are filled with air; these spaces also can easily be filled with dyes.

Both acellular and cellular cementum are separated by incremental lines into layers that indicate periodic formation (Figs. 126 and 128). While the cementum remains relatively thin, Sharpey's fibers can be observed crossing the entire thickness of the cementum. With further apposition of cementum, a larger part of the fibers is incorporated in the cementum. At the same time, the portion of the fibers lying in the deeper layers of the cementum becomes obscure. The attachment proper is confined to the most superficial or recently formed layers of cementum (Fig. 127). This would seem to indicate that the thickness of the cementum does not enhance functional efficiency by increasing the strength of attachment of the individual fibers. Continuous apposition of cementum is essential for the continuous eruptive movements of the functioning tooth, but it serves mainly to maintain a young and vital surface layer of the cementum, whose life span is restricted. Often the cells in the deeper layers of the cementum have degenerated, and the lacunae are empty (Fig. 127).

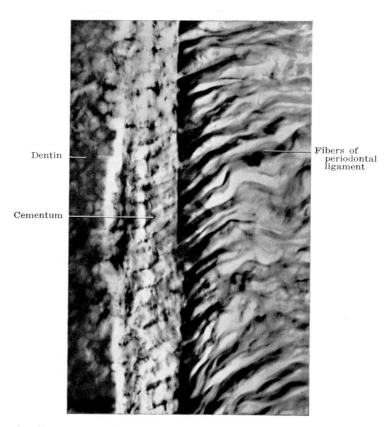

Dentin

Cementum

Fibers of periodontal ligament

Fig. 127. The fibers of the periodontal ligament continue into the surface layer of the cementum.

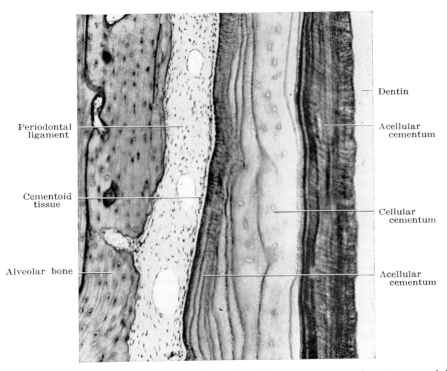

Fig. 128. Cellular cementum on the surface of acellular cementum, and again covered by acellular cementum (incremental lines). The lacunae of the cellular cementum are empty, indicating that this part of the cementum is necrotic.

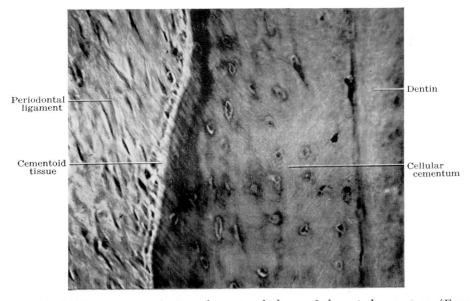

Fig. 129. Cellular cementum forming the entire thickness of the apical cementum. (From Orban, B.: Dental Histology and Embryology, Philadelphia, 1929, P. Blakiston's Son & Co.)

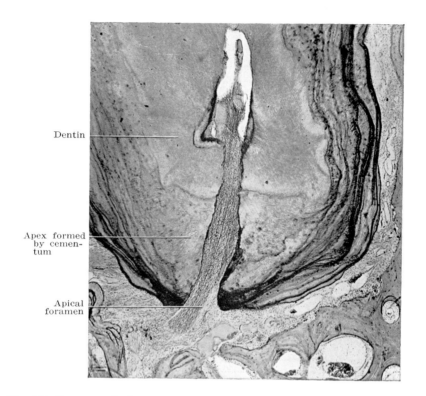

Dentin

Apex formed
by cemen-
tum

Apical
foramen

Fig. 130. Cementum thickest at apex, contributing to the length of the root.

The location of acellular and cellular cementum is not definite. Layers of acellular and cellular cementum may alternate in almost any arrangement. The acellular cementum, which is normally laid down on the surface of the dentin occasionally may be found on the surface of cellular cementum. (Fig. 128.) Cellular cementum usually is formed on the surface of acellular cementum (Fig. 128), but it may comprise the entire thickness of the apical cementum (Fig. 129). It is always thickest around the apex and, by its growth, contributes to the lengthening of the root (Fig. 130).

CEMENTOENAMEL JUNCTION

The relation between cementum and enamel at the cervical region of the teeth is variable.[21] In about 30 per cent of the examined teeth the cementum meets the cervical end of the enamel in a sharp line (Fig. 131, *A*). Here, the cementum, as well as the enamel, tapers into a knife-edge. In other teeth, about 60 per cent, the cementum overlaps the cervical end of the enamel for a short distance (Fig. 131, *B*). Developmentally, this can occur only when the dental epithelium that normally covers the entire enamel degenerates in its cervical

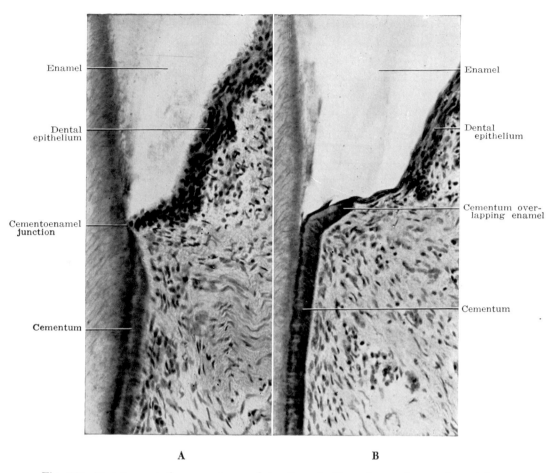

Fig. 131. Variations at the cementoenamel junction. **A,** Cementum and enamel meet in a sharp line. **B,** Cementum overlaps enamel.

end, permitting the connective tissue, which is responsible for the deposition of cementum, to come in contact with the enamel surface.

In about 10 per cent of all teeth various other aberrations of the cementoenamel junction may be observed. Occasionally, the dental epithelium which covers the cervical part of the root does not separate from the dentin surface at the proper time,[6] remains attached to the dentin of the root for variable distances (Fig. 132, *A*), and prevents the formation of cementum. In such cases there is no cementoenamel junction, but a zone of root dentin is devoid of cementum and covered by dental epithelium. In other instances cementum is formed at the cementoenamel junction for a short distance only, and apically Hertwig's epithelial root sheath remains in contact with the dentin in a limited area (Fig. 132, *B*). Enamel spurs, pearls, or drops may be formed by such epithelium.[6]

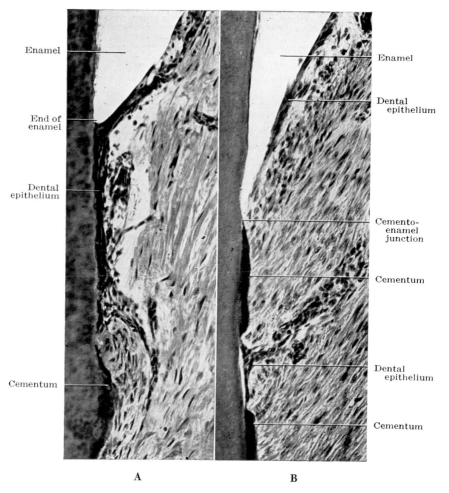

Enamel

End of
enamel

Dental
epithelium

Cementum

Enamel

Dental
epithelium

Cemento-
enamel
junction

Cementum

Dental
epithelium

Cementum

A   B

Fig. 132. Variations at the cementoenamel junction. **A,** Dental epithelium remained attached to dentin surface, preventing cementum formation. **B,** Dental epithelium breaking continuity of cementum near the cementoenamel junction.

CEMENTODENTINAL JUNCTION

The surface of the dentin upon which the cementum is deposited is normally smooth in permanent teeth. The cementodentinal junction in deciduous teeth, however, is sometimes scalloped. The attachment of the cementum to the dentin, in either case, is quite firm, although the nature of this attachment is not fully understood.

Sometimes the dentin is separated from the cementum by an intermediate layer, known as the intermediate cementum layer, which does not exhibit the characteristic features of either dentin or cementum (Fig. 133). This layer contains large and irregular cells. Its development may be due to localized, premature disintegration of Hertwig's epithelial sheath after its cells have induced

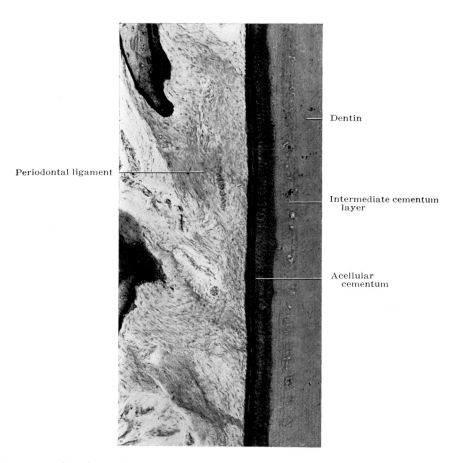

Fig. 133. Intermediate layer of cementum.

the differentiation of odontoblasts, but before the production of dentinal intercellular substance has begun. It is found mostly in the apical two-thirds of the root. Sometimes it is a continuous layer; sometimes it is found only in isolated areas.[18]

FUNCTION

The functions of cementum are as follows: (1) to anchor the tooth to the bony socket by attachment of fibers; (2) to compensate by its growth for loss of tooth substance due to occlusal wear; and (3) to contribute, by its continuous growth, to the continuous vertical eruption and mesial drift of the teeth.

The continued deposition of cementum is of great biologic importance.[6, 8, 13] In contrast to the alternating resorption and new formation of bone, cementum is not resorbed under normal conditions. If a layer ages or, functionally speaking, loses its vitality, the periodontal connective tissue and cementoblasts must produce a new layer of cementum on the surface to keep the attachment apparatus intact. In bone the loss of vitality can be recognized by the fact that the bone cells degenerate, and the bone lacunae are empty. Aging in acellular cementum cannot be so readily ascertained, but in cellular cementum the cells in the deepest layers may degenerate, and the lacunae may be empty (Fig. 127). In the surface layers, the lacunae contain normal cementocytes. The nuclei of degenerating cells in the deeper layers are pyknotic and the cells are shrunken; near the surface the cells fill the entire space of the cementum lacunae (Fig. 128), and the nuclei stain dark.[7, 8]

HYPERCEMENTOSIS

Hypercementosis is an abnormal thickening of the cementum. It may be diffuse or circumscribed, it may affect all teeth of the dentition or it may be confined to a single tooth, and it may even affect only parts of one tooth. If the overgrowth improves the functional qualities of the cementum, it is termed a cementum hypertrophy; if the overgrowth occurs in nonfunctional teeth or if it is not correlated with increased function, it is termed hyperplasia.

In localized hypertrophy a spur or pronglike extension of cementum may be

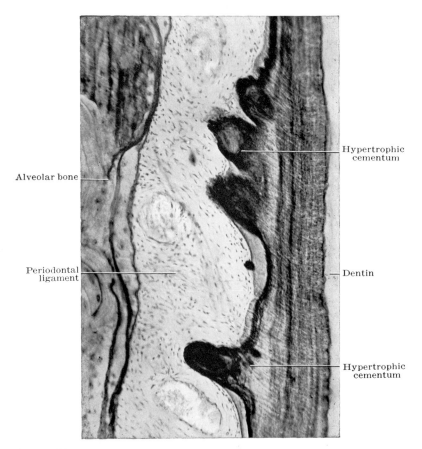

Fig. 134. Pronglike excementoses.

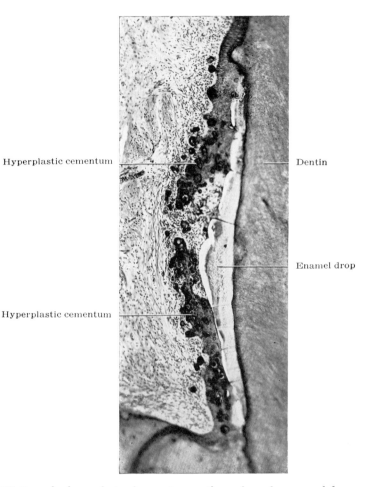

Hyperplastic cementum — Dentin

Enamel drop

Hyperplastic cementum

Fig. 135. Irregular hyperplasia of cementum on the surface of an enamel drop.

formed (Fig. 134). This condition frequently is found in teeth that are exposed to great stress. The pronglike extensions of cementum provide a larger surface area for the attaching fibers, thus securing a firmer anchorage of the tooth to the surrounding alveolar bone.[7]

Localized hypercementosis may sometimes be observed in areas where enamel drops have developed on the dentin. The hyperplastic cementum, covering the enamel drops (Fig. 135), occasionally is irregular and sometimes contains round bodies which may be calcified epithelial rests. The same type of embedded calcified round bodies frequently are found in localized areas of hyperplastic cementum. (Fig. 136.) Such knoblike projections are designated as excementoses. They, too, develop around disintegrated, degenerated epithelial rests.[6]

Extensive hyperplasia of the cementum of a tooth is found occasionally in connection with chronic periapical inflammation. Here the hyperplasia is circumscribed and surrounds the root like a cuff.

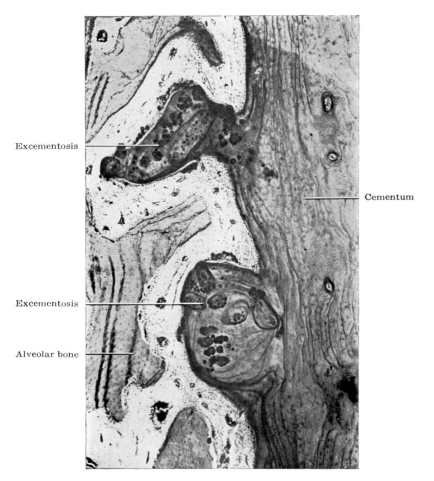

Excementosis

Cementum

Excementosis

Alveolar bone

Fig. 136. Excementoses in bifurcation of a molar. (From Gottlieb, B.: Oesterr. Ztschr. f. Stomatol. 19: 515, 1921.)

A thickening of the cementum is often observed on teeth that are not in function. The hyperplasia may extend around the entire root of the nonfunctioning teeth or may be localized in small areas (see Chapter VII). Hyperplasia of cementum in nonfunctioning teeth is characterized by the absence of Sharpey's fibers.

The cementum is thicker around the apex of all teeth and in the furcation of multirooted teeth than it is on other areas of the root. This thickening can be observed in embedded as well as in newly erupted teeth.[13]

In some cases an irregular overgrowth of cementum can be found with spike-like extensions and calcification of Sharpey's fibers, accompanied by numerous cementicles. This type of cementum hyperplasia can occasionally be observed on many teeth of the same dentition and is, at least in some cases, the sequela of injuries to the cementum (Fig. 137).

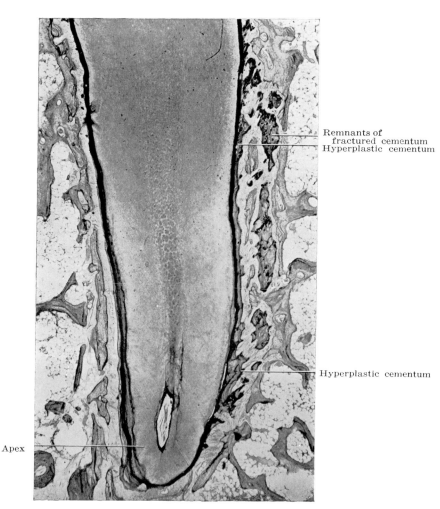

Remnants of
  fractured cementum
Hyperplastic cementum

Hyperplastic cementum

Apex

Fig. 137. Extensive spikelike hyperplasia of cementum formed during the healing of a cemental tear.

CLINICAL CONSIDERATIONS

The fact that cementum appears to be more resistant to resorption than bone renders orthodontic treatment possible. When a tooth is moved by means of an orthodontic appliance, bone is resorbed on the side of pressure, and new bone is formed on the side of tension. On the side toward which the tooth is moved, pressure is equal on the surfaces of bone and cementum. Resorption of bone, as well as of cementum, may be anticipated. However, in careful orthodontic treatment, cementum resorption, if it occurs, usually is localized and shallow, possibly because the cementum is, as a rule, covered by a continuous layer of cementoid tissue that is highly resistant to resorption. Moreover, resorptions are repaired readily if the intensity of pressure is reduced and if the surrounding connective tissue remains intact.

Excessive lateral stress may compress the periodontal connective tissue between bone and cementum and cause bleeding, thrombosis, and necrosis. After resorption of the damaged tissues, accompanied by bone resorption, repair may take place.[4, 9, 16, 23]

Resorption of cementum may continue into the dentin. After resorption has ceased, the damage usually is repaired, either by formation of acellular (Fig. 138, *A*) or cellular (Fig. 138, *B*) cementum, or by alternate formation of both (Fig. 138, *C*). In most cases of repair there is a tendency to re-establish the former outline of the root surface. However, if only a thin layer of cementum is deposited on the surface of a deep resorption, the root outline is not reconstructed, and a baylike recess remains. In such areas sometimes the periodontal space is restored to its normal width by formation of a bony projection, so that a proper functional relationship will result. The outline of the alveolar bone, in these cases, follows that of the root surface. (Fig. 139.) In contrast to anatomic repair, this change is called functional repair.[17]

If teeth are subjected to a severe blow, smaller or larger fragments of cementum may be severed from the dentin. The tear occurs frequently at the cementodentinal junction, but it may also be in the cementum or dentin. Trans-

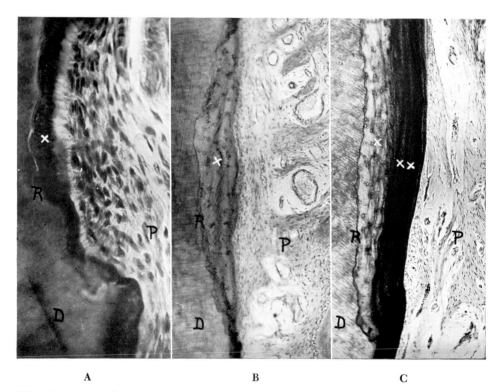

A   B   C

Fig. 138. Repair of resorbed cementum. **A,** Repair by acellular cementum (x). **B,** Repair by cellular cementum (x). **C,** Repair first by cellular (x) and later by acellular (xx) cementum. **D,** Dentin. **R,** Line of resorption. **P,** Periodontal ligament.

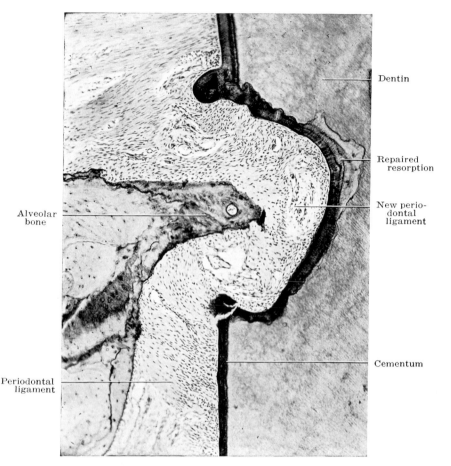

Fig. 139. Functional repair of cementum resorption by bone apposition. Normal width of periodontal ligament re-established.

verse fractures of the root may heal by formation of new cementum uniting the fragments.

Frequently, hyperplasia of cementum is secondary to periapical inflammation or extensive occlusal stress. The fact is of practical significance because the extraction of such teeth may necessitate the removal of bone. This also applies to extensive excementoses, as shown in Fig. 136. These can anchor the tooth so tightly to the socket that the jaw or parts of it may be fractured in an attempt to extract the tooth. This possibility indicates the necessity for taking roentgenograms before any extraction. Small fragments of roots left in the jaw after extraction of vital teeth may be surrounded by cementum and remain in the jaw without causing any disturbance.

If the cementum does not cover the cervical part of the root, recession of the gingiva will expose the highly sensitive dentin in the cervical area. When calculus is removed, it is impossible to avoid the removal of the thin cementum covering the cervical region of the exposed root. As the individual gets older, more cementum is gradually exposed and subject to the abrasive action of some dentifrices. Since the cementum is the softest of the hard dental tissues, a considerable amount of cementum may be removed by these mechanical means.[12] The denuded dentin is then highly sensitive to thermal, chemical, or mechanical stimuli. The hypersensitivity can often be relieved with astringent chemicals that coagulate the protoplasmic odontoblastic processes.

References

1. Becks, H.: Systemic Background of Paradentitis, J. A. D. A. **28**: 1447, 1941.
2. Black, G. V.: A Study of Histological Characters of the Periosteum and Peridental Membrane, D. Rev. 1886-1887; and W. T. Keener Co., Chicago, 1887.
3. Box, H. K.: The Dentinal Cemental Junction (Bull. No. 3), Canad. D. Res. Found., May, 1922.
4. Coolidge, E. D.: Traumatic and Functional Injuries Occurring in the Supporting Tissues of Human Teeth, J. A. D. A. **25**: 343, 1938.
5. Denton, G. H.: The Discovery of Cementum, J. D. Res. **18**: 239, 1939.
6. Gottlieb, B.: Zementexostosen, Schmelztropfen und Epithelnester (Cementexostosis, Enamel Drops and Epithelial Rests), Oesterr. Ztschr. f. Stomatol. **19**: 515, 1921.
7. Gottlieb, B.: Tissue Changes in Pyorrhea, J. A. D. A. **14**: 2178, 1927.
8. Gottlieb, B.: Biology of the Cementum, J. Periodont. **13**: 13, 1942.
9. Gottlieb, B., and Orban, B.: Die Veränderungen der Gewebe bei übermässiger Beanspruchung der Zähne (Experimental Traumatic Occlusion), Leipzig, 1931, Georg Thieme.
10. Gottlieb, B., and Orban, B.: Biology and Pathology of the Tooth (Translated by M. Diamond), New York, 1938, The Macmillan Co.
11. Kitchin, P. C.: The Prevalence of Tooth Root Exposure, J. D. Res. **20**: 565, 1941.
12. Kitchin, P. C., and Robinson, H. B. G.: The Abrasiveness of Dentifrices as Measured on the Cervical Areas of Extracted Teeth, J. D. Res. **27**: 195, 1948.
13. Kronfeld, R.: Die Zementhyperplasien an nicht funktionierenden Zähnen (Cementum Hyperplasia on Nonfunctioning Teeth), Ztschr. f. Stomatol. **25**: 1218, 1927.
14. Kronfeld, R.: The Biology of Cementum, J. A. D. A. **25**: 1451, 1938.
15. Malassez, M. L.: Sur le rôle des débris epitheliaux paradentaires (The Epithelial Rests Around the Root of the Teeth), Arch. de Physiol. **5**: 379, 1885.
16. Oppenheim, A.: Human Tissue Response to Orthodontic Intervention, Am. J. Orthodont. & Oral Surg. **28**: 263, 1942.
17. Orban, B.: Resorption and Repair on the Surface of the Root, J. A. D. A. **15**: 1768, 1928.
18. Orban, B.: Dental Histology and Embryology, Philadelphia, 1929, P. Blakiston's Son & Co.
19. Sicher, H., and Weinmann, J. P.: Bone Growth and Physiologic Tooth Movement, Am. J. Orthodont. & Oral Surg. **30**: 109, 1944.
20. Skillen, W. G.: Permeability: A Tissue Characteristic, J. A. D. A. **9**: 187, 1922.
21. Sorrin, S., and Miller, S. C.: The Practice of Pedodontia, New York, 1928, The Macmillan Co.
22. Stones, H. H.: The Permeability of Cementum, Brit. D. J. **56**: 273, 1934.
23. Stuteville, O. H.: Injuries Caused by Orthodontic Forces, Am. J. Orthodont. & Oral Surg. **24**: 103, 1938.
24. Tainter, M. L., and Epstein, S.: A Standard Procedure for Determining Abrasion, J. Am. Coll. Dentists **9**: 353, 1942.
25. Thomas, N. G., and Skillen, W. G.: Staining the Granular Layer, D. Cosmos **62**: 725, 1920.
26. Weinmann, J. P., and Sicher, H.: Bone and Bones. Fundamentals of Bone Biology, ed. 2, St. Louis, 1955, The C. V. Mosby Co.

Chapter VII • PERIODONTAL LIGAMENT*

INTRODUCTION

The periodontal ligament is the connective tissue that surrounds the root of the tooth and attaches it to the bony alveolus; it is continuous with the connective tissue of the gingiva. Various terms have been given to this tissue; peridental membrane, pericementum, dental periosteum, and alveolodental membrane. This tissue is called a membrane though it does not resemble other fibrous membranes, like fasciae, capsules of organs, perichondrium, or periosteum. It has some structural and functional similarities to these tissues, but it is different in that it serves not only as pericementum for the tooth and periosteum for the alveolar bone but also mainly as the suspensory ligament for the tooth. Therefore, the term periodontal *ligament* is most appropriate.

FUNCTION

The functions of the periodontal ligament are formative, supportive, protective, sensory, and nutritive. The formative function is fulfilled by the cementoblasts and the osteoblasts, which are essential in building cementum and bone, and by the fibroblasts, which form the fibers of the ligament. The supportive function is that of maintaining the relation of the tooth to the surrounding hard and soft tissues. Limiting the masticatory movements of the tooth, the periodontal ligament protects the tissues at the sites of pressure. This is achieved by connective tissue fibers that comprise the bulk of the ligament. Functions that are sensory and nutritive to the cementum and alveolar bone are carried out by the nerves and the blood vessels in the periodontal ligament.

DEVELOPMENT

The periodontal ligament is derived from the dental sac that envelops the developing tooth germ. Around the tooth germ three zones can be seen: an

---

*First draft submitted by Helmuth A. Zander.

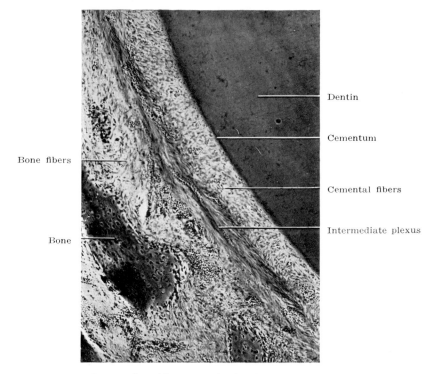

Dentin

Cementum

Cemental fibers

Intermediate plexus

Bone fibers

Bone

Fig. 140. Three zones in the periodontal ligament of a developing tooth.

outer zone containing fibers related to the bone, an inner zone of fibers adjacent to the tooth, and an intermediate zone of unoriented fibers between the other two (Fig. 140). During the formation of cementum, fibers of the inner zone become attached to the surface of the root. As the tooth moves toward the oral cavity, gradually a functional orientation of the fibers takes place.[19] Instead of loose and irregularly arranged fibers, fiber bundles extend from the bone to the tooth. When the tooth has reached the plane of occlusion and the root is fully formed, this functional orientation is complete. However, due to changes in functional stresses and the eruptive and drifting movements of the teeth, changes in the structural arrangement of the periodontal ligament occur throughout life.

STRUCTURAL ELEMENTS

The main tissue elements in the periodontal ligament are the principal fibers, all of which are attached to the cementum.[2, 3] The fiber bundles extend from the cementum to the alveolar wall, or across the crest of the interdental septum to the cementum of the adjacent tooth, or into the gingival tissue. The principal fibers of the periodontal ligament are white collagenous connective tissue fibers, and they cannot be lengthened. There are no elastic fibers in the periodontal ligament. The apparent elasticity of the periodontal ligament is due to the arrangement of the principal fiber bundles. They follow a wavy course from bone to cementum, thereby allowing slight movements of the tooth during mastication. Near the bone the fibers seem to form larger bundles before their insertion into it. Although the bundles run directly from bone to cementum, the single fibers do not span the entire distance. The bundles are spliced or braided together from shorter fibers in an intermediate plexus midway between cementum and bone. (Fig. 141A.) The presence of an intermediate plexus is common to the periodontal ligament of all mammalian teeth because they move occlusally by continuous eruption during their functional period and drift mesially or distally. These movements necessitate a continued adaptive readjustment of the suspensory ligament. This rearrangement does not occur by the embedding of new fibers in bone and cementum, as previously assumed, but by the formation of new links between the alveolar and the dental fibers in the intermediate plexus. How conspicuous or inconspicuous this plexus is depends on the rate of eruptive movements. In the rat incisor that has a daily eruptive rate of one-third of one

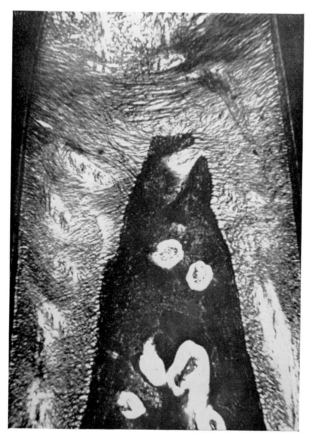

Fig. 141A. Periodontal ligament of premolars of a monkey. Interdental and alveolar bundles of principal fibers are seen. The fibers are intertwined between cementum and bone in an intermediate plexus.

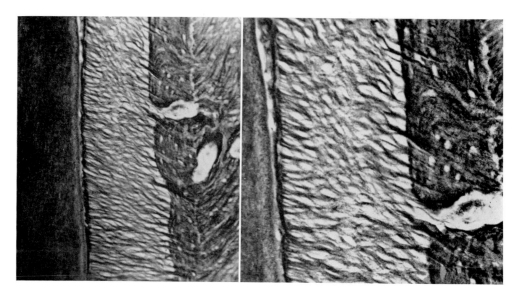

Fig. 141B   Fig. 141C

Fig. 141B. Periodontal ligament of a rat molar. Note the "braiding" of the periodontal fibers in the intermediate plexus. Silver impregnation. (×400.) (Courtesy Dr. Ino Sciaky, Jerusalem.)
Fig. 141C. Higher magnification of an area of **B.** (×800.) (Courtesy Dr. Ino Sciaky, Jerusalem.)

millimeter, this plexus is quite wide and conspicuous.[27, 28] In man, in whom eruptive movements and mesial drift are quite slow, the intermediate plexus is inconspicuous. However, during the time of fast eruptive movement before the teeth get into function, an intermediate plexus in human teeth has been observed.[19] The interdental or transseptal ligaments also consist of fibers that are shorter than the ligaments themselves. In contrast to alveolodental and interdental ligaments, the fibers of the gingival ligament seem to extend directly from the cementum into the gingiva.

The presence of an intermediate plexus and its significance for the rearrangement of fibers of the periodontal ligament make it clear that the continued apposition of cementum serves mainly the maintenance of the vitality of the cementum.

Principal fibers. The bundles of principal fibers are so arranged that they can be divided into the following ligaments: (1) gingival ligament, (2) interdental ligament, and (3) alveolodental ligament.

The fibers of the *gingival ligament* (Fig. 142) attach the gingiva to the cementum. The fiber bundles pass outward from the cementum into the free and attached gingiva. Usually they break up into a meshwork of smaller bundles and individual fibers, interlacing terminally with the fibrous tissue and the circular fibers of the gingiva.

The *transseptal, or interdental, ligaments* (Fig. 143) connect adjacent teeth.

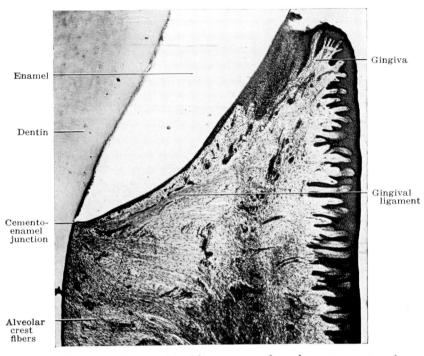

Enamel

Dentin

Cemento-
enamel
junction

Alveolar
crest
fibers

Gingiva

Gingival
ligament

Fig. 142. Gingival fibers of the periodontal ligament pass from the cementum into the gingiva.

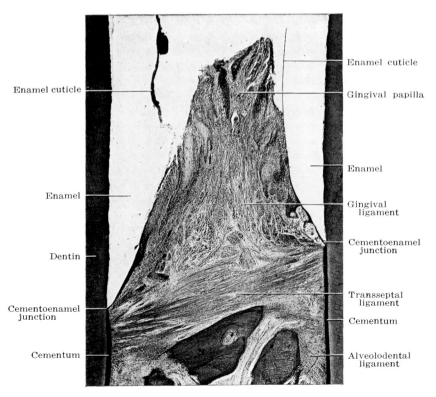

Enamel cuticle

Enamel

Dentin

Cementoenamel
junction

Cementum

Enamel cuticle

Gingival papilla

Enamel

Gingival
ligament

Cementoenamel
junction

Transseptal
ligament

Cementum

Alveolodental
ligament

Fig. 143. Transseptal ligament connects adjacent teeth.

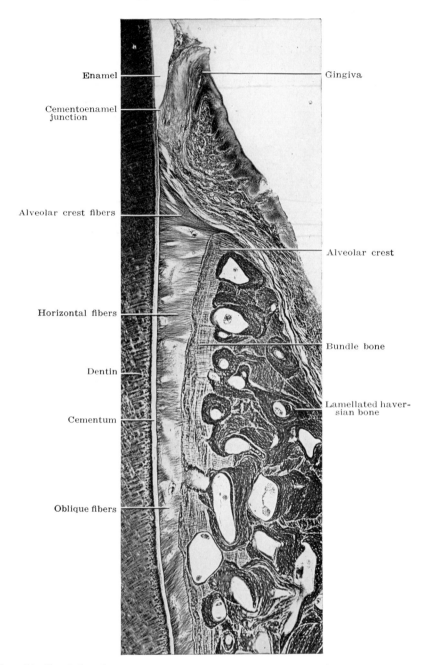

Enamel

Cementoenamel junction

Alveolar crest fibers

Horizontal fibers

Dentin

Cementum

Oblique fibers

Gingiva

Alveolar crest

Bundle bone

Lamellated haversian bone

Fig. 144. Alveolodental ligament.

The ligaments, but not the single fibers, run from the cementum of one tooth over the crest of the alveolus to the cementum of the neighboring tooth.

The *alveolodental ligament* (Fig. 114) attaches the tooth to the bone of the alveolus. It consists of five groups of bundles.

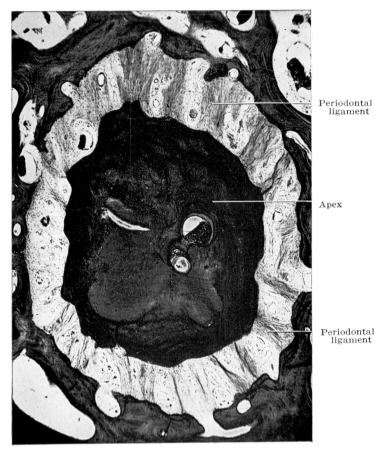

Periodontal
ligament

Apex

Periodontal
ligament

Fig. 145. Apical fibers of the periodontal ligament. (From Orban, B.: Dental Histology and Embryology, Philadelphia, 1929, P. Blakiston's Son & Co.)

1. *Alveolar crest group:* The fiber bundles of this group radiate from the crest of the alveolar process and attach themselves to the cervical part of the cementum.

2. *Horizontal group:* The bundles run at right angles to the long axis of the tooth, from the cementum to the bone.

3. *Oblique group:* The bundles run obliquely. They are attached in the cementum somewhat apically from their attachment to the bone. These fiber bundles are most numerous and constitute the main support of the tooth against masticatory forces.

4. *Apical group:* The bundles are irregularly arranged and radiate from the apical region of the root to the surrounding bone (Fig. 145).

5. *Interradicular group:* From the crest of the interradicular septum, bundles extend to the furcation of multirooted teeth.

The arrangement of the bundles in the different groups is well adapted to fulfill the functions of the periodontal ligament. No matter from which direction a force is applied to the tooth, it is counteracted by some or all of the fiber groups. The alveolar principal fibers, as a whole, may be regarded as a ligament, alveolo-dental ligament, by which the tooth is attached to the alveolar bone. Its function is primarily to transform pressure exerted upon the tooth into traction on cementum and bone.[24]

The periodontal ligament, as other ligaments, has also a protective function, limiting the masticatory movements of the tooth. In the areas toward which the roots move, the numerous capillaries are emptied for a short time during mastication, thus dissipating any pressure on the cellular elements. Therefore, normal masticatory forces do not lead to the differentiation of osteoclasts in "pressure areas." The structure of the periodontal ligament changes continuously to meet the requirements of the continuously moving tooth.[9, 21]

Fibroblasts. Most cells of the periodontal ligament are typical fibroblasts. They are long, slender, stellate connective tissue cells whose nuclei are large and oval in shape. These cells lie between the fibers, they are active in the formation and maintenance of the principal fibers and especially in the dissolution of old and the establishment of new fiber connections in the intermediate plexus.

Osteoblasts and osteoclasts. As is true of bone elsewhere in the body, the bone of the alveolus is constantly resorbed and rebuilt. Resorption of bone is brought about by the osteoclasts; formation of new bone is initiated by the activity of the osteoblasts.

Where bone formation is in progress, osteoblasts are found along the surface of the wall of the bony socket, the periodontal ligament fibers passing between them. These cells usually are irregularly cuboid in shape, with large single nuclei containing large nucleoli and fine chromatin particles. The fibers of the periodontal ligament are secured to the bone by the formation of bone around the ends of the fibers. Osteoclasts are mostly multinucleated and are believed to originate from undifferentiated mesenchymal cells in the periodontal ligament; they are found only during the process of active bone resorption. Presumably the osteoclasts produce enzymes that dissolve the organic components of bone and probably produce chelating agents capable of bringing the calcium salts into solution.[31] Where their cytoplasm is in contact with bone, hollows or depressions called Howship's lacunae, or resorption lacunae, are formed. When bone resorption ceases, the osteoclasts disappear. These cells are also active when resorption of the roots of teeth occurs (see Chapters VIII and XII).

Cementoblasts. Cementoblasts are connective tissue cells found on the surface of cementum between the fibers. They are large cuboidal cells with spheroid or ovoid nuclei, which are active in the formation of cementum (see Chapter VI). The cells have irregular, fingerlike projections that fit around the fibers that extend from the cementum.

Interstitial tissue. The blood vessels, lymphatics, and nerves of the periodontal ligament are contained in spaces between the principal fiber bundles (Fig. 146). They are surrounded by loose connective tissue in which fibroblasts, histiocytes,

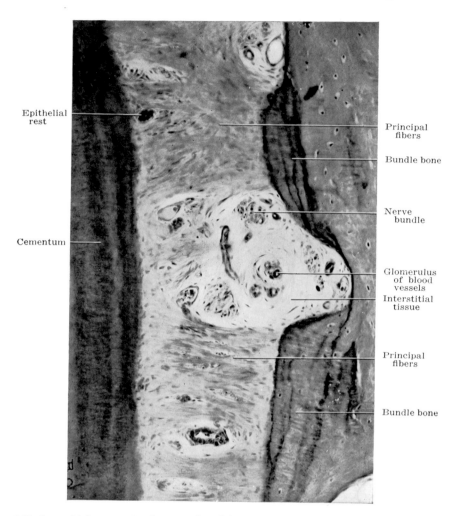

Epithelial rest

Principal fibers

Bundle bone

Nerve bundle

Cementum

Glomerulus of blood vessels

Interstitial tissue

Principal fibers

Bundle bone

Fig. 146. Interstitial spaces in the periodontal ligament contain loose connective tissue and carry glomerulus-like arranged blood vessels and nerves. (From Orban, B.: J. A. D. A. **16:** 405, 1929.)

undifferentiated mesenchymal reserve cells, and lymphocytes are found. Many arteriovenous anastomoses exist in these glomerulus-like arrangements of blood vessels.[10a]

Blood vessels. The blood supply of the periodontal ligament is derived from three sources: (1) blood vessels of the periapical area arise from the blood vessels for the pulp; (2) vessels branching from the interalveolar arteries pass into the membrane through openings in the wall of the alveolus (Fig. 147)—they are the main source of blood supply; and (3) arteries of the gingiva anastomose across the alveolar crest with those of the periodontal tissues. The capillaries form a rich network in the periodontal ligament.[29]

Lymphatics. A network of lymphatic vessels, following the path of the blood

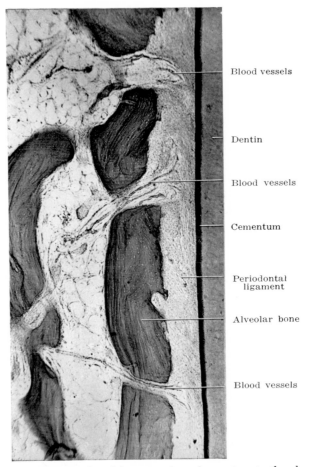

Fig. 147. Blood vessels enter the periodontal ligament through openings in the alveolar bone. (From Orban, B.: Dental Histology and Embryology, Philadelphia, 1929, P. Blakiston's Son & Co.)

vessels, provides the lymph drainage of the periodontal ligament. The flow is from the ligament toward and into the adjacent alveolar bone.[17, 25]

Nerves. The nerves of the periodontal ligament follow the path of the blood vessels, both from the periapical area and from the interdental and interradicular arteries through the alveolar wall. A rich plexus is formed in the periodontal ligament. Three types of nerve endings are found, one terminating in a knoblike swelling, another forming loops or rings around bundles of the principal fibers, and the third, free nerve endings that are receptors of pain. The terminal branches are free of myelin sheaths. Many nerve endings are receptors for proprioceptive stimuli. Any pressure to the crown of the tooth is transmitted to the nerve endings through the medium of the periodontal ligament. The proprioceptive endings allow accurate localization of degree and direction of pressure. Proprioceptive reflexes regulate the masticatory musculature and, by inhibition of muscular activity, protect the tooth in sudden overload. Pain reflexes are a second line of defense in an emergency, as in biting upon hard particles, bone, or birdshot.

The proprioceptive and pain sensations are not impaired by removal of the apical parts of the membrane, as in root resection, or by removal of its gingival portion, gingivectomy, since the nerves of the periodontal ligament arise from the interdental nerves running in the interdental septum. As elsewhere in the body, fibers from the sympathetic system supply the blood vessels of the periodontal ligament.[1, 14]

Epithelial structures. In the periodontal ligament epithelial cells are found which usually lie close to the cementum but not in contact with it (Fig. 148). They were first described by Malassez in 1884.[15] They are remnants of the epithelium of Hertwig's epithelial root sheath[5] (see Chapter II). At the time

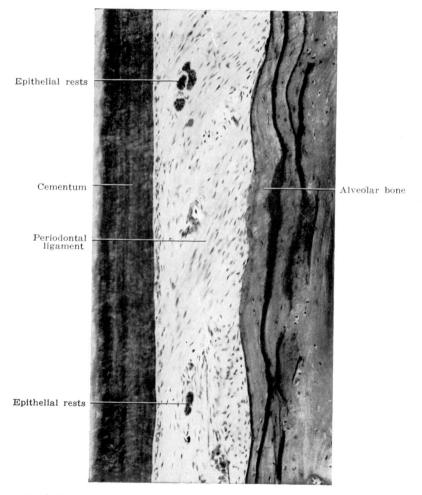

Fig. 148. Epithelial rests in the periodontal ligament.

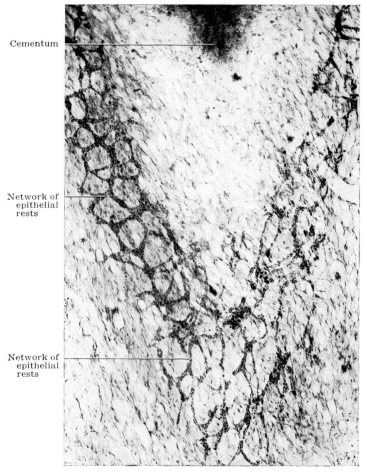

Cementum

Network of
epithelial
rests

Network of
epithelial
rests

Fig. 149. Network of epithelial rests in the periodontal ligament. (Tangential section almost parallel to root surface.)

of formation of cementum, the continuous layer of epithelium lining the dentin surface breaks into strands that persist as a network parallel to the surface of the root (Fig. 149). Only in sections almost parallel to the root can the true arrangement of these epithelial strands be seen.[6] Cross or longitudinal sections through the tooth cut through the strands of the network, and thus only isolated nests of epithelial cells appear in the sections. It is not clear whether the epithelial sheath breaks up because of degeneration of the epithelial cells, or because of active proliferation of the connective tissue, or both. The disintegration of the epithelium enables the connective tissue to approach the outer surface of the dentin and to deposit cementum on its surface. Frequently epithelial rests appear in sections as long strands (Fig. 150) or as tubules (Fig. 151). Under pathologic conditions they may proliferate and give rise to epithelial masses, associated with granulomas, cysts, or tumors of dental origin.

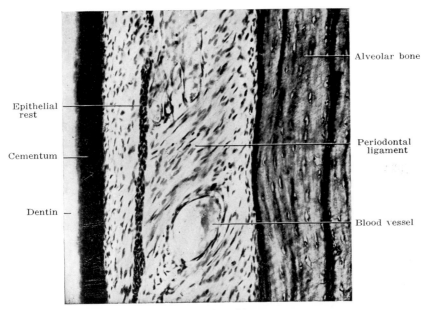

Fig. 150. Long strand of epithelium in the periodontal ligament.

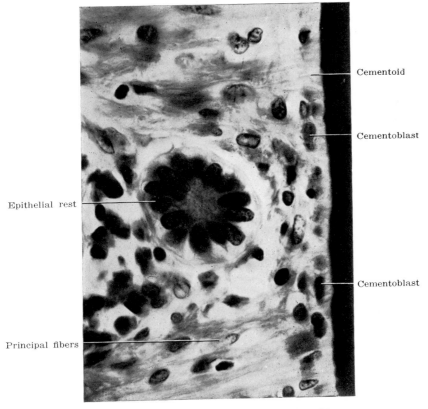

Fig. 151. Pseudoglandular structure of epithelial rest in the periodontal ligament.

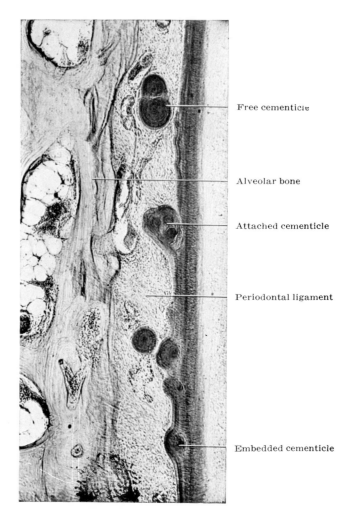

Fig. 152. Cementicles in the periodontal ligament.

Cementicles. Calcified bodies, cementicles, are sometimes found in the periodontal ligament, especially in older persons. These bodies may remain free in the connective tissue, they may fuse into large calcified masses, or they may be joined with the cementum (Fig. 152). As the cementum thickens with advancing age, it may envelop these bodies. When they are adherent to the cementum, they form excementoses. The origin of these calcified bodies is not established; it is presumed that degenerated epithelial cells form the nidus for their calcification.

PHYSIOLOGIC CHANGES

Measurements and changes in dimensions during life. Several studies of the width of the periodontal ligament in human specimens have been reported.[7, 8, 12, 13]

Table 3. Thickness of periodontal ligament of 154 teeth from 14 human jaws[*]

	Average at alveolar crest (mm.)	Average at midroot (mm.)	Average at apex (mm.)	Average for the entire tooth (mm.)
Ages 11-16 83 teeth from 4 jaws	0.23	0.17	0.24	0.21
Ages 32-50 36 teeth from 5 jaws	0.20	0.14	0.19	0.18
Ages 51-67 35 teeth from 5 jaws	0.17	0.12	0.16	0.15

[*]The table shows that the width of the periodontal ligament decreases with age and that it is wider at the crest and at the apex than at the midroot. (From Coolidge, E. D.: J. A. D. A. 24: 1260, 1937.)

Table 4. Comparison of periodontal ligament in different locations around the same tooth (subject 11 years of age)[*]

	Mesial (mm.)	Distal (mm.)	Labial (mm.)	Lingual (mm.)
Upper right central incisor, mesial and labial drift	0.12	0.24	0.12	0.22
Upper left central incisor, no drift	0.21	0.19	0.24	0.24
Upper right lateral incisor, distal and labial drift	0.27	0.17	0.11	0.15

[*]The table shows the variation in width of the mesial, distal, labial, and lingual sides of the same tooth. (From Coolidge, E. D.: J. A. D. A. 24: 1260, 1937.)

All reports agree that the thickness of the periodontal ligament varies in different individuals, in different teeth in the same person, and in different locations on the same tooth, as is illustrated in Tables 3 and 4.

The measurements shown in the tables indicate that it is not feasible to refer to an average figure of normal width of the periodontal ligament. Measurements of a large number of cases range from 0.15 to 0.38 mm. The fact that the periodontal ligament is thinnest in the middle region of the root seems to indicate that the fulcrum of physiologic movement is in this region. The thickness of the periodontal ligament seems to be maintained by the functional movements of the tooth. It is thinner in functionless and embedded teeth, but cementum and bone do not fuse even in functionless teeth.

Physiologic changes. Physiologic movement of human teeth is characterized by their tendency to migrate mesially in compensation for the wear at their contact areas.[30] In mesial drift a difference can be observed in the periodontal ligament in the distal and mesial areas (Fig. 153). On the distal side of the tooth, the interstitial spaces with their blood vessels, lymph vessels, and nerves appear in sections elliptic in contrast to those on the mesial side that appear round.[9] Bone resorption on the mesial side of the tooth sometimes opens marrow spaces to the periodontal ligament (Fig. 153, *A*). Frequently, however, the drift is so gradual

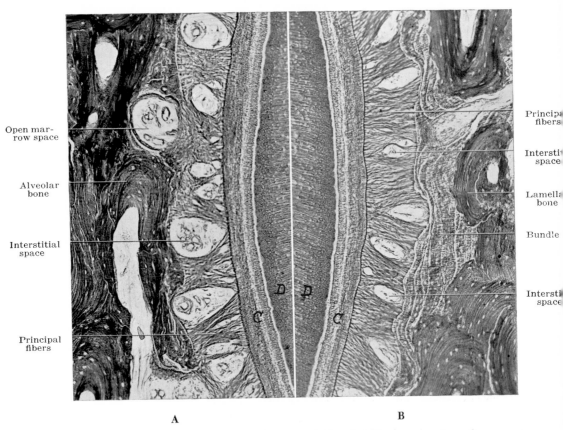

Open mar-
row space

Alveolar
bone

Interstitial
space

Principal
fibers

Principa
fibers

Interstit
space

Lamella
bone

Bundle

Intersti
space

A   B

Fig. 153. Interstitial spaces between the principal fiber bundles are round on the pressure side, **A**, and elliptic on the tension side, **B**. Marrow spaces open up on the pressure side and become interstitial spaces. **C**, Cementum. **D**, Dentin.

that bone formation in the marrow spaces keeps pace with the resorption on the periodontal side, and the thickness of the alveolar bone is maintained. Due to the shift of the tooth, epithelial rests may become incorporated in the bone on the side from which the tooth moves.[21]

CLINICAL CONSIDERATIONS

The complex functional interrelation of the teeth and their supporting tissues brings about continuous structural changes during life. Between the two extremes of occlusal trauma and loss of function there are many intermediate stages. In loss of function the periodontal ligament becomes narrower because of decreased use of that particular tooth.[8, 11, 12] The regular arrangement of the principal fibers is lost, and the periodontal *ligament* is changed into a *membrane* with irregularly arranged collagenous fibers. The cementum becomes thicker but finally aplastic; it contains no Sharpey's fibers. Also, the alveolar bone is in an aplastic state and lacks Sharpey's fibers (Fig. 154, *B*).

For restorative dentistry the importance of these changes in structure is obvious.[20] The supporting tissues of a tooth long out of function are unable to carry the load suddenly placed upon the tooth by a restoration. This applies to bridge abutments, teeth opposing bridges or dentures, and teeth used as anchorage for removable bridges. This may account for the inability of a patient to use a restoration immediately following its placement. Some time must elapse before the supporting tissues become again adapted to the new functional demands. An adjustment period, likewise, must be permitted following orthodontic treatment.

Acute trauma of the periodontal ligament, accidental blows, condensing of

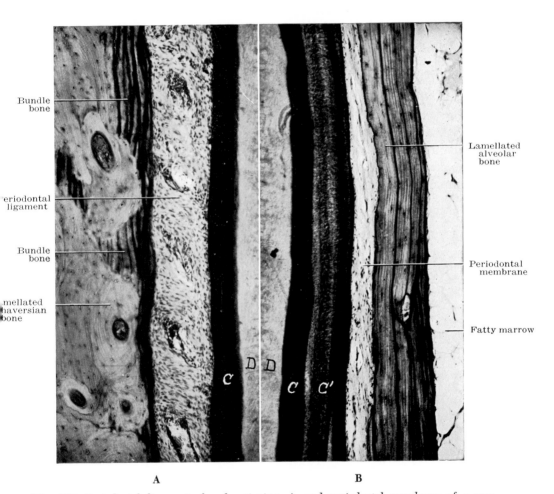

Fig. 154. Periodontal *ligament* of a functioning, **A**, and periodontal *membrane* of a nonfunctioning, **B**, tooth. In the functioning tooth the periodontal ligament is wide, and principal fibers are present. Cementum, **C**, is thin. Bundle bone with Sharpey's fibers. In the nonfunctioning tooth the periodontal space is narrow, and no principal fiber bundles are present. Cementum is thick, **C** and **C′**. Alveolar bone is lamellated, containing no Sharpey's fibers. **D**, Dentin.

foil, or rapid mechanical separation, may produce pathologic changes such as fractures or resorption of the cementum, tears of fiber bundles, hemorrhage, and necrosis. The adjacent alveolar bone is resorbed, the periodontal ligament lengthened, and the tooth becomes loose. When trauma is eliminated repair usually takes place. Occlusal trauma is always restricted to the intra-alveolar tissues and does not cause changes of the gingiva such as recession or pocket formation or gingivitis.

Orthodontic tooth movement depends upon bone resorption and bone formation stimulated by properly regulated pressure and tension.[18] These stimuli are transmitted through the medium of the periodontal ligament. If the movement of teeth is within physiologic limits (which may vary with the individual), the initial compression of the periodontal ligament on the pressure side is compensated for by bone resorption, whereas the stretch of the bundles of the periodontal ligament on the tension side is balanced by bone apposition. The presence of an intermediate plexus in the alveolodental and interdental ligaments allows a rather speedy adjustment after orthodontic movements. The absence of an intermediate plexus in the gingival fiber bundles prolongs such a readjustment and is responsible for the relapse, for instance, after rotation of a tooth.[23]

Under the stimulus of inflammation such as occurs in a dental granuloma, the epithelial rests of the periodontal ligament may proliferate to form a periodontal cyst around the root end of the tooth. Careful studies[10, 16] have shown that 100 per cent of dental granulomas contain either proliferating or resting epithelium. Therefore, all dental granulomas must be considered as potential periodontal cysts.

References

1. Berkelbach van der Sprenkel, H.: Zur Neurologie des Zahnes (Neurology of the Tooth), Ztschr. f. mikr.-anat. Forsch. **38**: 1, 1935.
2. Black, G. V.: A Study of the Histological Characters of the Periosteum and Peridental Membrane, Chicago, 1887, W. T. Keener Co.
3. Black, G. V.: The Fibers and Glands of the Peridental Membrane, D. Cosmos **41**: 101, 1899.
4. Box, K. F.: Evidence of Lymphatics in the Periodontium, J. Canad. D. A. **15**: 8, 1949.
5. Brunn, A. v.: Ueber die Ausdehnung des Schmelzorganes und seine Bedeutung für die Zahnbildung (The Extension of the Enamel Organ and Its Significance in Tooth Development), Arch. f. mikr. Anat. **29**: 367, 1887.
6. Bruszt, P.: Ueber die netzartige Anordnung des paradentalen Epithels (The Network Arrangement of the Epithelium in the Periodontal Membrane), Ztschr. f. Stomatol. **30**: 679, 1932.
7. Coolidge, E. D.: Clinical Pathology and Treatment of the Dental Pulp and Periodontal Tissues, Philadelphia, 1939, Lea & Febiger.
8. Coolidge, E. D.: The Thickness of the Human Periodontal Membrane, J. A. D. A. **24**: 1260, 1937.
9. Gottlieb, B.: Paradental Pyorrhoë und Alveolar atrophie (Paradental Pyorrhea and Alveolar Atrophy), Fortschr. d. Zahnheilk. **2**: 363, 1926.
10. Hill, T. J.: The Epithelium in Dental Granulomata, J. D. Res. **10**: 323, 1930.
10a. Ishimitsu, K.: Beitrag zur Kenntnis der Morphologie und Entwicklungsgeschichte der Glomeruli periodontii (Contribution of the Knowledge of Morphology and Development of the Periodontal Glomeruli), Yokohama med. Bull. **11**: 415, 1960.

11. Kellner, E.: Histologische Befunde an antagonistenlosen Zähnen (Histologic Findings on Teeth Without Antagonists), Ztschr. f. Stomatol. **26:** 271, 1928.

12. Klein, A.: Systematische Untersuchungen über die Periodontalbreite (Systematic Investigations on the Width of the Periodontal Membrane), Ztschr. f. Stomatol. **26:** 417, 1928.

13. Kronfeld, R.: A Case of Tooth Fracture, With Special Emphasis on Tissue Repair and Adaptation Following Traumatic Injury, J. D. Res. **15:** 429, 1935-1936.

14. Lehner, J., and Plenk, H.: Die Zähne (the Teeth). *In* von Möllendorff, W. (editor): Handbuch der mikroskopischen Anatomie des Menschen, vol. 5, pt. 3, Berlin, 1936, Julius Springer, p. 449.

15. Malassez, M. L.: Sur l'existence de masses epithéliales dans le ligament alveolodentaire (On the Existence of Epithelial Masses in the Periodontal Membrane), Compt. rend. Soc. de biol. **36:** 241, 1884.

16. McCrea, M. W.: Histologic Studies on the Occurrence of Epithelium in Dental Granulomata, J. A. D. A. **24:** 1133, 1937.

17. Noyes, F. B.: A Review of Work on the Lymphatics of Dental Origin, J. A. D. A. **14:** 714, 1927.

18. Oppenheim, A.: Human Tissue Response to Orthodontic Intervention of Short and Long Duration, Am. J. Orthodont. & Oral Surg. **28:** 263, 1942.

19. Orban, B.: Entwicklungsgeschichte und Histogenese (Embryology and Histogenesis), Fortschr. d. Zahnheilk. **3:** 749, 1927.

20. Orban, B.: Biologic Considerations in Restorative Dentistry, J. A. D. A. **28:** 1069, 1941.

21. Orban, B.: A Contribution to the Knowledge of the Physiologic Changes in the Periodontal Membrane, J. A. D. A. **16:** 405, 1929.

22. Orban, B.: Dental Histology and Embryology, Philadelphia, 1929, P. Blakiston's Son & Co.

23. Reitan, K.: Tissue Behavior During Orthodontic Tooth Movement, Am. J. Orthodontics **46:** 881, 1960.

24. Robinson, H. B. G.: Some Clinical Aspects of Intra-Oral Age Changes, Geriatrics **2:** 9, 1947.

25. Schweitzer, G.: Die Lymphgefässe des Zahnfleisches und der Zähne (Lymph Vessels of the Gingivae and Teeth), Arch. f. mikr. Anat. **69:** 807, 1907; **74:** 927, 1909.

26. Sicher, H.: Bau und Funktion des Fixationsapparates der Meerschweinchenmolaren (Structure and Function of the Supporting Apparatus in the Teeth of Guinea Pigs), Ztschr. f. Stomatol. **21:** 580, 1923.

27. Sicher, H.: The Axial Movement of Continuously Growing Teeth, J. D. Res. **21:** 201, 1942.

28. Sicher, H.: The Principal Fibers of the Periodontal Membrane, Bur **55:** 2, 1954.

29. Weinmann, J. P.: Progress of Gingival Inflammation Into the Supporting Structures of the Teeth, J. Periodont. **12:** 71, 1941.

30. Weinmann, J. P.: Bone Changes Related to Eruption of the Teeth, Angle Orthodontist **11:** 83, 1941.

31. Weinmann, J. P., and Sicher, H.: Bone and Bones, ed. 2, 1955, The C. V. Mosby Co.

Chapter VIII • MAXILLA AND MANDIBLE (ALVEOLAR PROCESS)*

DEVELOPMENT OF THE MAXILLA AND THE MANDIBLE

In the beginning of the second month of fetal life the skull consists of three parts: (1) the chondrocranium, which is cartilaginous, comprises the base of the skull with the otic and nasal capsules; (2) the desmocranium, which is membranous, forms the lateral walls and roof of the brain case; (3) the appendicular or visceral part of the skull consist of the cartilaginous skeletal rods of the branchial arches.

The bones of the skull develop either by endochondral ossification, replacing the cartilage, or by intramembranous ossification in the mesenchyme. Intramembranous bone may develop in close proximity to cartilaginous parts of the skull, or directly in the desmocranium, the membranous capsule of the brain. (Plate 2.)

The endochondral bones are the bones of the base of the skull: ethmoidal bone; inferior concha (turbinate bone); body, lesser wings, basal part of greater wings, and the lateral plate of pterygoid process of the sphenoid bone; petrosal part of the temporal bone; basilar, lateral, and lower part of the squamous portion of the occipital bone. The following bones develop in the desmocranium: frontal bones; parietal bones; squamous and tympanic parts of the temporal bone; parts of the greater wings and the medial plate of pterygoid process of the sphenoid bone; the upper part of the squamous portion of the occipital bone. All the bones of the upper face develop by intramembranous ossification, most of them close to the cartilage of the nasal capsule. The mandible develops as intramembranous bone, lateral to the cartilage of the mandibular arch. This cartilage, Meckel's cartilage, is in its proximal parts the primordium for two of the auditory ossicles: the incus (anvil) and the malleus (hammer). The third auditory ossicle, the stapes (stirrup), develops from the proximal part of the skeleton in the second branchial arch, which then gives rise to the styloid process, the stylohyoid ligament, and part of the hyoid bone, which is completed by the derivatives of the third arch. The fourth and fifth arches form the skeleton of the larynx.

---

*First draft submitted by Harry Sicher and Joseph P. Weinmann.

A

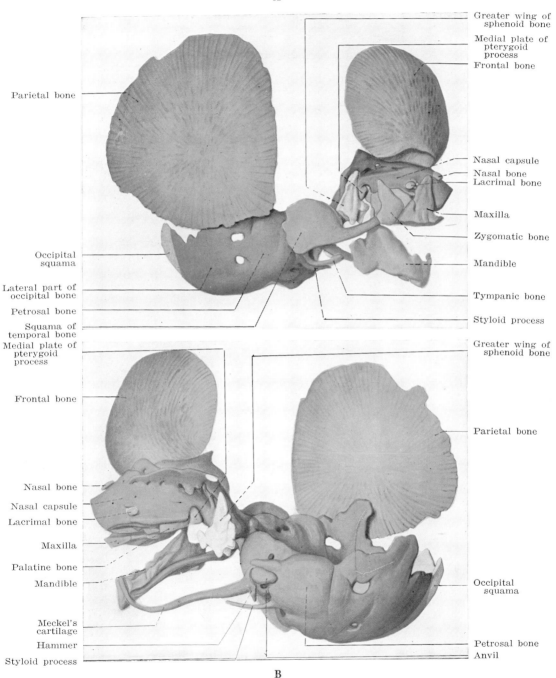

Greater wing of
sphenoid bone

Medial plate of
pterygoid
process

Frontal bone

Parietal bone

Nasal capsule
Nasal bone
Lacrimal bone

Maxilla

Zygomatic bone

Occipital
squama

Mandible

Lateral part of
occipital bone

Petrosal bone

Squama of
temporal bone

Tympanic bone

Styloid process

Medial plate of
pterygoid
process

Greater wing of
sphenoid bone

Frontal bone

Parietal bone

Nasal bone

Nasal capsule

Lacrimal bone

Maxilla

Palatine bone

Mandible

Occipital
squama

Meckel's
cartilage

Hammer

Styloid process

Petrosal bone
Anvil

B

Plate 2. Reconstruction of the skull of a human embryo 80 mm. long. Cartilage, green. Intra-membranous bones, pink. Endochondral bones, white. A, Right lateral view. B, Left lateral view after removal of left intramembranous bones. (From Sicher, H., and Tandler, J.: Anatomie für Zahnärzte [Anatomy for Dentists], Vienna, 1928, Julius Springer.)

Maxilla. The human maxilla is homologous to two bones, the maxilla proper and the premaxilla. The latter, in most animals a separate bone, carries the incisors and forms the anterior part of the hard palate and the rim of the piriform aperture. The ossification centers of premaxilla and maxilla may be separate for a very short time,[23] or only one center of ossification, common to both premaxilla and maxilla, appears. That man, therefore, may not have an independent premaxilla, even in the first developmental stages, does not change the fact that man possesses the homologue of a premaxilla. The composition of the human maxilla from premaxilla and maxilla is indicated by the incisive fissure, well visible in young skulls on the palate, extending from the incisive foramen to the alveolus of the canine.

Mandible. The mandible makes its appearance as a bilateral structure in the sixth week of fetal life as a thin plate of bone lateral to, and at some dis-

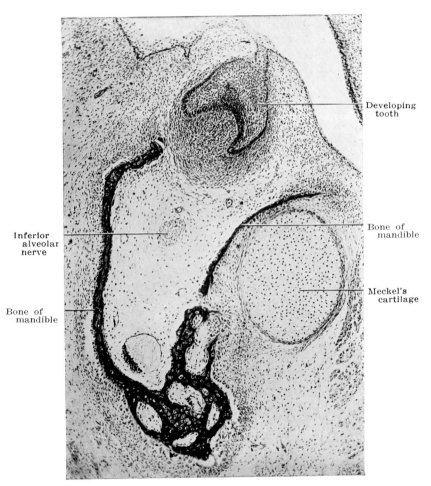

Fig. 155. Development of the mandible as intramembranous bone lateral to Meckel's cartilage (human embryo 45 mm. long).

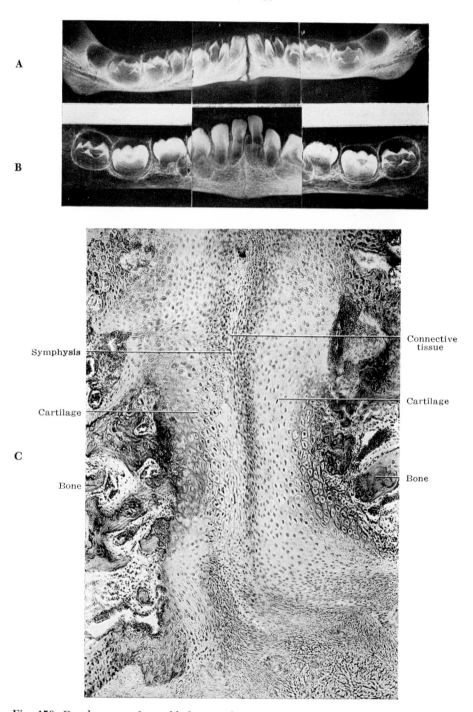

Fig. 156. Development of mandibular symphysis. **A,** Newborn infant. Symphysis wide open. Mental ossicle (roentgenogram). **B,** Child 9 months. Symphysis partly closed. Mental ossicles fused to mandible (roentgenogram). **C,** Frontal section through mandibular symphysis of newborn infant. Connective tissue in midline connects plates of cartilage on either side. The cartilage is later replaced by bone.

tance from, Meckel's cartilage (Fig. 155). The latter is a cylindrical rod of cartilage; its proximal end (close to the base of the skull) is continuous with the hammer and is in contact with the anvil. Its distal end at the midline is bent upward and is in contact with the cartilage of the other side. (Plate 2.) The greater part of Meckel's cartilage disappears without contributing to the formation of the bone of the mandible. Only a small part of the cartilage, some distance from the midline, is the site of endochondral ossification. Here the cartilage calcifies and is destroyed by chondroclasts, replaced by connective tissue and then by bone. Throughout fetal life the mandible is a paired bone; right and left mandibles are joined in the midline by fibrocartilage in the mandibular symphysis. The cartilage at the symphysis is not derived from Meckel's cartilage but differentiates from the connective tissue in the midline. In it, small irregular bones, known as the mental ossicles, develop and at the end of the first year fuse with the mandibular body. At the same time the two halves of the mandible unite by ossification of the symphysial fibrocartilage. (Fig. 156.)

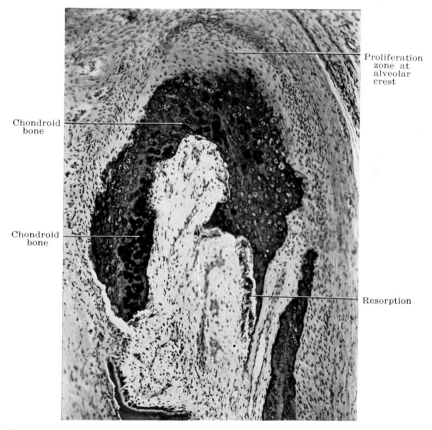

Fig. 157. Vertical growth of mandible at alveolar crest. Formation of chondroid bone that later is replaced by typical bone.

DEVELOPMENT OF THE ALVEOLAR PROCESS

Near the end of the second month of fetal life, the maxilla, as well as the mandible, form a groove which is open toward the surface of the oral cavity (Fig. 155). The tooth germs are contained in this groove, which also includes the alveolar nerves and vessels. Gradually, bony septa develop between the adjacent tooth germs, and much later the primitive mandibular canal is separated from the dental crypts by a horizontal plate of bone.

An alveolar process in the strict sense of the word develops only during the eruption of the teeth. It is important to realize that during growth part of the alveolar process is gradually incorporated into the maxillary or mandibular body, while it grows at a fairly rapid rate at its free borders. During the period of rapid growth, a tissue may develop at the alveolar crest that combines characteristics of cartilage and bone; it is called chondroid bone (Fig. 157).

STRUCTURE OF THE ALVEOLAR PROCESS

The alveolar process may be defined as that part of the maxilla and the mandible that forms and supports the sockets of the teeth (Fig. 158). Anatomically, no distinct boundary exists between the body of the maxilla or the mandible and their respective alveolar processes. In some places the alveolar process is fused with, and partly masked by, bone which is not functionally related to the teeth. In the anterior part of the maxilla the palatine process fuses with the oral plate of the alveolar process. In the posterior part of the mandible the oblique line is superimposed upon the bone of the alveolar process (Figs. 158, *D* and *E*).

As a result of its adaptation to function, two parts of the alveolar process can be distinguished. The first consists of a thin lamella of bone that surrounds the root of the tooth and gives attachment to principal fibers of the periodontal ligament. This is the alveolar bone proper. The second part is the bone that surrounds the alveolar bone and gives support to the socket. This has been called supporting alveolar bone.[13] The latter, in turn, consists of two parts: (1) compact bone, cortical plates, forming the vestibular, or buccolabial, and oral, or lingual, plates of the alveolar processes; and (2) the spongy bone between these plates and the alveolar bone proper. (Fig. 158.)

The cortical plates, continuous with the compact layers of maxillary and mandibular body, are generally much thinner in the maxilla than in the mandible. They are thickest in the premolar and molar regions of the lower jaw, especially on the buccal side. In the maxilla the outer cortical plate is perforated by many small openings through which blood and lymph vessels pass. In the lower jaw the cortical bone of the alveolar process is dense. In the region of the anterior teeth of both jaws the supporting bone usually is very thin. No spongy bone is found here, and the cortical plate is fused with the alveolar bone proper. (Figs. 158, *B* and *C*.) In such areas, notably in the premolar and molar regions of the maxilla, defects of the outer alveolar wall are fairly common. Such defects, where

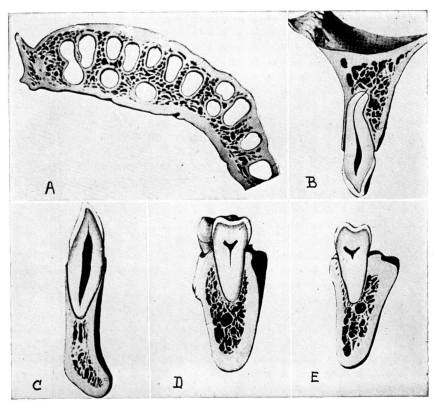

Fig. 158. Gross relations of alveolar processes: **A**, Horizontal section through upper alveolar process. **B**, Labiolingual section through upper lateral incisor. **C**, Labiolingual section through lower canine. **D**, Labiolingual section through lower second molar. **E**, Labiolingual section through lower third molar. (From Sicher, H., and Tandler, J.: Anatomie für Zahnärzte [Anatomy for Dentists], Vienna, 1928, Julius Springer.)

periodontal tissues and covering mucosa fuse, do not impair the firm attachment and function of the tooth.

The shape of the outlines of the crest of the alveolar septa in the roentgenogram is dependent upon the position of the adjacent teeth. In a healthy mouth the distance between the cementoenamel junction and the free border of the alveolar bone proper is fairly constant. In consequence the alveolar crest often is oblique if the neighboring teeth are inclined. In the majority of individuals the inclination is most pronounced in the premolar and molar regions, the teeth being tipped mesially. Then the cementoenamel junction of the mesial tooth is situated in a more occlusal plane than that of the distal tooth, and the alveolar crest, therefore, slopes distally. (Fig. 159.)

The interdental and interradicular septa contain the perforating canals of Zuckerkandl and Hirschfeld, which house the interdental and interradicular arteries, veins, lymph vessels, and nerves.

Histologically, the cortical plates consist of longitudinal lamellae and haversian systems (Fig. 160). In the lower jaw circumferential or basic lamellae reach from the body of the mandible into the cortical plates.

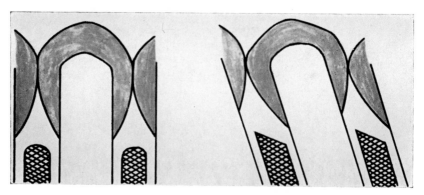

Fig. 159. Diagrammatic illustration of the relation between the cementoenamel junction of adjacent teeth and the shape of the crests of the alveolar septa. (From Ritchey, B., and Orban, B.: J. Periodont. **24:** 75, 1953.)

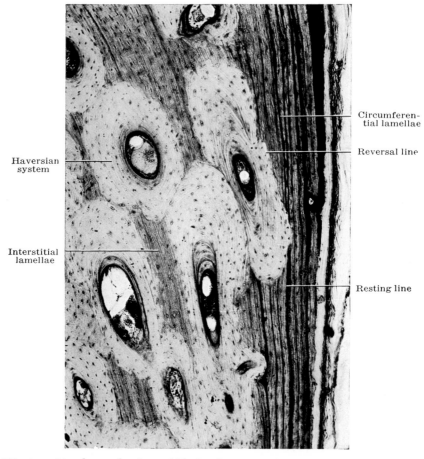

Fig. 160. Appositional growth of mandible by formation of circumferential lamellae. These are replaced by haversian bone; remnants of circumferential lamellae in the depth persisting as interstitial lamellae.

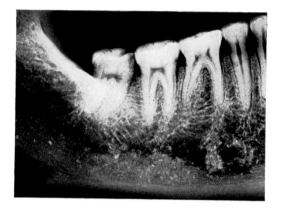

A

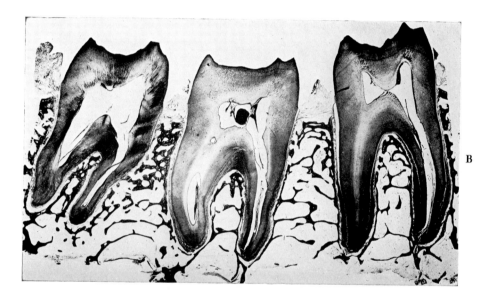

B

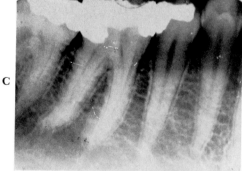

C

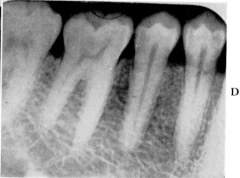

D

Fig. 161. Supporting trabeculae between alveoli. **A,** Roentgenogram of a mandible. **B,** Mesio-distal section through mandibular molars showing alveolar bone proper and supporting bone. **C,** Type I of alveolar spongiosa. Note regular horizontal trabeculae. **D,** Type II of alveolar spongiosa. Note irregularly arranged trabeculae. (Courtesy Dr. N. Brescia, Chicago, Ill.)

The study of roentgenograms permits the classification of the spongiosa of the alveolar process into two main types. In Type I the interdental and interradicular trabeculae are regular and horizontal in a ladderlike arrangement. (Fig. 161, *A*, *B*, and *C*.) Type II shows irregularly arranged numerous and delicate interdental and interradicular trabeculae. (Fig. 161, *D*.) Both types show a variation in thickness of trabeculae and size of marrow spaces. The architecture of Type I fits well into the general idea of trajectorial pattern of spongy bone; Type II, though evidently functionally satisfactory, lacks a distinct trajectorial pattern, which seems to be compensated for by the greater number of trabeculae in any given area. From the apical part of the socket of lower molars trabeculae are sometimes seen radiating in a slightly distal direction. These trabeculae are less prominent in the upper jaw because of the proximity of the nasal cavity and the maxillary sinus. The marrow spaces in the alveolar process may contain hemo-

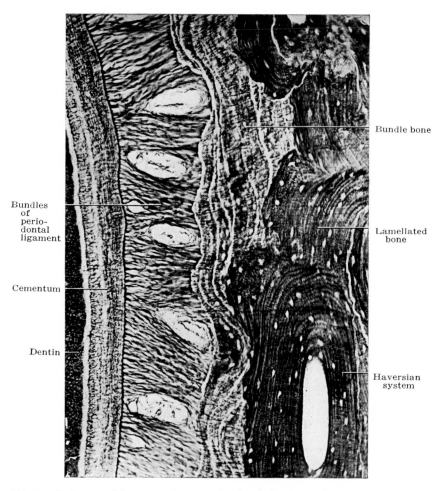

Fig. 162. Bundle bone and haversian bone on the distal alveolar wall, separated by a reversal line (silver impregnation).

poietic marrow, but they usually contain fatty marrow. In the condylar process, in the angle of the mandible, in the maxillary tuberosity, and in other foci, hemopoietic cellular marrow is found frequently, even in adults.[4, 17]

The alveolar bone proper, which forms the inner wall of the socket (Fig. 161), is perforated by many openings that carry branches of the interalveolar nerves and blood vessels into the periodontal ligament (see Chapter VII), and it is, therefore, called the cribriform plate. The alveolar bone proper consists partly of lamellated, partly of bundle bone. Some lamellae of the lamellated bone are arranged roughly parallel to the surface of the adjacent marrow spaces, whereas others form haversian systems. Bundle bone is that bone in which the principal fibers of the periodontal ligament are anchored. The term bundle bone was chosen because the bundles of the principal fibers continue into the bone as Sharpey's fibers. The bundle bone is characterized by the scarcity of the fibrils in the intercellular substance. These fibrils, moreover, are all arranged at right angles to the Sharpey's fibers. The bundle bone appears much lighter in preparations stained with silver than lamellated bone because of the reduced number of fibrils. (Fig. 162.) In some areas the alveolar bone proper consists mainly of bundle bone. Such areas are visible in a roentgenogram by their greater radiopacity.

PHYSIOLOGIC CHANGES IN THE ALVEOLAR PROCESS

The internal structure of bone is adapted to mechanical stresses. It changes continuously during growth and alteration of functional stresses. In the jaws structural changes are correlated to the growth, eruption, movements, wear, and loss of teeth. All these processes are made possible only by a coordination of destructive and formative activities. Specialized cells, the osteoclasts, have the function of eliminating overaged bony tissue or bone that is no longer adapted to mechanical forces, whereas osteoblasts produce new bone.

Osteoclasts are as a rule multinucleated giant cells (Fig. 163, A). The number of nuclei in one cell may rise to a dozen or more. However, occasionally uninuclear osteoclasts are found. The nuclei are vesicular, showing a prominent nucleolus and little chromatin. The cell body is irregularly oval or club-shaped and may show many branching processes. In general, osteoclasts are found in baylike depressions in the bone that are called Howship's lacunae; they are formed by the activity of the osteoclasts. The cytoplasm that is in contact with the bone is striated. These striations have been explained as the expression of a secretory activity of these cells. The osteoclasts seem to produce proteolytic enzymes that destroy or dissolve the organic constituents of the bone matrix and chelating substances that bring about the solubility of the otherwise insoluble bone salts. A decalcification of bone in the living organism has often been claimed but has never been demonstrated.

Osteoclasts differentiate from undifferentiated mesenchymal reserve cells by division of nuclei, without a following division of the cytoplasm, or by

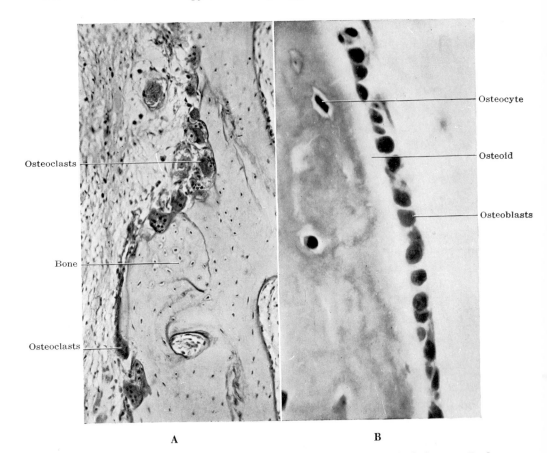

Fig. 163. Resorption and apposition of bone. **A,** Osteoclasts in Howship's lacunae. **B,** Osteoblasts along a bone trabecula. Layer of osteoid tissue as a sign of bone formation (high magnification).

fusion of several cells. The stimulus that leads to the differentiation of mesenchymal cells into osteoclasts is not known. Osteoclastic resorption of bone is partly genetically patterned, partly functionally determined. Overaged bone seems to stimulate the differentiation of osteoclasts,[8] possibly by chemical changes that are the consequence of degeneration and final necrosis of the osteocytes.

New bone is produced by the activity of osteoblasts (Fig. 163, *B*). These cells also differentiate probably from undifferentiated mesenchymal reserve cells of the connective tissue. Functioning osteoblasts are arranged along the surface of the growing bone in a continuous layer.

The osteoblasts produce the intercellular substance of bone. It is at first devoid of mineral salts and at this stage is termed osteoid tissue. While the matrix is produced, some of the osteoblasts become embedded in the matrix as osteocytes. Normally, the organic matrix calcifies immediately after formation.[3, 12, 23]

INTERNAL RECONSTRUCTION OF BONE

The bone in the alveolar process is identical to bone elsewhere in the body and is in a constant state of flux. During the growth of the maxilla and the mandible, bone is deposited on the outer surfaces of the cortical plates. In the mandible, with its thick, compact cortical plates, bone is deposited in the shape of basic or circumferential lamellae (Fig. 160). When the lamellae reach a certain thickness they are replaced from the inside by haversian bone. This reconstruction is correlated to the functional and nutritional demands of the bone. In the haversian canals, closest to the surface, osteoclasts differentiate and resorb the haversian lamellae and part of the circumferential lamellae. The resorbed bone is replaced by proliferating loose connective tissue. After a time the resorption ceases and new bone is apposed onto the old. The scalloped outline of Howship's lacunae that turn their convexity toward the old bone remains visible as a darkly stained cementing line, reversal line. This is in contrast to those cementing lines

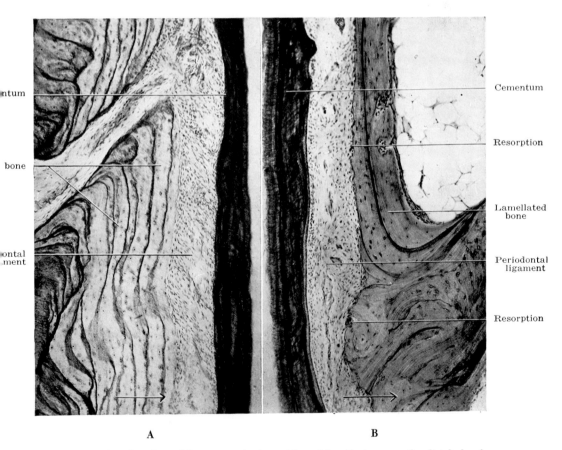

Fig. 164. Mesial drift indicated by arrow. A, Apposition of bundle bone on the distal alveolar wall. B, Resorption of bone on the mesial alveolar wall. (From Weinmann, J. P.: Angle Orthodontist 11: 83, 1941.)

that correspond to a rest period in an otherwise continuous process of bone apposition; they are called resting lines (Fig. 160). Resting and reversal lines are found between layers of bone of varying age.

Wherever a muscle, tendon, or ligament is attached to the surface of bone, Sharpey's fibers can be seen penetrating the basic lamellae. During replacement of the latter by haversian systems, fragments of bone containing Sharpey's fibers remain in the deeper layers. Thus, the presence of interstitial lamellae containing Sharpey's fibers indicates the former level of the surface.[21]

Alterations in the structure of the alveolar bone are of great importance in connection with the physiologic movements of the teeth. These movements are directed mesio-occlusally. At the alveolar fundus the continual apposition of bone can be recognized by resting lines separating parallel layers of bundle bone; when the bundle bone has reached a certain thickness it is resorbed partly from the marrow spaces and then replaced by lamellated bone or spongy trabeculae. The

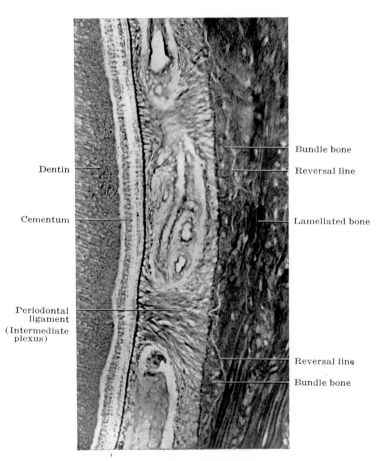

Dentin

Cementum

Periodontal
ligament
(Intermediate
plexus)

Bundle bone

Reversal line

Lamellated bone

Reversal line

Bundle bone

Fig. 165. Mesial alveolar wall consisting mostly of lamellated bone, islands of bundle bone anchoring principal fibers of the periodontal ligament.

presence of bundle bone indicates the level at which the alveolar fundus was situated previously. During the mesial drift of a tooth, bone is apposed on the distal and resorbed on the mesial alveolar wall (Fig. 164.). The distal wall is made up almost entirely of bundle bone. However, the osteoclasts in the adjacent marrow spaces remove part of the bundle bone when it reaches a certain thickness. In its place lamellated bone is laid down. (Fig. 162.)

On the mesial alveolar wall of a drifting tooth signs of active resorption are the presence of Howship's lacunae containing osteoclasts (Fig. 164). Bundle bone, however, on this side is always present in some areas, but forms merely a thin layer (Fig. 165). This is due to the fact that the mesial drift of a tooth does not occur simply as a bodily movement. Thus, resorption does not involve the entire mesial surface of the alveolus at one and the same time. Moreover, periods of resorption alternate with periods of rest and repair. It is during these periods of repair that bundle bone is formed, and detached periodontal fibers are again secured. Islands of bundle bone are separated from the lamellated bone by reversal lines that turn their convexities toward the lamellated bone (Fig. 165).

During these changes compact bone may be replaced by spongy bone or spongy bone may change into compact bone. This type of internal reconstruction of bone can be observed in physiologic mesial drift or in orthodontic mesial or distal movement of teeth. In these movements an interdental septum shows apposition on one, resorption on the other surface. If the alveolar bone proper is thickened by apposition of bundle bone, the interdental marrow spaces widen and advance in the direction of apposition. Conversely, if the plate of the alveolar bone proper is thinned by resorption, apposition of bone occurs on those surfaces that face the marrow spaces. The result is a reconstructive shift of the interdental septum.

CLINICAL CONSIDERATIONS

Bone, though one of the hardest tissues of the human body, is, biologically, a highly plastic tissue. Where bone is covered by a vascularized connective tissue, it is exceedingly sensitive to pressure, whereas tension acts, generally, as a stimulus to the production of new bone. It is this biologic plasticity that enables the orthodontist to move teeth without disrupting their relations to the alveolar bone. Bone is resorbed on the side of pressure and apposed on the side of tension, thus allowing the entire alveolus to shift with the tooth.

The adaptation of bone to function is quantitative as well as qualitative. Whereas increase in functional forces leads to formation of new bone, decreased function leads to a decrease in the volume of bone. This can be observed in the supporting bone of teeth that have lost their antagonists.[10] Here, the spongy bone around the alveolus shows marked rarefication: the bone trabeculae are less numerous and very thin. (Fig. 166.) The alveolar bone proper, however, is generally well preserved because it continues to receive some stimuli by the tension of the periodontal tissues.

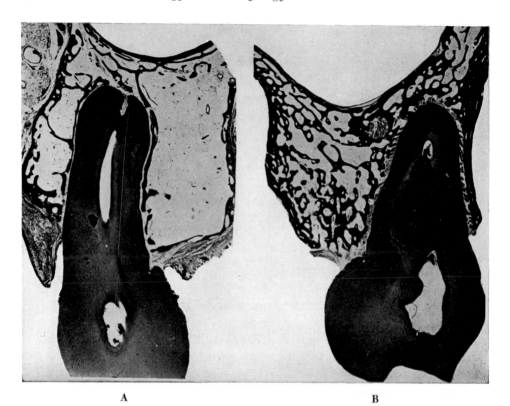

A   B

Fig. 166. Osteoporosis of alveolar process caused by inactivity of the tooth that has no antagonist. Labiolingual sections through upper molars of the same individual. **A,** Disappearance of bony trabeculae after loss of function. Plane of mesiobuccal root. Alveolar bone proper remains intact. **B,** Normal spongy bone in the plane of mesiobuccal root of functioning tooth. (From Kellner, E.: Ztschr. f. Stomatol. **18:** 59, 1920.)

During healing of fractures or extraction wounds, an embryonic type of bone is formed, which only later is replaced by mature bone. The embryonic bone, immature or coarse fibrillar bone, is characterized by the greater number, size, and irregular arrangement of the osteocytes and the irregular course of its fibrils. The greater number of cells and the reduced volume of calcified intercellular substance render this immature bone more radiolucent than mature bone. This explains why bony callus cannot be seen in roentgenograms at a time when histologic examination of a fracture reveals a well-developed union between the fragments, and why a socket after an extraction wound appears to be empty at a time when it is almost filled with immature bone. The visibility in radiograms lags two to three weeks behind actual formation of new bone.

References

1. Becks, H.: Dangerous Consequences of Vitamin D Overdosage on Dental and Paradental Structures, J. A. D. A. **29:** 1947, 1942.
2. Becks, H.: The Effect of Deficiencies of the Filtrate Fraction of the Vitamin B Complex and Nicotinic Acid on Teeth and Oral Structures, J. Periodont. **13:** 18, 1942.

3. Bloom, W., and Bloom, M. A.: Calcification and Ossification. Calcification of Developing Bones in Embryonic and Newborn Rats, Anat. Rec. **78**: 497, 1940.
4. Box, H. K.: Red Bone Marrow in Human Jaws, Toronto, 1933, University of Toronto Press.
5. Breitner, C.: Bone Changes Resulting From Experimental Orthodontic Treatment, Am. J. Orthodont. & Oral Surg. **26**: 521, 1940.
6. Brodie, A. G.: Some Recent Observations on the Growth of the Mandible, Angle Orthodontist **10**: 63, 1940.
7. Brodie, A. G.: On the Growth Pattern of the Human Head From the Third Month to the Eighth Year of Life, Am. J. Anat. **68**: 209, 1941.
8. Gottlieb, B.: Zur Aetiologie und Therapie der Alveolarpyorrhoe (Etiology and Therapy of Alveolar Pyorrhea), Oesterr. Ztschr. f. Stomatol. **18**: 59, 1920.
9. Ham, A. W.: Histology, ed. 2, Philadelphia, 1953, J. B. Lippincott Co.
10. Kellner, E.: Histologische Befunde an antagonistenlosen Zähnen (Histological Findings on Teeth Without Antagonists), Ztschr. f. Stomatol. **26**: 271, 1928.
11. Lehner, J., and Plenk, H.: Die Zähne (The Teeth). In von Möllendorff, W. (editor): Handbuch der mikroskopischen Anatomie des Menschen, vol. 5, pt. 3, Berlin, 1936, Julius Springer.
12. McLean, F. C., and Bloom, W.: Calcification and Ossification. Calcification in Normal Growing Bone, Anat. Rec. **78**: 333, 1940.
13. Orban, B.: Dental Histology and Embryology, ed. 1, Chicago, 1928, Rogers Printing Co.
14. Orban, B.: A Contribution to the Knowledge of the Physiologic Changes in the Periodontal Membrane, J. A. D. A. **16**: 405, 1929.
15. Ritchey, B., and Orban, B.: The Crests of the Interdental Alveolar Septa, J. Periodont. **24**: 75, 1953.
16. Schaffer, J.: Die Verknöcherung des Unterkiefers (Ossification of the Mandible), Arch. f. mikr. Anat. **32**: 266, 1888.
17. Schoenbauer, F.: Histologische Befunde bei Kieferosteomyelitis (Histologic Findings in Osteomyelitis of the Jaw), Ztschr. f. Stomatol. **35**: 820, 1937.
18. Schour, I., and Massler, M.: Endocrines and Dentistry, J. A. D. A. **30**: 595, 763, 943, 1943.
19. Sicher, H., and Tandler, J.: Anatomie für Zahnärzte (Anatomy for Dentists), Vienna, 1928, Julius Springer.
20. Sicher, H.: Oral Anatomy, ed. 2, St. Louis, 1952, The C. V. Mosby Co.
21. Weinmann, J. P.: Das Knochenbild bei Störungen der physiologischen Wanderung der Zähne (Bone in Disturbances of the Physiologic Mesial Drift), Ztschr. f. Stomatol. **24**: 397, 1926.
22. Weinmann, J. P.: Bone Changes Related to Eruption of the Teeth, Angle Orthodontist **11**: 83, 1941.
23. Weinmann, J. P., and Sicher, H.: Bone and Bones, ed. 2, St. Louis, 1955, The C. V. Mosby Co.

Chapter IX • ORAL MUCOUS MEMBRANE*

GENERAL CHARACTERISTICS

The oral cavity, as the first part of the digestive tract, serves a variety of functions. It is both the portal of entry and the place of mastication of food. It contains the taste organs. The saliva secreted into the oral cavity not only lubricates the food to facilitate swallowing but also contains enzymes that initiate digestion. The oral cavity is lined throughout by a mucous membrane. This term designates the lining of body cavities that communicate with the outside.

The morphologic structure of the mucous membrane varies in the different areas of the oral cavity in correlation with the functions of specific zones and the mechanical influences that bear upon them. Around the teeth and on the hard palate, for example, the mucous membrane is exposed to mechanical forces in the mastication of rough and hard food, whereas on the floor of the mouth it is largely protected by the tongue. This is the reason the mucous membrane around the teeth and on the hard palate differs in structure from that of the floor of the mouth, cheeks, and lips.

The mucous membrane is attached to the underlying structures by a layer of connective tissue, the submucosa, which varies in character in different areas. The oral mucous membrane itself is composed of two layers, the lamina propria and the surface epithelium. (Fig. 167.) A basement membrane separates the lamina propria from the stratified squamous epithelium.

In man the stratified squamous epithelium is keratinized in some areas only, namely, the gingiva and the hard palate. Keratinized epithelium and nonkera-

---

*First draft submitted by Balint J. Orban and Harry Sicher.

tinized epithelium differ not only by the presence or the lack of a horny layer. In both types, the basal cells form a single layer of high cuboidal cells that are anchored to the basement membrane by short protoplasmic processes. In the next layers the cells are irregularly polyhedral, larger in nonkeratinized areas than in the keratinized zones. In keratinizing epithelium, intercellular spaces and, therefore, intercellular bridges are conspicuous, but are insignificant or absent in nonkeratinizing areas, for instance, in the cheek. However, in all zones they are referred to as prickle cells, though the "prickly" appearance of isolated cells is characteristic for cells with conspicuous intercellular bridges. Toward the surface the cells everywhere flatten and at the same time widen considerably. No further changes occur in the nonkeratinizing epithelium. In areas where the epithelium is keratinized, the cells of the prickle cell layer flatten and pass first into the granular layer and then into the keratinous layer as they move toward the surface. The cells of the granular layer contain keratohyalin granules that are basophil and stain blue in hematoxylin-eosin preparation. The nuclei of the flattened cells are pyknotic. The keratinous layer is characterized by its acidophil

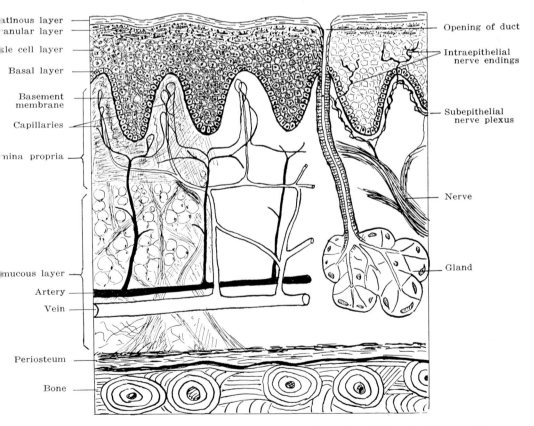

Fig. 167. Diagrammatic drawing of oral mucous membrane (epithelium, lamina propria, and submucosa).

nature; here most if not all the nuclei have disappeared. The structure of the granular and keratinous layers varies in the different regions of the oral cavity. A stratum lucidum, such as is seen in regions of the skin where cornification is abundant, is, as a rule, missing in the oral mucosa.

The lamina propria is a layer of dense connective tissue of variable thickness. Its papillae, which indent the epithelium, carry both blood vessels and nerves. Some of the latter actually pass into the epithelium. The papillae of the lamina propria vary considerably in length and width in different areas. The inward epithelial projections between the papillae are described as epithelial pegs because of their appearance in sections. In reality, however, they form a continuous network of epithelial ridges. The arrangement of the papillae increases the area of contact between lamina propria and epithelium and facilitates the exchange of material between blood vessels and epithelium. The presence of papillae permits the subdivision of the lamina propria into the outer papillary and the deeper reticular layer.

The submucosa consists of connective tissue of varying thickness and density. It attaches the mucous membrane to the underlying structures. Whether this attachment is loose or firm depends upon the character of the submucosa. Glands, blood vessels, nerves, and also adipose tissue are present in this layer. It is in the submucosa that the larger arteries divide into smaller branches, which then enter the lamina propria. Here they again divide to form a subepithelial capillary network in the papillae. The veins originating from the capillary network follow the course of the arteries. The blood vessels are accompanied by a rich network of lymph vessels. The sensory nerves of the mucous membrane traverse the submucosa. The nerve fibers are myelinated but lose their myelin sheath in the mucous membrane before splitting into their end arborizations. Sensory nerve endings of various types are found in the papillae; some of the fibers enter the epithelium, where they terminate between the epithelial cells as free nerve endings. The blood vessels are accompanied by nonmyelinated visceral nerve fibers that supply their smooth muscles; other visceral fibers supply the glands.

The oral cavity can be divided into two parts: the vestibulum oris, vestibule, and the cavum oris proprium, oral cavity proper. The vestibule is that part of the oral cavity which is bounded by the lips and cheeks on the outer side and by the teeth and alveolar processes on the inner side. The oral cavity proper lies within the dental arches and bones of the jaws, being limited posteriorly toward the pharynx by the anterior pillars of the fauces, or the palatoglossal arches.

TRANSITION BETWEEN SKIN AND MUCOUS MEMBRANE

The transitional zone between the skin covering the outer surface of the lip and the true mucous membrane lining the inner surface, is the red zone or the vermilion border of the lip. It is present in man only (Fig. 168). The skin of the lip is covered by a hornified epithelium of moderate thickness; the papillae of the connective tissue are few and short. Many sebaceous glands are found in

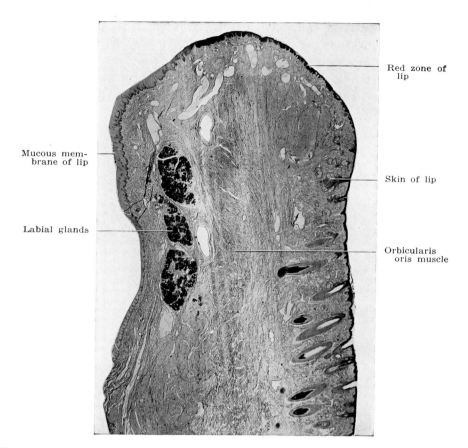

Red zone of lip

Mucous membrane of lip

Skin of lip

Labial glands

Orbicularis oris muscle

Fig. 168. Section through lip.

connection with the hairs; sweat glands occur between them. The epidermis is a keratinized stratified squamous epithelium with a rather thick keratin layer. The transitional region is characterized by numerous densely arranged long papillae of the lamina propria, reaching deep into the epithelium and carrying large capillary loops close to the surface. Thus, blood is visible through the thin parts of the translucent epithelium covering the papillae; hence, the red color of the lips. Because this transitional zone contains only occasional single sebaceous glands, it is particularly subject to drying if not moistened by the tongue.

The boundary between the red zone of the lip and the mucous membrane is found where keratinization of the transitional zone ends. The epithelium of the mucous membrane of the lip is not keratinized.

SUBDIVISIONS OF THE ORAL MUCOSA

In studying any mucous membrane the following features should be considered: (1) type of covering epithelium; (2) structure of lamina propria, especially as to its density, thickness, and presence or lack of elasticity; (3) the type of junction between epithelium and lamina propria; and (4) its fixation to the underlying structures, in other words, the submucous layer. A submucosa may be present or absent as a separate and well-defined layer. Looseness or density of its texture determines whether the mucous membrane is movably or immovably attached to the deeper layers. Presence or absence and location of adipose tissue or glands should also be noted.

The oral mucosa may be divided primarily into three different types. During mastication some parts are subjected to strong forces of pressure and friction. These parts, gingiva and covering of the hard palate, may be termed *masticatory mucosa*. The second type of oral mucosa is that which is merely the protective lining of the oral cavity. These areas may be termed *lining mucosa*. They comprise the mucosa of the lips and the cheeks, the mucosa of the vestibular fornix and that of the upper and lower alveolar process peripheral to the gingiva proper, the mucosa of the floor of the mouth extending to the inner surface of the lower alveolar process, the mucosa of the inferior surface of the tongue, and, finally, the mucous membrane of the soft palate. The third type of mucosa is represented by the covering of the dorsal surface of the tongue and is highly specialized; hence, the term *specialized mucosa*.

Masticatory mucosa

Gingiva and covering of the hard palate have in common the thickness and keratinization of the epithelium, the thickness, density, and firmness of the lamina propria, and, finally, their immovable attachment to the deep structures. In the gingiva, formation of true keratin, orthokeratosis, is in a majority of individuals replaced by parakeratosis. Sometimes the epithelium is nonkeratinized though the gingiva has to be regarded as normal. In the structure of the sub-mucosa, the areas of gingiva and hard palate differ markedly. In the gingiva, a well-differentiated submucous layer cannot be recognized; instead, the dense and inelastic connective tissue of the lamina propria fuses with the periosteum of the alveolar process or is attached to the cervical region of the tooth and the mar-ginal areas of the alveolar process.

In contrast to this, the covering of the hard palate has, with the exception of narrow areas, a distinct submucous layer. It is absent only in the peripheral zone, where the palatine tissue is identical with the gingiva, and in a narrow zone along the midline, starting in front with the palatine or incisive papilla and continuing as the palatine raphe over the entire length of the hard palate. In spite of the presence of a well-defined submucous layer in the wide lateral fields of the hard palate between palatine raphe and palatine gingiva, the mucous membrane is immovably attached to the periosteum of maxillary and palatine bones. This attachment is accomplished by dense bands and trabeculae of fibrous connective tissue that join the lamina propria of the mucous mem-brane to the periosteum. The submucous space is thus subdivided into irregular intercommunicating compartments of various sizes. These are filled with adipose tissue in the anterior part and with glands in the posterior part of the hard palate. The presence of fat or glands in the submucous layer acts as a cushion comparable to that which we find in the subcutaneous tissue of the palm of the hand and the sole of the foot.

GINGIVA

The gingiva surrounding the teeth is subjected to forces of friction and pressure in the process of mastication. The character of this tissue shows that it is adapted to these forces. The gingiva is limited sharply on the outer surface of both jaws by a scalloped line, the mucogingival junction, which separates it from the alveolar mucosa (Fig. 169). The gingiva is normally pink, sometimes with a grayish tinge, dependent on the variable thickness of the stratum corneum. The alveolar mucosa is red, showing numerous small vessels close to the surface. A similar line of demarcation is found on the inner surface of the lower jaw between the gingiva and the mucosa on the floor of the mouth. On the palate, there is no sharp dividing line because of the dense structure and firm attachment of the entire palatal mucosa.

According to the behavior of the surface layer, four types of gingival epithelium can be distinguished. They are described as follows (Fig. 170).

1. In fully keratinized epithelium the surface layers consist of flat, tightly packed, horny scales, the transformed surface cells. Nuclei are absent.

2. In parakeratosis the surface cells seem to consist of keratin but have retained pyknotic nuclei.

3. In incomplete parakeratosis specific stains, e.g., Mallory's stain, show the surface layer divided into two layers. The deeper layer stains like keratin, but this stain is lost in the superficial layer, probably by the influence of oral fluids on the incompletely differentiated keratin of the nuclei-containing cells.

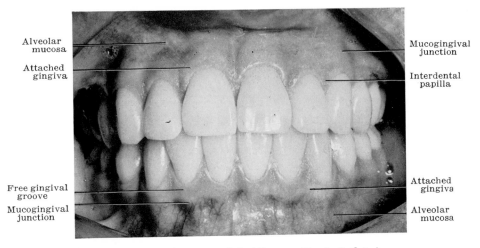

Fig. 169. Surface of the gingiva of a young adult. (Courtesy Dr. A. Ogilvie.)

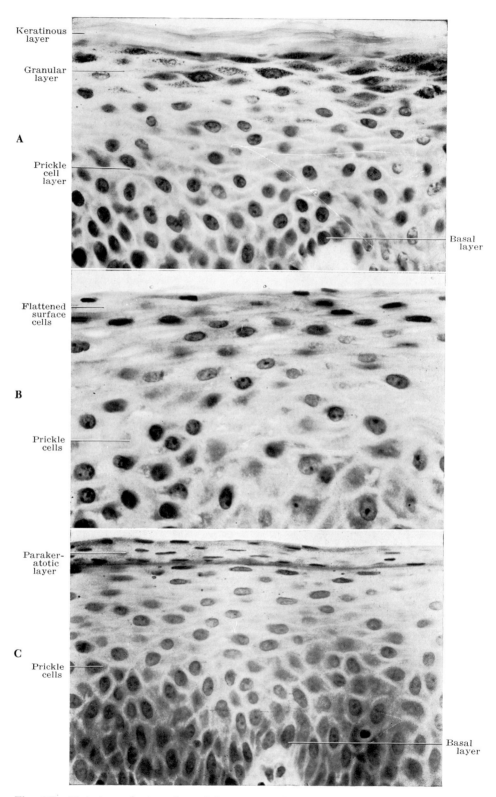

Keratinous
layer

Granular
layer

A

Prickle
cell
layer

Basal
layer

Flattened
surface
cells

B

Prickle
cells

Paraker-
atotic
layer

C

Prickle
cells

Basal
layer

Fig. 170. Variations of gingival epithelium. **A,** Orthokeratosis. **B,** Lack of keratinization. **C,** Parakeratosis.

4. Where keratinization is lacking, the flat surface cells retain their nuclei.

The most frequent type is parakeratosis, about 50 per cent. The next frequent type is incomplete parakeratosis, 25 per cent. Then follows full keratinization, 15 per cent, and nonkeratinization, 10 per cent. Presence of inflammation and/or glycogen seems progressively to interfere with keratinization.

The rate of cell renewal is expressed in the mitotic index, i.e., the number of cells in mitosis of 1,000 cells counted. The index increases with age. In individuals between 50 and 70 years of age it is higher by 50 per cent than in the group between 25 and 35 years of age. In the latter it was calculated as 1.37, which is higher than the index in the epidermis. Presence or lack of a granular layer also influences the mitotic index. It is twice as high in the absence of the granular layer. There is, however, no correlation of the mitotic index to the variations of keratinization.

The gingival epithelium covers the margin of the gingiva and continues into the epithelial lining of the gingival sulcus to terminate on the surface of the tooth as the epithelial attachment (see section on Structure of Epithelial Attachment).

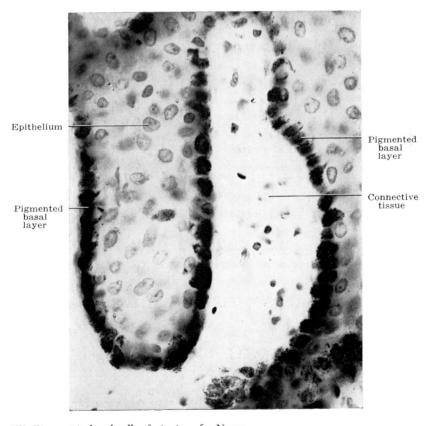

Epithelium

Pigmented basal layer

Pigmented basal layer

Connective tissue

Fig. 171. Pigment in basal cells of gingiva of a Negro.

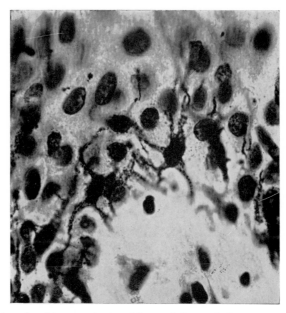

Fig. 172. Dendritic melanoblasts in the basal layer of the epithelium. Biopsy of normal gingiva. (×1,000.) (From Aprile, E. C. de: Arch. hist. normal y Pat. **3:** 473, 1947.)

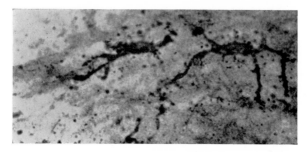

Fig. 173. Macrophages in the normal gingiva. Rio Hortega stain. (×1,000.) (From Aprile, E. C. de: Arch hist. normal y Pat. **3:** 473, 1947.)

The cells of the basal layer may contain pigment granules (melanin) (Fig. 171). While pigmentation is a normal occurrence in Negroes, it is often found, too, in the Caucasian race, especially in people with a dark complexion. It is most abundant in the bases of the interdental papillae. It may increase considerably in cases of Addison's disease, destruction of the adrenal cortex. The melanin pigment is stored by the basal cells of the epithelium, but these cells do not produce the pigment. The melanin is elaborated by specific cells, melanoblasts, situated in the basal layer of the epithelium (Fig. 172). These cells have long processes and are also termed dendritic cells. In the usual hematoxylin-eosin specimen, these cells have a clear cytoplasm and are also known as clear cells.

Cells of human oral epithelium show, as human epidermal epithelium, a sex difference. In females the nuclei contain a large chromatin particle adjacent to the nuclear membrane.[20]

The lamina propria of the gingiva consists of dense connective tissue that is not highly vascular. Macrophages are present in the perivascular loose connective tissue of the normal gingiva (Fig. 173). These cells have an important function in the defense mechanism of the body. The papillae of the connective tissue are characteristically long, slender, and numerous. The presence of these high papillae permits the sharp demarcation of the gingiva and alveolar mucosa in which the papillae are quite low (Fig. 174). The tissue of the lamina propria contains only few elastic fibers that are, for the most part, confined to the walls of the blood vessels. The gingival fibers of the periodontal ligament enter into the lamina propria, attaching the gingiva firmly to the teeth (see Chapter VII). The gingiva is also immovably and firmly attached to the periosteum of the alveolar bone; here, a dense connective tissue, consisting of coarse collagenous bundles (Fig. 175, *A*), extends from the bone to the lamina propria. In contrast, the submucosa underlying the alveolar mucous membrane is loosely textured (Fig. 175, *B*). The fiber bundles of the lamina propria of the alveolar

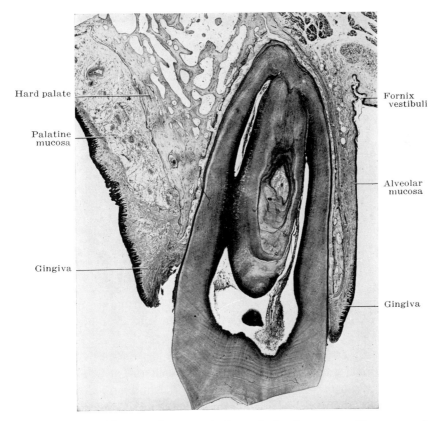

Hard palate

Palatine mucosa

Gingiva

Fornix vestibuli

Alveolar mucosa

Gingiva

Fig. 174. Structural differences between gingiva and alveolar mucosa. Upper premolar.

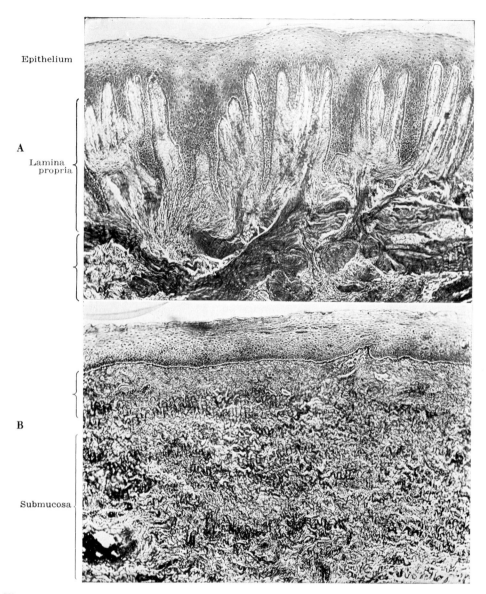

Epithelium

A

Lamina propria

B

Submucosa

Fig. 175. Differences between gingiva, **A**, and alveolar mucosa, **B**. Silver impregnation of collagenous fibers. Note the coarse bundles of fibers in gingiva and finer fibers in alveolar mucosa.

mucosa are thin and regularly interwoven. The alveolar mucosa and submucosa contain numerous elastic fibers that are thin in the lamina propria and thick in the submucosa.

Collagen fibers arranged in strong bundles arise from the cervical area of cementum (gingival group of periodontal ligament fibers), in part from the outer surface of the alveolar process. They interlace with bundles of varying direction. Circular fibers in the attached gingiva are sometimes quite conspicuous. The gingival fibers are functionally arranged in the following groups[8]:

1. *Gingival ligament:* Extends from cervical cementum into the lamina propria of the gingiva. The fibers of the gingival ligament constitute the most numerous group of gingival fibers.

2. *Alveologingival group:* The fibers arise from the alveolar crest and extend into the lamina propria.

3. *Circular group:* A small group of fibers that circle the tooth and interlace with the other fibers.

4. *Dentoperiosteal fibers:* These fibers can be followed from the cementum into the periosteum of the alveolar crest and of the vestibular and oral surfaces of the alveolar bone.

Blood and nerve supply. The blood supply of the gingiva is derived chiefly from the branches of the alveolar arteries that penetrate the interdental septa.[39] The interdental alveolar arteries perforate the alveolar crest in the interdental spaces and end in the gingiva, supplying the interdental papilla and the adjacent areas of the buccal and lingual gingiva. In the gingiva these branches anastomose with superficial branches of arteries that supply the oral and vestibular mucosa and marginal gingiva, for instance, with branches of the lingual, buccinator, mental, and palatine arteries. There is a rich network of lymph vessels in the gingiva along the blood vessels leading to submental and submaxillary lymph nodes.

The gingiva is well innervated.[10] Different types of nerve endings can be observed, such as the Meissner or Krause corpuscles, end bulbs, loops, or fine fibers that enter the epithelium as "ultraterminal" fibers. (Figs. 176A and 176B.)

The gingiva can be divided into the *free gingiva*, the *attached gingiva* (Figs. 177A and 177B),[27] and the *interdental papillae*. The dividing line between the free and the attached gingiva is the *free gingival groove*, which runs parallel to the margin of the gingiva at a distance of 0.5 to 1.5 mm. The free gingival groove, not always visible macroscopically, appears in histologic sections (Fig. 178) as a shallow V-shaped notch corresponding to the heavy epithelial ridge that divides the free and the attached gingiva. The free gingival groove develops at the level of, or somewhat apical to, the bottom of the gingival sulcus. In some cases, the free gingival groove is not as well defined as in others, and then the division between the free and the attached gingiva is not clear. The free gingival groove and the epithelial ridge are probably caused by functional impacts upon the free gingiva, folding the movable free part back upon the attached and immovable zone.

The attached gingiva is characterized by high connective tissue papillae elevating the epithelium, so that the surface of the attached gingiva appears stippled (Fig. 178). Between the elevations there are shallow depressions that correspond to the center of heavier epithelial ridges and show signs of degeneration and keratinization at their depth. The stippling is probably a functional adaptation to mechanical impacts.

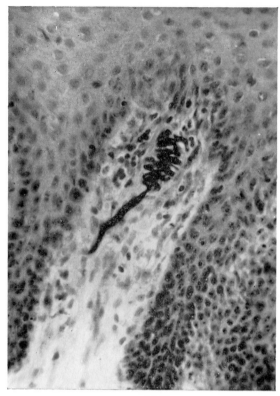

Fig. 176A. Meissner tactile corpuscle in the human gingiva. Silver impregnation after Bielschowsky-Gros. (From Gairns, F. W., and Aitchison, J. A.: D. Rec. **70:** 180, 1950.)

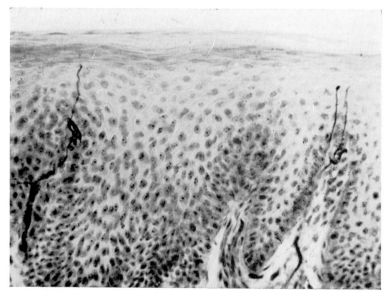

Fig. 176B. Intraepithelial "ultraterminal" extensions and nerve endings in the human gingiva. Silver impregnation after Bielschowsky-Gros. (From Gairns, F. W., and Aitchison, J. A.: D. Rec. **70:** 180, 1950.)

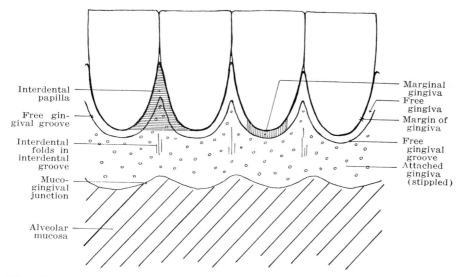

Interdental papilla

Free gingival groove

Interdental folds in interdental groove

Mucogingival junction

Alveolar mucosa

Marginal gingiva
Free gingiva
Margin of gingiva

Free gingival groove

Attached gingiva (stippled)

Fig. 177A. Diagram illustrating the surface characteristics of the gingiva.

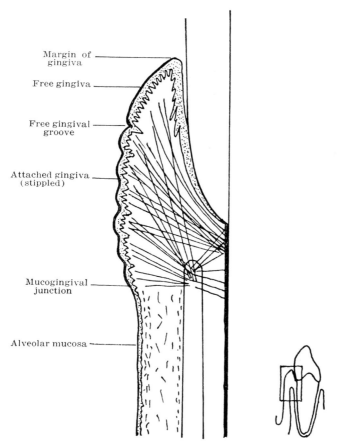

Margin of gingiva

Free gingiva

Free gingival groove

Attached gingiva (stippled)

Mucogingival junction

Alveolar mucosa

Fig. 177B. Diagram illustrating the difference between the free gingiva, attached gingiva, and alveolar mucosa.

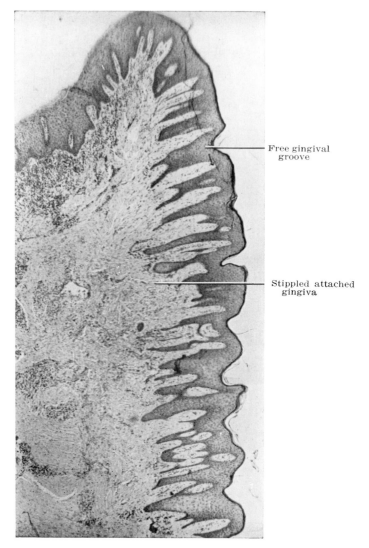

Free gingival
groove

Stippled attached
gingiva

Fig. 178. Biopsy specimen of gingiva showing free gingival groove and stippled attached gingiva.

While the degree of stippling (Fig. 169) and the texture of the collagenous fibers vary with different individuals, there are also differences according to age and sex. In younger female persons the connective tissue is more finely textured than that of the male; however, with increasing age, the collagenous fiber bundles become more coarse in both sexes.[41] The disappearance of stippling is an indication of edema, an expression of an involvement of the attached gingiva in a progressing gingivitis.

The attached gingiva appears slightly depressed between adjacent teeth, corresponding to the depression on the alveolar process between eminences of the sockets. In these depressions, the attached gingiva often forms slight vertical folds.

The interdental papilla is that part of the gingiva that fills the space between two adjacent teeth and is limited at its base by a line connecting the margin of the gingiva at the center of one tooth and the center of the next. The interdental papilla is tent-shaped. Vestibular and oral corners are elevated; the ridge of the papilla is concave. Vestibular and oral parts of the papilla partly fill the embrasures between two adjacent teeth. The interdental part in the strict sense of the term seems to lack keratinization.

DENTOGINGIVAL JUNCTION[*]

Physiologically and clinically, the juncture of the soft oral tissues to the hard dental tissues is of great importance. This union is unique in many ways and does constitute a point of lessened resistance to mechanical and bacterial attack. The gingiva consists of two elements that, though integrated in their function, show a division of labor in protecting the underlying structures. The resistance to the mechanical forces of mastication rests mainly on the strength of the dense, unelastic but resilient connective tissue, the lamina propria. The protection against chemical and bacterial injuries is the function of the thick and mostly parakeratinized or keratinized epithelium.

Both of these layers are attached to the tooth, and the structure of each of these components contributes to the security of the dentogingival junction. Again, the firmness of this junction is the function of the connective tissue attached to the tooth through the gingival division of the periodontal ligament. This dental attachment of the lamina propria is reinforced by fibers that reach into the gingiva from the edge of the alveolar bone and by circular fiber bundles in the free gingiva.[2]

The biologic protection, the sealing off of the dentogingival junction, is the function of the epithelial attachment. The epithelium of the gingiva is continuous over the free gingival margin and then, in the real sense of the word, is attached to the surface of the tooth. This attached epithelium has the shape of a collar or cuff and can, therefore, be termed either *epithelial attachment* or *attached epithelial cuff*.

While the attachment of the epithelium to the tooth surface is a well-documented fact, the mode of attachment of the epithelial cuff is not understood in all details. It seems important to analyze the development of this attachment during and after eruption of the tooth.

Development. At the conclusion of enamel matrix formation the ameloblasts produce a thin membrane on the surface of the enamel, the *primary enamel cuticle*. It is a limiting membrane, connected with the interprismatic enamel

---

[*]First draft of the section on Structure of the Epithelial Attachment submitted by Bernhard Gottlieb.

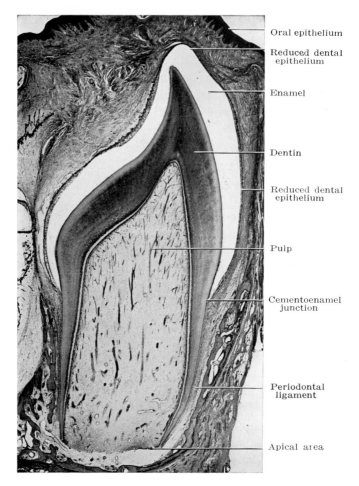

Oral epithelium

Reduced dental
epithelium

Enamel

Dentin

Reduced dental
epithelium

Pulp

Cementoenamel
junction

Periodontal
ligament

Apical area

Fig. 179. Human permanent incisor. The entire surface of the enamel is covered by reduced dental epithelium. Mature enamel is lost by decalcification. (From Gottlieb, B., and Orban, B.: Biology of the Investing Structures of the Teeth. In Gordon, S. M., editor: Dental Science and Dental Art, Philadelphia, 1938, Lea & Febiger.)

substance and the ameloblasts.[36] The ameloblasts shorten after the primary enamel cuticle has been formed, and the epithelial dental organ is reduced to a few layers of flat cuboidal cells that are then called *reduced dental epithelium.* Under normal conditions it covers the entire enamel surface, extending to the cementoenamel junction (Fig. 179), and remains attached to the primary enamel cuticle. During eruption the tip of the tooth approaches the oral mucosa, and the reduced dental epithelium fuses with the oral epithelium (Fig. 180).

The epithelium that covers the tip of the crown degenerates in its center, and the crown emerges through this perforation into the oval cavity (Fig. 181). The reduced dental epithelium remains organically attached to that part of the enamel which has not yet erupted. Once the tip of the crown has emerged, the

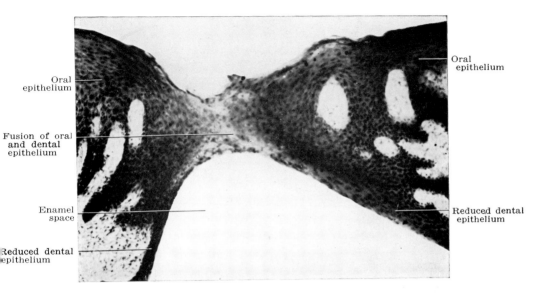

Oral epithelium

Oral epithelium

Fusion of oral and dental epithelium

Enamel space

Reduced dental epithelium

Reduced dental epithelium

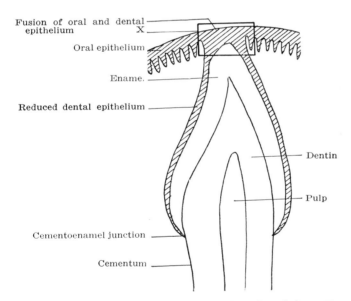

Fusion of oral and dental epithelium — X

Oral epithelium

Enamel

Reduced dental epithelium

Dentin

Pulp

Cementoenamel junction

Cementum

Fig. 180. Reduced dental epithelium fuses with oral epithelium. **X** in the diagram indicates area from which the photomicrograph was taken.

reduced dental epithelium is termed the *epithelial attachment*[11] or, better, the *attached epithelial cuff*. At the margin of the gingiva the attached epithelium continues into the oral epithelium. (Fig. 182.) As the tooth erupts, the attached epithelium is gradually separated from its surface. The shallow groove that develops between the gingiva and the surface of the tooth and extends around its circumference is the *gingival sulcus*. (Fig. 182.) It is bounded by the surface of

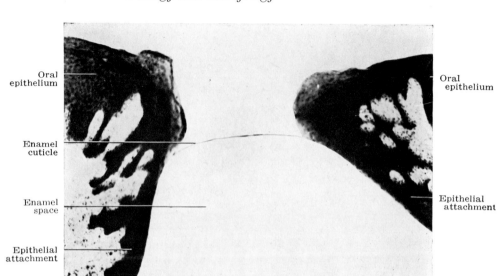

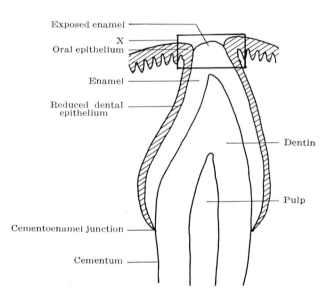

Fig. 181. Tooth emerges through a perforation in the fused epithelia. **X** in the diagram indicates area from which the photomicrograph was taken.

the tooth on one side and by the free gingiva on the other side. The bottom of the sulcus is found where the epithelial attachment separates from the surface of the tooth. The part of the gingiva that is coronal to the bottom of the sulcus is the free or *marginal gingiva*. The attached epithelium elaborates while the tooth erupts a cuticular product termed the *secondary enamel* or *dental cuticle*.[12] It is a noncellular keratinized layer that may measure up to 10 microns in thickness.

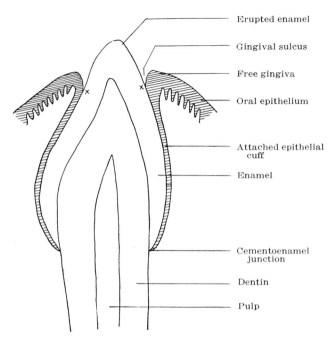

Erupted enamel

Gingival sulcus

Free gingiva

Oral epithelium

Attached epithelial
cuff

Enamel

Cementoenamel
junction

Dentin

Pulp

Fig. 182. Diagrammatic illustration of the attached epithelial cuff and gingival sulcus at an early stage of tooth eruption. Bottom of the sulcus at x.

In erupting teeth the attached epithelial cuff extends to the cementoenamel junction (Fig. 182). Occasionally, the epithelium degenerates in the cervical areas of the enamel; then the surrounding connective tissue may deposit cementum upon the enamel. Different sections of the same tooth may, and frequently do, show varying relationships in the area where enamel and cementum meet (Fig. 183).

Structure of the epithelial attachment. The epithelial attachment is the derivative of the reduced enamel epithelium. In some cases, ameloblasts may still function near the cementoenamel junction when the tip of the crown has already emerged through the oral mucosa. This is the rule in continuously growing teeth and high-crowned teeth of many animals. The ameloblasts flatten out rapidly and then the reduced dental epithelium is called the epithelial attachment. This is thin at first and consists of 3 to 4 layers of cells (Figs. 186 and 187), but it thickens gradually with advancing age to about 10 to 20 rows of cells, or more (Figs. 188 and 189).

The epithelium that forms the attachment is a stratified squamous epithelium. As a rule the basement membrane at the junction between epithelial attachment and connective tissue is smooth. It may be considered as a sign of irritation if the epithelial attachment sends projections, epithelial ridges, into the connective tissue. The cells within the epithelial attachment are elongated and are arranged more or less parallel to the surface of the tooth (Fig. 184).

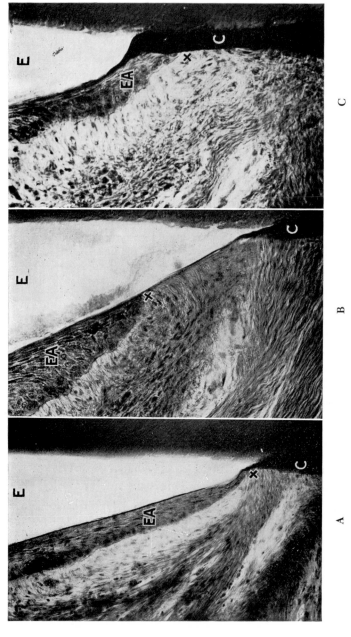

Fig. 183. Three sections of the same tooth showing different relations of tissues at the cementoenamel junction. A, Epithelial attachment reaching to the cementoenamel junction. B, Epithelial attachment ends coronal to the cementoenamel junction. C, Epithelial attachment covers part of the cementum. Cementum overlaps the edge of the enamel. EA, Epithelial attachment. E, Enamel (lost in decalcification). C, Cementum. x, End of epithelial attachment. (From Orban, B.: J. A. D. A. 17: 1977, 1930.)

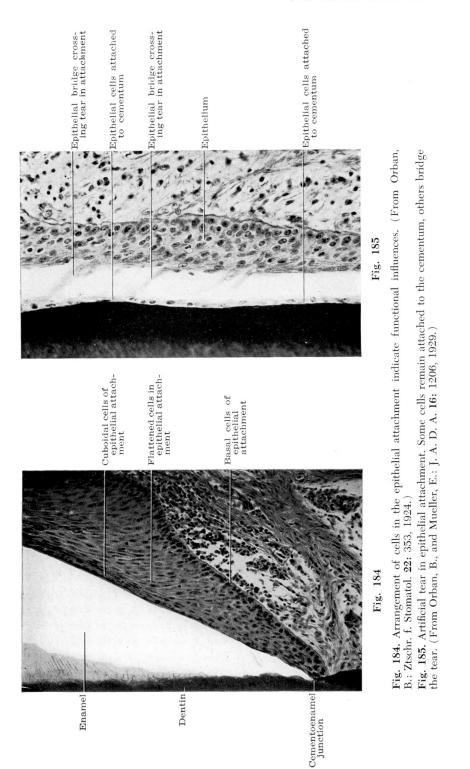

Epithelial bridge cross-
ing tear in attachment

Epithelial cells attached
to cementum

Epithelial bridge cross-
ing tear in attachment

Epithelium

Epithelial cells attached
to cementum

Fig. 185

Cuboidal cells of
epithelial attach-
ment

Flattened cells in
epithelial attach-
ment

Basal cells of
epithelial
attachment

Enamel

Dentin

Cementoenamel
junction

Fig. 184

Fig. 184. Arrangement of cells in the epithelial attachment indicate functional influences. (From Orban, B.: Ztschr. f. Stomatol. **22:** 353, 1924.)

Fig. 185. Artificial tear in epithelial attachment. Some cells remain attached to the cementum, others bridge the tear. (From Orban, B., and Mueller, E.: J. A. D. A. **16:** 1206, 1929.)

There is a distinct pattern in the direction of these flattened cells that may be the result of functional influences upon the attachment.[26] The attachment of the surface cells to enamel or cementum seems to be more firm than the connection of these cells to the deeper layers of the epithelium. For this reason tears occur frequently between the cuboidal cells attached to the tooth and the rest of the epithelial attachment. Such tears are found as artifacts in microscopic specimens (Fig. 185) but may also occur during life,[24] or in experimental flap operations.[30]

Shift of the dentogingival junction. The relation between the gingiva and the surface of the tooth changes constantly. When the tip of the enamel first emerges through the mucous membrane of the oral cavity, the epithelium covers almost the entire enamel (Fig. 186). Tooth eruption is relatively fast until the tooth reaches the plane of occlusion (see Chapter XI). This causes the epithelial attachment to separate from the enamel surface, while the crown gradually emerges into the oral cavity. When the tooth reaches the plane of occlusion,

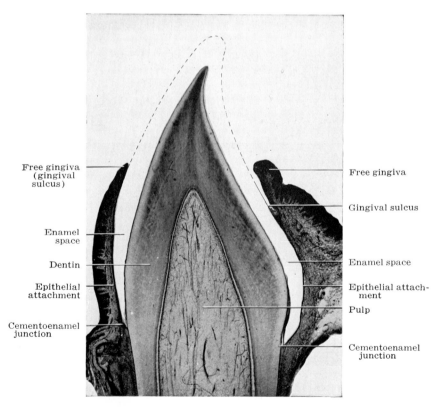

Free gingiva (gingival sulcus)

Enamel space

Dentin

Epithelial attachment

Cementoenamel junction

Free gingiva

Gingival sulcus

Enamel space

Epithelial attachment

Pulp

Cementoenamel junction

Fig. 186. Epithelial attachment and gingival sulcus in an erupting tooth. Erupted part of enamel is indicated by dotted line. Enamel lost in decalcification. (From Kronfeld, R.: J. A. D. A. **18:** 382, 1936.)

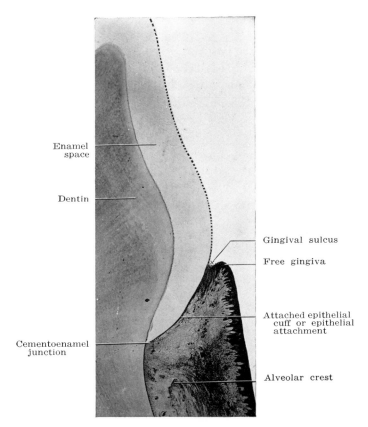

Enamel
space

Dentin

Gingival sulcus

Free gingiva

Attached epithelial
cuff or epithelial
attachment

Cementoenamel
junction

Alveolar crest

Fig. 187. Tooth in occlusion. One-fourth of the enamel is still covered by the epithelial attachment. (From Kronfeld, R.: J. A. D. A. 18: 382, 1936.)

one-third to one-fourth of the enamel is still covered by the gingiva (Fig. 187). The gradual exposure of the crown by separation of the epithelial attachment from the enamel and by recession of the gingiva is termed passive eruption; the actual movement of the teeth toward the occlusal plane is termed active eruption (see Chapter XI).

First stage. The bottom of the gingival sulcus remains in the region of the enamel-covered crown for some time, and the apical end of the attached epithelial cuff stays at the cementoenamel junction. This relation of the epithelial attachment to the tooth characterizes the *first stage* in passive exposure. (Fig. 188.) It persists in primary teeth almost up to one year before shedding and, in permanent teeth, usually to the age of about 20 or 30; however, this relation is subject to a wide range of variations.

Second stage. The epithelial attachment forms, at first, a wide band or cuff around the cervical part of the crown that is gradually narrowed as the separation of epithelium from the enamel surface proceeds. Long before the bottom of the sulcus reaches the cementoenamel junction, the epithelium proliferates along the surface of the cementum, and the apical end of the epithelial attachment is then found on the cementum in the cervical part of the root. This is the *second stage* in passive eruption. In this phase the bottom of the gingival sulcus is still on the enamel; the apical end of the epithelial attachment has shifted to the surface of the cementum. (Fig. 189.)

The downgrowth of the epithelial attachment along the cementum is but one facet of the shift of the dentogingival junction. This entails detachment of fiber bundles that were anchored in the cervical parts of the cementum, now covered by the epithelium, and an apical shift of the gingival and transseptal fibers. It is still questionable whether the degeneration of the fibers or the proliferation of the epithelium is the primary change.[38] Recent findings indicate that destruction of the fibers is caused by the proliferating epithelial cells actively dissolving the principal fibers by enzyme action, desmolysis. The second stage of passive tooth exposure may persist to the age of 40 or later.

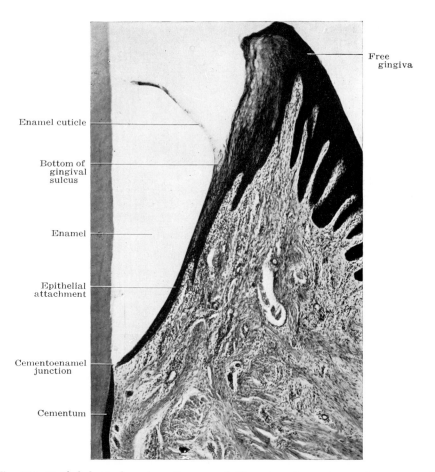

Fig. 188. Epithelial attachment on the enamel. First stage in passive tooth exposure. (From Gottlieb, B., and Orban, B.: Biology and Pathology of the Tooth [Translated by M. Diamond], New York, 1938, The Macmillan Co.)

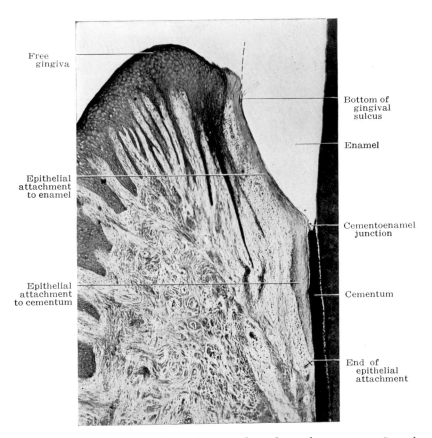

Free
gingiva

Bottom of
gingival
sulcus

Enamel

Epithelial
attachment
to enamel

Cementoenamel
junction

Epithelial
attachment
to cementum

Cementum

End of
epithelial
attachment

Fig. 189. Epithelial attachment partly on the enamel, partly on the cementum. Second stage in passive tooth exposure. (From Gottlieb, B., and Orban, B.: Biology and Pathology of the Tooth [Translated by M. Diamond], New York, 1938, The Macmillan Co.)

Third stage. For a short time the bottom of the gingival sulcus is at the cementoenamel junction, the epithelial attachment is entirely on the cementum, and the enamel-covered crown is fully exposed (Fig. 190). This is the *third stage* in passive eruption. Because of the continuous active eruption and passive exposure of the teeth, the epithelium shifts gradually along the surface of the tooth, and the attachment does not remain at the linear cementoenamel junction for any length of time. The third stage in passive eruption is often only a transitional stage in a more or less continuous, but normally slow, process.

Fourth stage. If a part of the cementum is already exposed by separation of the epithelial attachment from the tooth surface, the *fourth stage* of passive eruption is reached. The entire epithelial cuff is attached to the cementum. (Fig. 191.)

It would appear that the epithelial attachment has to maintain a certain minimal width, 0.25 to 6.0 mm., to assure normal function of the tooth. Therefore, the proliferation of the epithelium along the cementum should be considered a physiologic process, if it is in correlation to active eruption and

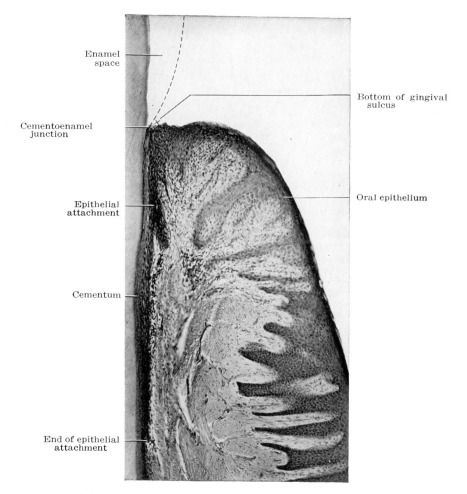

Enamel space

Bottom of gingival sulcus

Cementoenamel junction

Epithelial attachment

Oral epithelium

Cementum

End of epithelial attachment

Fig. 190. Epithelial attachment on the cementum. Bottom of the gingival sulcus at the cementoenamel junction. Third stage in passive tooth exposure. (From Gottlieb, B.: J. A. D. A. **14:** 2178, 1927.)

attrition. If it progresses too rapidly or precociously and therefore loses correlation to active eruption, it must be considered as a pathologic process.

An atrophy of the gingiva is correlated with the apical shift of the dento-gingival junction, exposing more and more of the crown, and, later, of the root, to the oral cavity. The recession of the gingiva is therefore a physiologic process if it is correlated both to the occlusal wear and to the compensatory active eruption.

The rate of passive eruption varies in different persons and in different teeth of the same individual, as well as on different surfaces of the same tooth. In some cases the fourth stage of passive eruption is observed in persons during their twenties; in others, even at the age of 50 or later the teeth are still in the first or second stage of eruption. The rate varies also in different teeth of the same jaw

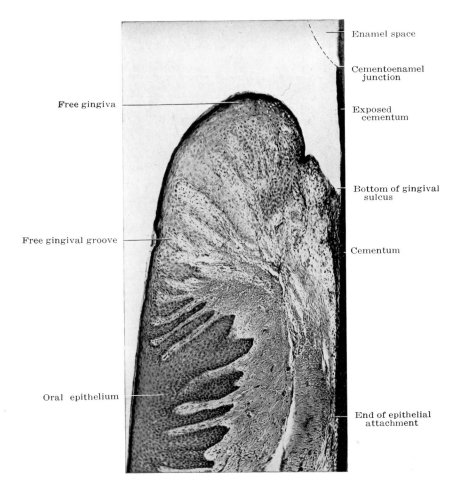

Fig. 191. Epithelial attachment on the cementum. Bottom of the gingival sulcus also on the cementum. Fourth stage in passive tooth exposure. (From Gottlieb, B.: J. A. D. A. **14:** 2178, 1927.)

and on different surfaces of the same tooth. One side may be in the first stage, the other in the second or even the fourth stage. (Fig. 192.) Hardly at any time are all parts of the bottom of the gingival sulcus in the same relation to the tooth.

Gradual exposure of the tooth to the oral cavity makes it possible to distinguish between the anatomic and the clinical crowns of the tooth (Fig. 193). That part of the tooth which is covered by enamel is the anatomic crown; the clinical crown is that part of the tooth exposed in the oral cavity.[13] In the first and second stages, the clinical crown is smaller than the anatomic crown. In the third stage, the entire enamel-covered part of the tooth is exposed, and the clinical crown is equal to the anatomic crown. However, this condition is not actually encountered because the bottom of the gingival sulcus is never at the same level all around

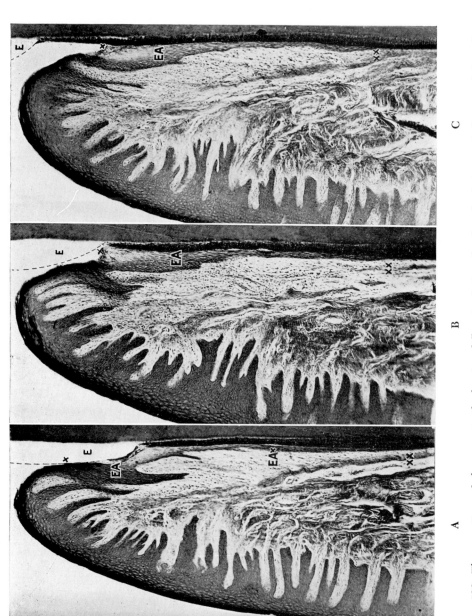

Fig. 192. Three sections of the same tooth showing different relation of soft to hard tissues. **A,** Bottom of the sulcus on the enamel (second stage). **B,** Bottom of the sulcus at the cementoenamel junction (third stage). **C,** Bottom of the sulcus on the cementum (fourth stage). **E,** Enamel lost in decalcification. **EA,** Epithelial attachment. **x,** Bottom of gingival sulcus. **xx,** End of epithelial attachment.

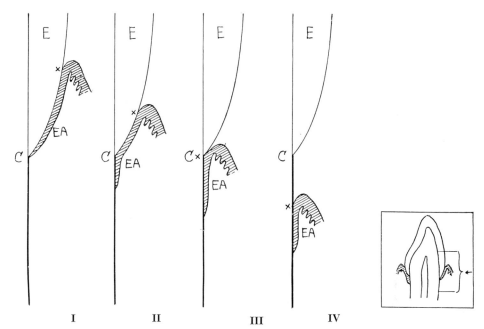

Fig. 193. Diagrammatic illustration of the four stages in passive eruption. In Stages I and II the anatomic crown is larger than the clinical. In Stage III anatomic and clinical crowns are equal. In Stage IV the clinical crown is larger than the anatomic crown. The arrow in the small diagram indicates the area from which the drawings were made. **E,** Enamel. **EA,** Epithelial attachment. **C,** Cementoenamel junction. **x,** Bottom of gingival sulcus.

the tooth. In the fourth stage the clinical crown is larger than the anatomic crown because parts of the root have been exposed.

Mode of attachment of epithelium. For a long time the epithelium was thought to be only in close contact with the enamel. The contact was supposed to be maintained by the turgor of the connective tissue elements of the gingiva, and thus a capillary space was supposed to extend between gingiva and enamel to the cementoenamel junction. Although this concept has lately been resurrected,[37] there seems hardly any doubt of the existence of an organic, true attachment of the epithelium to the enamel and later also to the cementum, in the form of a rather broad cuff. It is true, however, as was mentioned before, that this epithelial attachment is but a part of the dentogingival junction.

A most important problem is that of the mode or mechanism of the epithelial attachment. As long as enamel maturation is not completed, there is every evidence for a primary organic union between ameloblasts and the enamel, mediated by the primary enamel cuticle.[36] It was thought that this primary union persists after the maturation of the enamel and calcification of the primary cuticle in the erupted and functioning tooth.

However, there is considerable doubt that this primary union could persist into the functioning period of the tooth. It seems more probable that it is replaced by

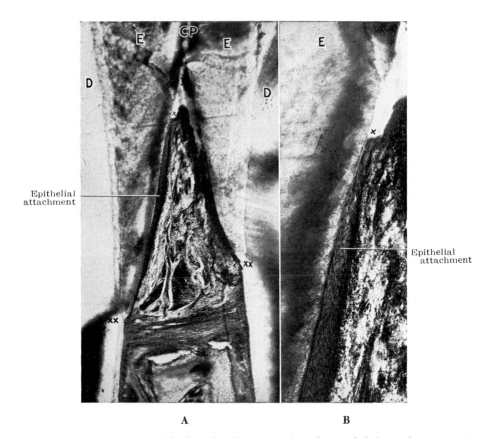

Epithelial
attachment

Epithelial
attachment

A   B

Fig. 194. Ground section of hard and soft tissues of teeth. Epithelial attachment to the enamel. **A,** General view of interdental papilla. **B,** Higher magnification of gingival sulcus and epithelial attachment. **E,** Enamel. **D,** Dentin. **CP,** Contact point. **x,** Bottom of gingival sulcus. **xx,** End of epithelial attachment (cementoenamel junction). (From Bodecker, C. F., and Applebaum, E.: D. Cosmos **176:** 1127, 1934.)

a secondary attachment through the formation of a cementing substance, namely, the keratinoid secondary enamel cuticle. The replacement starts from the coronal parts of the crown, gradually progressing cervically. When the epithelium proliferates beyond the cementoenamel junction, it gains an organic attachment to the cementum. The secondary enamel cuticle extends now along the cementum. (Figs. 195 and 196.) Secondary enamel cuticle and the cemental cuticle are referred to as dental cuticle. The function of the dental cuticle as a cementing substance is supported by findings of extensions of the cuticle into the minute spaces of the cementum formerly occupied by Sharpey's fibers. (Fig. 196.)

Though the mechanical resistance of the dentogingival junction is mainly due to the connective tissue attachment and to the fiber bundles in the gingiva, the attachment of the epithelium to the enamel is by no means loose or weak. This could be demonstrated by microscopic studies of ground sections of frozen

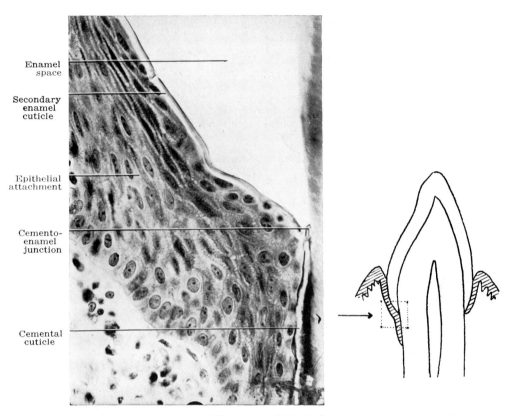

Enamel
space

Secondary
enamel
cuticle

Epithelial
attachment

Cemento-
enamel
junction

Cemental
cuticle

Fig. 195. Secondary enamel cuticle follows epithelial attachment to the cementum forming the dental cuticle. Arrow in diagram indicates area from which the photomicrograph was taken.

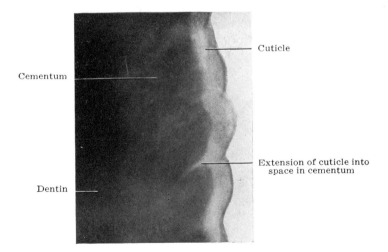

Cuticle

Cementum

Extension of cuticle into
space in cementum

Dentin

Fig. 196. Horny substance of the dental cuticle extends into the spaces of the cementum. (From Gottlieb, B., and Orban, B.: Biology and Pathology of the Tooth [Translated by M. Diamond], New York, 1938, The Macmillan Co.)

specimens where enamel and soft tissues are retained in their normal relation.[35] If, in such specimens, an attempt is made to detach the gingiva from the tooth, the epithelium tears rather than peeling off the enamel surface. Similar results were obtained when gingival flaps were pulled away from the tooth in vivo or post mortem.[30]

The firmness of the epithelial attachment may also be shown by studying ground sections prepared by a special method of investing soft and hard tissues[4] (Fig. 194).

Gingival sulcus. The gingival sulcus forms when the tip of the crown emerges through the oral mucosa. It deepens as a result of separation of the reduced dental epithelium from the actively erupting tooth. Shortly after the tip of the crown has appeared in the oral cavity, the tooth establishes occlusion with its antagonist. At first the epithelium separates rapidly from the surface of the tooth. Later, after occlusal relations are established, separation of the epithelial attachment from the surface of the tooth slows down.

The formation and relative depth of the gingival sulcus at different ages is still a controversial subject. Until the epithelial attachment was recognized, it was believed that the gingival sulcus extended to the cementoenamel junction from the time the tip of the crown had pierced the oral mucosa. (Fig. 197, *I.*) It was assumed that the attachment of the gingival epithelium to the tooth was

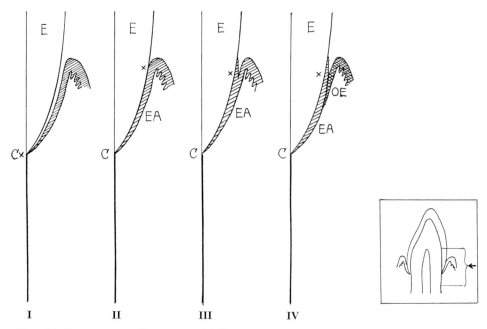

Fig. 197. Diagrammatic illustration of different views on the formation of the gingival sulcus as discussed in the text. Arrow in the small diagram indicates area from which the drawings were made.

linear at the cementoenamel junction. After the epithelial attachment had been discovered, it was recognized that no cleft exists between epithelium and enamel but that these tissues are organically connected. The gingival sulcus is merely a shallow groove, the bottom of which is at the point of separation of the attached epithelium from the tooth. (Fig. 197, *II.*)

Some investigators contend that the deepening of the gingival sulcus is due to a tear in the attached epithelium (Fig. 197, *III.*) Tears may deepen the gingival sulcus when the free margin of the gingiva is exposed to excessive mechanical trauma.

Others claim[1, 34] that the gingival sulcus forms at the line of fusion between the enamel epithelium attached to the surface of the enamel, and the oral epithelium (Fig. 197, *IV*). The oral epithelium proliferates at the connective tissue side of the epithelial cuff and replaces the former enamel epithelium, which degenerates progressively.

The depth of the normal gingival sulcus has been a frequent cause of disagreement, investigations, and measurements.[23] Under normal conditions, the depth of the sulcus varies from near zero to 6 mm.; 45 per cent of all measured sulci were below 0.5 mm., the average being 1.8 mm. The more shallow the sulcus, the more favorable are the conditions at the gingival margin. Every sulcus may be termed normal, regardless of its depth, if there are no signs of pathologic, mainly inflammatory, changes in the gingival tissues.

The presence of lymphocytes and plasma cells in the connective tissue at the bottom of the gingival sulcus should not, in itself, be considered a pathologic condition. It is evidence, rather, of a defense reaction in response to the constant presence of bacteria in the gingival sulcus or of a barrier against the invasion of bacteria and the penetration of their toxins.[9]

HARD PALATE

The mucous membrane of the hard palate is tightly fixed to the underlying periosteum and, therefore, immovable. Its color is pink, like that of the gingiva. The epithelium is uniform in character throughout the hard palate, with a rather thick keratinized layer and numerous long papillae. The lamina propria, a layer of dense connective tissue, is thicker in the anterior than in the posterior parts of the palate. Various regions in the hard palate differ because of the varying structure of the submucous layer. The following zones can be distinguished (Fig. 198): (1) the gingival region, adjacent to the teeth; (2) the palatine raphe, also known as the median area, extending from the incisive or palatine papilla posteriorly; (3) the anterolateral area or fatty zone between raphe and gingiva; (4) the posterolateral zone or glandular zone between raphe and gingiva.

The marginal area shows the same structure as the other regions of the gingiva. In this zone, a submucous layer cannot be differentiated from the lamina propria or periosteum. (Fig. 199.) Similarly, the layers of the lamina

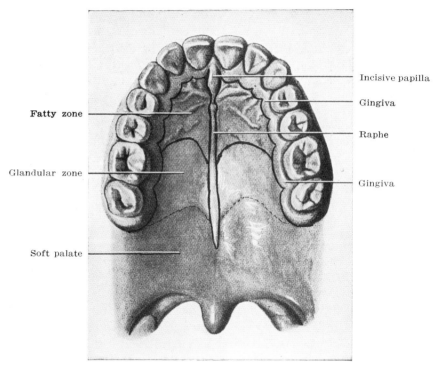

Fatty zone

Incisive papilla

Gingiva

Raphe

Glandular zone

Gingiva

Soft palate

Fig. 198. Surface view of hard and soft palate. The different zones of palatine mucosa.

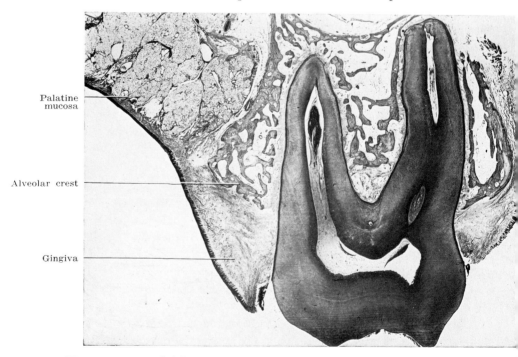

Palatine
mucosa

Alveolar crest

Gingiva

Fig. 199. Structural differences between gingiva and palatine mucosa. Region of first mo

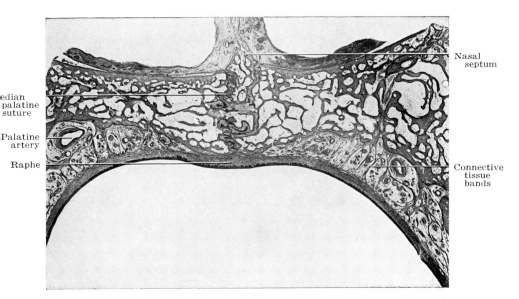

Fig. 200. Transverse section through hard palate. Palatine raphe. Fibrous bands connecting mucosa and periosteum in the lateral areas. Palatine vessels. (From Pendleton, E. C.: J. A. D. A. **21:** 488, 1934.)

propria, submucosa, and periosteum cannot be distinguished in the palatine raphe, or median area (Fig. 200). If a palatine torus is present, the mucous membrane is noticeably thin, and the otherwise narrow raphe spreads over the entire torus.

In the lateral areas of the hard palate (Fig. 201), in both fatty and glandular zones, the lamina propria is fixed to the periosteum by bands of dense fibrous connective tissue that are at right angles to the surface and divide the submucous layer into irregularly shaped spaces. The distance between lamina propria and periosteum is smaller in the anterior than in the posterior parts. In the anterior zone the connective tissue spaces contain fat (Fig. 200), whereas in the posterior part mucous glands are packed into the spaces (Fig. 201). The glandular layer of the hard palate continues posteriorly into that of the soft palate.

In the sulcus between alveolar process and hard palate, the anterior palatine vessels and nerves are surrounded by loose connective tissue. This area, wedge-shaped in cross section (Fig. 202), is relatively large in the posterior parts of the palate and gradually diminishes in size anteriorly.

Incisive papilla. The pear-shaped or oval incisive or palatine papilla is formed of dense connective tissue. It contains the oral parts of the vestigial nasopalatine ducts. These are blind epithelial ducts of varying lengths. They are lined by a simple or pseudostratified columnar epithelium, rich in goblet cells; small mucous glands open into the lumen of the ducts. Frequently the ducts are surrounded by small, irregular islands of hyalin cartilage, vestigial extensions of the paraseptal

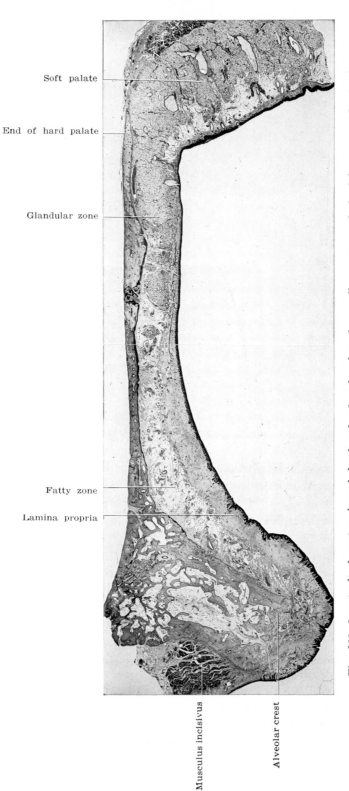

Soft palate

End of hard palate

Glandular zone

Fatty zone

Lamina propria

Musculus incisivus

Alveolar crest

Fig. 201. Longitudinal section through hard and soft palate lateral to midline. Fatty and glandular zones of hard palate.

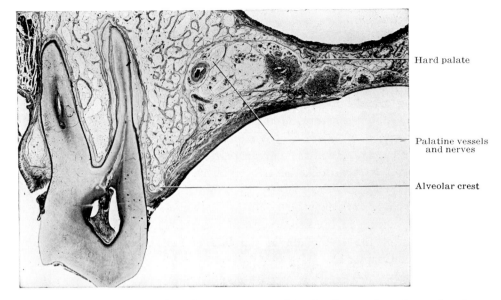

Hard palate

Palatine vessels
and nerves

Alveolar crest

Fig. 202. Transverse section through posterior part of hard palate, region of second molar. Loose connective tissue in the furrow between alveolar process and hard palate around palatine vessels and nerves.

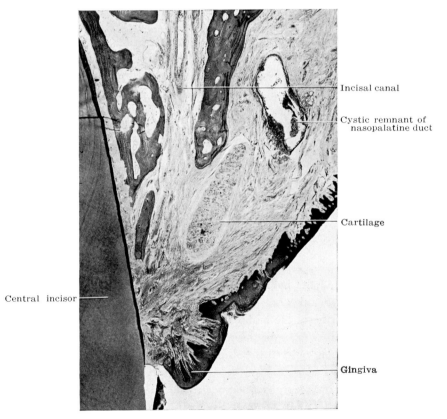

Incisal canal

Cystic remnant of
nasopalatine duct

Cartilage

Central incisor

Gingiva

Fig. 203. Sagittal section through palatine papilla and anterior palatine canal. Cartilage in papilla.

cartilages. The nasopalatine ducts are patent in most mammals and, together with Jacobson's organ, are considered as auxiliary olfactory sense organs. The cartilage is sometimes found in the anterior parts of the papilla; it then shows no apparent relation to nasopalatine ducts (Fig. 203).

Palatine rugae (transverse palatine ridges). The palatine rugae, irregular and often asymmetric in man, are ridges of mucous membrane extending laterally from the incisive papilla and the anterior part of the raphe. Their core is a dense connective tissue layer with fine interwoven fibers.

Epithelial pearls. In the midline, especially in the region of the incisive papilla, epithelial pearls may be found in the lamina propria. They consist of concentrically arranged epithelial cells that are frequently keratinized. They are remnants of the epithelium in the line of fusion between the palatine processes (see Chapter I).

Lining mucosa

All the zones of the lining mucosa are characterized by a relatively thin, non-keratinized epithelium and by the thinness of the lamina propria. They differ from one another in the structure of their submucosa. Where the lining mucosa reflects from the movable lips, cheeks, and tongue to the alveolar bone, the submucosa is loosely textured. In regions where the lining mucosa covers muscles, as on the lips, cheeks, and underside of the tongue, it is immovably fixed to the epimysium or fascia of the respective muscle. In these regions the mucosa is also highly elastic. These two characteristics safeguard the smoothness of the mucous lining in any functional phase of the muscle and prevent a heavy folding which may lead to injuries of lips or cheeks if such folds were caught between the teeth. The mucosa of the soft palate is a transition between this type of lining mucosa and that which is found in the fornix vestibuli and in the sublingual sulcus at the floor of the oral cavity. In the latter zones, the submucosa is loose and of considerable volume; the mucous membrane is movably attached to the deep structures, which allows for the free movement of lips and cheeks and also tongue.

LIP AND CHEEK

The epithelium of the mucosa on the lips (Fig. 168) and on the cheek (Fig. 204) is stratified squamous nonkeratinized epithelium.

The lamina propria of the labial and buccal mucosa consists of dense connective tissue that sends short, irregular papillae into the epithelium.

The submucous layer connects the lamina propria to the thin fascia of the muscles and consists of strands of densely grouped collagenous fibers. Between these strands is found loose connective tissue containing fat and small mixed glands. The strands of dense connective tissue limit the mobility of the mucous membrane against the musculature and prevent its elevation into folds. Small wrinkles appear in the mucosa during the contraction of the muscles, thus pre-

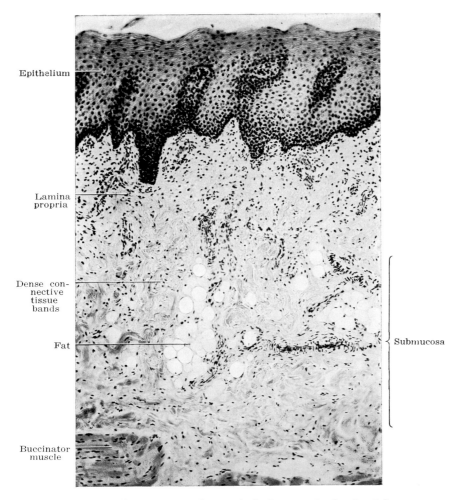

Epithelium

Lamina
propria

Dense con-
nective
tissue
bands

Fat

Submucosa

Buccinator
muscle

Fig. 204. Section through mucous membrane of cheek. Note the bands of dense connective tissue attaching the lamina propria to the fascia of the buccinator muscle.

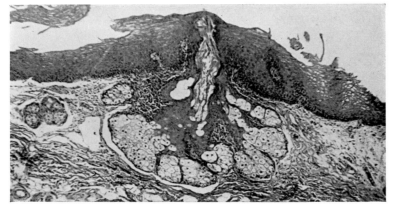

Fig. 205. Sebaceous gland in the cheek, Fordyce spot. Biopsy specimen.

venting the mucous membrane of the lips and cheeks from lodging between the biting surfaces of the teeth during mastication. The mixed glands of the lips are situated in the submucosa, whereas the larger glands of the cheek are usually found between the bundles of the buccinator muscle, and sometimes on its outer surface. A horizontal middle zone on the cheek, lateral to the corner of the mouth, may contain isolated sebaceous glands, Fordyce spots (Fig. 205).

VESTIBULAR FORNIX AND ALVEOLAR MUCOSA

In the vestibular fornix the mucosa of lips and cheeks reflects into the mucosa covering the bone. The mucous membrane of cheeks and lips is attached firmly to the buccinator muscle in the cheeks and the orbicularis oris muscle in the lips. In the fornix, the mucosa is loosely connected to the underlying structures and thus permits the necessary movements of lips and cheeks. The mucous membrane covering the outer surface of the alveolar process is attached loosely to the periosteum in the area close to the fornix. It continues into, but is sharply limited from, the gingiva, which is firmly attached to the periosteum of the alveolar crest and to the teeth.

The median and lateral labial frenula are folds of the mucous membrane, containing loose connective tissue. No muscle fibers are found in these folds.

Gingiva and alveolar mucosa are separated by a scalloped line, the mucogingival junction. The firmly attached gingiva is stippled, firm, thick, lacks a separate submucous layer, is immovably attached to the bone, and has no glands. The gingival epithelium is thick and mostly parakeratinized or keratinized; the epithelial ridges and the papillae of the lamina propria are high. The alveolar mucosa is thin and loosely attached to the periosteum by a well-defined submucous layer of loose connective tissue, and it may contain small mixed glands. The epithelium is thin, not keratinized, and the epithelial ridges and papillae are low and are often entirely missing. These differences cause the difference in color between the pale pink gingiva and the dark red lining mucosa.

MUCOUS MEMBRANE OF THE INFERIOR SURFACE OF THE TONGUE AND OF THE FLOOR OF THE ORAL CAVITY

The mucous membrane on the floor of the oral cavity is thin and loosely attached to the underlying structures to allow for the free mobility of the tongue. The epithelium is not keratinized and the papillae of the lamina propria are short. (Fig. 206.) The submucosa contains adipose tissue. The sublingual glands lie close to the covering mucosa in the sublingual fold. The sublingual mucosa joins the lingual gingiva in a sharp line that corresponds to the mucogingival line on the vestibular surface of the jaws. At the inner border of the horseshoe-shaped sublingual sulcus, the sublingual mucosa reflects onto the lower surface of the tongue and continues as the ventral lingual mucosa.

The mucous membrane of the inferior surface of the tongue is smooth and relatively thin (Fig. 207). The epithelium is not keratinized; the papillae of the

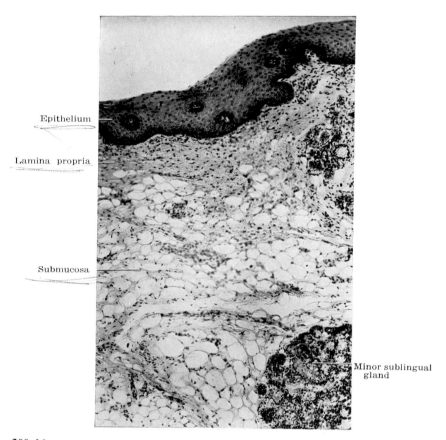

Epithelium

Lamina propria

Submucosa

Minor sublingual gland

Fig. 206. Mucous membrane from floor of mouth.

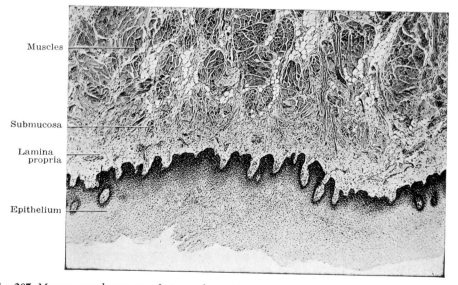

Muscles

Submucosa

Lamina propria

Epithelium

Fig. 207. Mucous membrane on inferior surface of tongue.

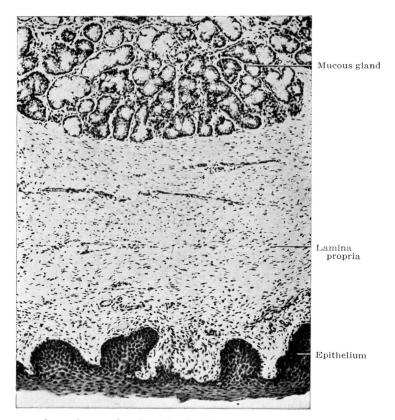

Fig. 208. Mucous membrane from oral surface of soft palate.

connective tissue are numerous but short. Here, the submucosa cannot be identified as a separate layer; it binds the mucous membrane tightly to the connective tissue surrounding the bundles of the muscles of the tongue.

SOFT PALATE

The mucous membrane on the oral surface of the soft palate is highly vascularized and of reddish color, noticeably differing from the pale color of the hard palate. The papillae of the connective tissue are few and short. The stratified squamous epithelium is not keratinized. (Fig. 208.) The lamina propria shows a distinct layer of elastic fibers separating it from the submucosa. The latter is relatively loose and contains an almost continuous layer of mucous glands. Typical oral mucosa continues around the free border of the soft palate for a variable distance and is then replaced by nasal mucosa with its pseudostratified, ciliated columnar epithelium.

Specialized mucosa

Dorsal lingual mucosa. The superior surface of the tongue is rough and irregular (Fig. 209). A V-shaped line divides it into an anterior part, or body, and

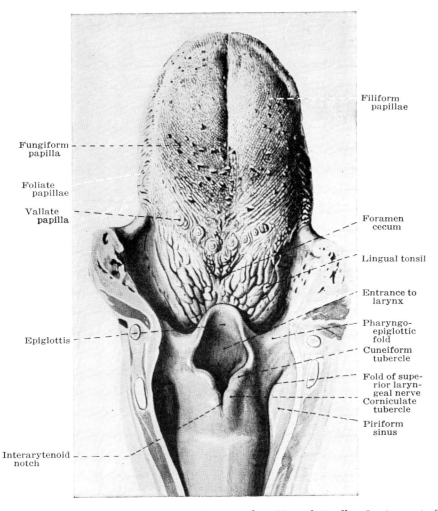

Filiform
papillae

Fungiform
papilla

Foliate
papillae

Vallate
papilla

Foramen
cecum

Lingual tonsil

Entrance to
larynx

Pharyngo-
epiglottic
fold

Epiglottis

Cuneiform
tubercle

Fold of supe-
rior laryn-
geal nerve
Corniculate
tubercle

Piriform
sinus

Interarytenoid
notch

Fig. 209. Surface view of human tongue. (From Sicher, H., and Tandler, J.: Anatomie für Zahnärzte [Anatomy for Dentists], Vienna, 1928, Julius Springer.)

a posterior part, or base. The former comprises about two-thirds of the length of the organ, the latter forms the posterior one-third. The fact that these two parts develop from different areas of the branchial region (see Chapter I) accounts for the different source of nerves of general sense: the anterior two-thirds are supplied by the trigeminal nerve through its lingual branch; the posterior one-third by the glossopharyngeal nerve.

The body and the base of the tongue differ widely in the structure of the mucous membrane. The anterior part can be termed the papillary, the posterior part, the lymphatic portion of the dorsal lingual mucosa. On the anterior part are found numerous fine-pointed, cone-shaped papillae that give it a velvetlike appearance. These projections, the filiform thread-shaped papillae, consist of a core of connective tissue that carries secondary papillae (Fig. 210, *A*). The

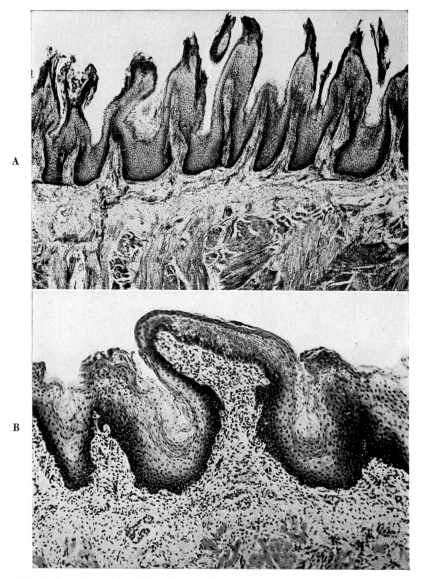

Fig. 210. Filiform, **A,** and fungiform, **B,** papillae.

covering epithelium is keratinized and forms at the apex of the papillae, hairlike tufts over the secondary papillae of the connective tissue.

Interspersed between the filiform papillae are the isolated mushroom-shaped or fungiform papillae (Fig. 210, *B*), which are round, reddish prominences. Their color is derived from a rich capillary network visible through the relatively thin epithelium. Fungiform papillae contain a few taste buds.

In front of the dividing V-shaped terminal sulcus, between the body and the base of the tongue, are the vallate, walled-in, papillae (Fig. 211); they are 8 to

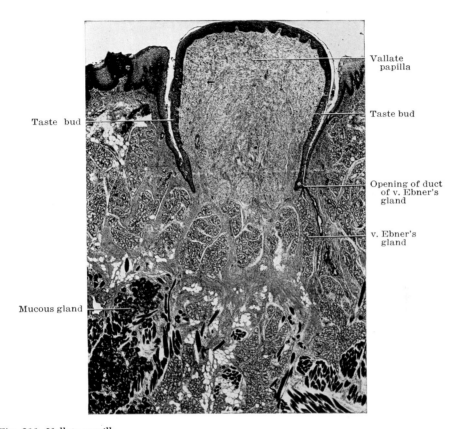

Fig. 211. Vallate papilla.

10 in number. They do not protrude above the surface of the tongue but are bounded by a deep circular furrow that seems to cut them out of the substance of the tongue. They are slightly narrower at their base. Their free surface shows numerous secondary papillae that are covered by a thin, smooth epithelium. On the lateral surface of the vallate papillae and occasionally on the walls surrounding them, the epithelium contains numerous taste buds. Into the trough open the ducts of small serous glands, von Ebner's glands, which serve to wash out the soluble elements of food that stimulate the taste buds from the deep circular groove.

At the angle of the V-shaped terminal groove on the tongue is located the foramen cecum, the remnant of the thyroglossal duct (see Chapter I). Posterior to the terminal sulcus, the surface of the tongue is irregularly studded with round or oval prominences, the lingual follicles. Each of these shows one or more lymph nodules, sometimes containing a germinal center (Fig. 212). Most of these prominences have a small pit at the center, the lingual crypt, which is lined with stratified squamous epithelium. Innumerable lymphocytes migrate into the crypts through the epithelium. Ducts of the small posterior lingual mucous glands open into the crypts. Together the lingual follicles form the lingual tonsil.

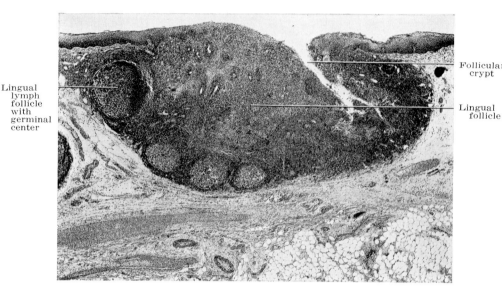

Lingual lymph follicle with germinal center

Follicular crypt

Lingual follicle

Fig. 212. Lingual lymph follicle.

On the lateral border of the posterior parts of the tongue sharp parallel clefts of varying length can often be observed. They bound narrow folds of the mucous membrane and are the vestige of the large foliate papillae found in many mammals. They contain taste buds.

Taste buds. Taste buds are small ovoid or barrel-shaped intraepithelial organs about 80 microns in height and 40 microns thick (Fig. 213). They touch with their broader base the basement membrane, while their narrower tip almost reaches the surface of the epithelium. The tip is covered by a few flat epithelial cells, which surround a small opening, the taste pore. It leads into a narrow space between the peripheral ends of the sustentacular supporting cells of the taste bud. The outer supporting cells are arranged like the staves of a barrel; the inner and shorter ones are spindle-shaped. Between the latter are arranged 10 to 12 neuroepithelial cells, the receptors of taste stimuli. They are slender, dark-staining cells that carry a stiff hairlike process at their superficial end. The hairs reach into the space beneath the taste pore.

A rich plexus of nerves is found below the taste buds. Some fibers enter the taste bud from the base and end in contact with the taste cells. Others end in the epithelium between the taste buds.

Taste buds are numerous on the inner wall of the trough surrounding the vallate papillae, in the folds of the foliate papillae, on the posterior surface of the epiglottis, and on some of the fungiform papillae at the tip and the lateral borders of the tongue.

The primary taste sensations, namely, sweet, salty, bitter, and sour, are not perceived in all regions of the tongue. Sweet is tasted at the tip, salty at the lateral border of the body of the tongue. Bitter and sour are recognized in the

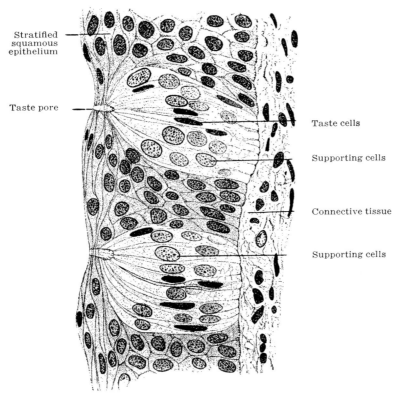

Fig. 213. Taste buds from the slope of a vallate papilla. (From Schaffer, J.: Lehrbuch der Histologie und Histogenese [Textbook of Histology and Histogenesis], ed. 2, Leipzig, 1922, Wilhelm Engelmann.)

posterior part of the tongue, bitter in the middle, sour in the lateral areas. The distribution of the receptors for primary taste qualities can, diagrammatically and somewhat arbitrarily, be correlated to the different types of papillae. The vallate papillae recognize bitter taste; the foliate papillae, sour taste. The taste buds on the fungiform papillae at the tip of the tongue are receptors for sweet taste, those at the borders, for salty taste. Bitter and sour taste sensations are mediated by the glossopharyngeal nerve, sweet and salty taste, by the intermediofacial nerve via the chorda tympani.

CLINICAL CONSIDERATIONS

To understand the pathogenesis of periodontal disease and the pathologic involvements of the different structures, it is essential to be thoroughly familiar with the structure of cementum, periodontal ligament, alveolar bone, marginal gingiva, gingival sulcus, and dentogingival junction, as well as their biologic interrelations. Periodontal disturbances frequently have their origin in the gingival sulcus and marginal gingiva, leading to the formation of a deep gingival pocket. The reduction of the depth of the gingival pocket is the primary objective of treatment. Any given method of treatment should be judged by its ability to accomplish this end, whether the method be surgical, chemical, or electrical.

In restorative dentistry, the extent of the epithelial attachment plays an important role. In young persons, the attachment of the epithelium to the enamel is of considerable length, and the clinical crown is smaller than the anatomic crown. The enamel cannot be removed entirely without destroying the epithelial attachment. It is, therefore, very difficult to prepare a tooth properly for an abutment or crown in young individuals. On the other hand, the preparation may be mechanically inadequate when it is extended only to the bottom of the gingival sulcus. It should be understood, therefore, that in young persons a restoration may be only temporary and may require later replacement.

When large areas of the root are exposed and a restoration is to be placed, the preparation need not cover the entire clinical crown. The first requirement is that the restoration be adapted to mechanical needs.

In extending the gingival margin of any restoration in the direction of the bottom of the gingival sulcus, the following rules should be observed: If the epithelial attachment is still on the enamel, and the gingival papilla fills the entire interdental space, the gingival margin of a cavity should be placed below the marginal gingiva. Special care should be taken to avoid injury to the gingiva and the dentogingival junction to prevent premature recession of the gingiva. When the gingiva is pathologically affected, treatment should precede the placing of a restoration. If the gingiva has receded from the enamel, if the gingival papilla does not fill the interdental space, and if the gingival sulcus is very shallow, the margin of a cavity need not necessarily be carried below the free margin of the gingiva. The gingival margin of a cavity should be placed far enough from the contact point to permit proper cleansing.

With exposure of the cervical part of the anatomic root, cemental caries or abrasion may occur. Improperly constructed clasps, overzealous scaling, and strongly abrasive dentifrices may result in marked abrasion. After loss of the cementum, the dentin may be extremely sensitive to thermal or chemical stimuli. Drugs, judiciously applied, may be used to accelerate sclerosis of the tubules and reparative dentin formation.

The difference in the structure of the submucosa in various regions of the oral cavity is of great clinical importance. Wherever the submucosa consists of a layer of loose connective tissue, edema or hemorrhage causes much swelling, and infections spread speedily and extensively. As a rule, inflammatory infiltrations in such parts are not very painful. If possible, injections should be made into loose submucous connective tissue. Such areas are the region of the fornix and the neighboring parts of the alveolar mucosa. The only place in the palate where larger amounts of fluid can be injected without damaging the tissues is the loose connective tissue in the furrow between the palate and the alveolar process (Fig. 202).

The gingiva is exposed to heavy mechanical stresses during mastication.

Moreover, the epithelial attachment to the tooth is relatively weak, and injuries or infections can cause permanent damage here. Strong keratinization of the gingiva may afford relative protection. Therefore, steps taken to increase keratinization can be considered preventive measures. One of the methods of inducing keratinization is mechanical stimulation, such as massage or brushing.

Unfavorable mechanical irritations of the gingiva may ensue from sharp edges of carious cavities, overhanging fillings or crowns, and accumulation of calculus. These may cause chronic inflammation of the gingival tissue.

Many systemic diseases cause characteristic changes in the oral mucosa. For instance, metal poisoning (lead, bismuth) causes characteristic discoloration of the gingival margin. Leukemia, pernicious anemia, and other blood dyscrasias can be diagnosed by characteristic infiltrations of the oral mucosa. In the first stages of measles, small red spots with bluish-white centers can be seen in the mucous membrane of the cheeks, even before the skin rash appears; they are known as Koplik's spots. Endocrine disturbances, including those of the sex hormones and of the pancreas, may be reflected in the oral mucosa.

Changes of the tongue are sometimes diagnostically significant. In scarlet fever, the atrophy of the lingual mucosa causes the peculiar redness of the strawberry tongue. Systemic diseases such as pernicious anemia and vitamin deficiencies, especially B complex deficiency, lead to characteristic changes, such as magenta tongue and beefy-red tongue.[29]

In denture construction it is important to observe the firmness or looseness of attachment of the mucous membrane. Denture-bearing areas should be those where the attachment of the mucosa is firm.[31, 32]

In old age, the mucous membrane of the mouth may atrophy in the cheeks and lips; it is then thin and parchmentlike. The atrophy of the lingual papillae leaves the upper surface of the tongue smooth, shiny, and varnished in appearance. Atrophy of major and minor salivary glands may lead to xerostomia, dry mouth, and sometimes to a secondary atrophy of the mucous membrane. In a large percentage of individuals, the sebaceous glands of the cheek are visible as fairly large, yellowish patches, Fordyce spots. They do not represent a pathologic change (Fig. 205).

References

1. de Aprile, E. C.: Contribucion al estudio de los elementos reticulo endoteliales de la mucosa gingival, Arch. hist. normal y Pat. **3:** 473, 1947.
2. Arnim, S. S., and Hagerman, D. A.: The Connective Tissue Fibers of the Marginal Gingiva, J. A. D. A. **47:** 271, 1953.
3. Becks, H.: Normal and Pathological Pocket Formation, J. A. D. A. **16:** 2167, 1929.
4. Bodecker, C. F., and Applebaum, E.: The Clinical Importance of the Gingival Crevice, D. Cosmos **176:** 1127, 1934.
5. Cattoni, M.: Melanoblasts in the Inflamed Gingiva, Oral Surg., Oral Med., & Oral Path. **6:** 1095, 1952.
6. Emslie, R. D., and Weinmann, J. P.: The Architectural Pattern of the Boundary Between Epithelium and Connective Tissue of the Gingiva in the Rhesus Monkey, Anat. Rec. **105:** 35, 1949.

7. Erausquin, Jorge: Histologia Dentaria Humana, Buenos Aires, 1953, Progrental.
8. Fehr, C., and Mühlemann, H. R.: The Surface of the Free and Attached Gingiva, Studied With the Replica Method, Oral Surg., Oral Med., & Oral Path. **8:** 649, 1955.
9. Fish, E. W.: Bone Infection, J. A. D. A. **26:** 691, 1939.
10. Gairns, F. W., and Aitchison, J. A.: A Preliminary Study of the Multiplicity of Nerve Endings in the Human Gum, D. Rec. **70:** 180, 1950.
11. Gottlieb, B.: Der Epithelansatz am Zähne (The Epithelial Attachment), Deutsche Monatschr. f. Zahnh. **39:** 142, 1921.
12. Gottlieb, B.: Aetiologie und Prophylaxe der Zahnkaries (Etiology and Prophylaxis of Caries), Ztschr. f. Stomatol. **19:** 129, 1921.
13. Gottlieb, B.: Tissue Changes in Pyorrhea, J. A. D. A. **14:** 2178, 1927.
14. Gottlieb, B., and Orban, B.: Biology of the Investing Structures of the Teeth. In Gordon, S. M. (editor): Dental Science and Dental Art, Philadelphia, 1938, Lea & Febiger.
15. Gottlieb, B., and Orban, B.: Biology and Pathology of the Tooth (Translated by M. Diamond), New York, 1938, The Macmillan Co.
16. Keller, G. J., and Cohen, D. W.: India Ink Profusion of the Vascular Plexus of Oral Tissues, Oral Surg., Oral Med., & Oral Path. **8:** 539, 1955.
17. Kronfeld, R.: The Epithelial Attachment and So-Called Nasmyth's Membrane, J. A. D. A. **17:** 1889, 1930.
18. Kronfeld, R.: Increase in Size of the Clinical Crown of Human Teeth With Advancing Age, J. A. D. A. **18:** 382, 1936.
19. Lehner, J.: Ein Beitrag zur Kenntniss vom Schmelzoberhäutchen (Contribution to the Knowledge of the Dental Cuticle), Ztschr. f. mikr.-anat. Forsch. **27:** 613, 1931.
20. Marvah, A. S., and Weinmann, J. P.: A Sex Difference in the Epithelial Cells of Human Gingiva, J. Periodont. **26:** 11, 1955.
21. Meyer, J., Marwah, A. S., and Weinmann, J. P.: Mitotic Rate of Gingival Epithelium in Two Age Groups, J. Invest. Dermat. **27:** 237, 1956.
22. Meyer, W.: Ueber strittige Fragen in der Histologie des Schmelzoberhäutchens (Controversial Questions in the Histology of the Enamel Cuticle), Vrtljsschr. f. Zahnh. **46:** 42, 1930.
23. Orban, B., and Kohler, J.: Die physiologische Zahnfleischtasche, Epithelansatz und Epitheltiefenwucherung (The Physiologic Gingival Sulcus), Ztschr. f. Stomatol. **22:** 353, 1924.
24. Orban, B., and Mueller, E.: The Gingival Crevice, J. A. D. A. **16:** 1206, 1929.
25. Orban, B.: Hornification of the Gums, J. A. D. A. **17:** 1977, 1930.
26. Orban, B.: Zahnfleischtasche und Epithelansatz (Gingival Sulcus and Epithelial Attachment), Ztschr. f. Stomatol. **22:** 353, 1924.
27. Orban, B.: Clinical and Histologic Study of the Surface Characteristics of the Gingiva, Oral Surg., Oral Med., & Oral Path. **1:** 827, 1948.
28. Orban, B., and Sicher, H.: The Oral Mucosa, J. D. Educ. **10:** 94, 163, 1946.
29. Orban, B., and Wentz, F. M.: Atlas of Clinical Pathology of the Mucous Membrane, St. Louis, 1955, The C. V. Mosby Co.
30. Orban, B., Bhatia, H., Kollar, J. A., Wentz, F. M.: The Epithelial Attachment, J. Periodont. **27:** 167, 1956.
31. Pendleton, E. C.: The Minute Anatomy of the Denture Bearing Area, J. A. D. A. **21:** 488, 1934.
32. Pendleton, E. C., and Glupker, H.: Research on the Reaction of Tissues Supporting Full Dentures, J. A. D. A. **22:** 76, 1935.
33. Robinson, H. B. G., and Kitchin, P. C.: The Effect of Massage With the Toothbrush on Keratinization of the Gingivae, Oral Surg., Oral Med., & Oral Path. **1:** 1042, 1948.
34. Skillen, W. G.: The Morphology of the Gingivae of the Rat Molar, J. A. D. A. **17:** 645, 1930.
35. Toller, J. R.: Studies of the Epithelial Attachment on Young Dogs, Northwestern Univ. Bull. **40:** 13, 1940. (Abst.)
36. Ussing, M. J.: The Development of the Epithelial Attachment, Acta odont. scandinav. **13:** 123, 1955.
37. Waerhaug, J.: Gingival Pocket. Anatomy, Pathology, Deepening and Elimination, Odont. Tskr. **60** (supp. 1): 5, 1952.
38. Wassermann, F.: Personal communication.

39. Weinmann, J. P.: Progress of Gingival Inflammation Into the Supporting Structures of the Teeth, J. Periodont. **12**: 71, 1941.
40. Weinmann, J. P.: The Keratinization of the Human Oral Mucosa, J. D. Res. **19**: 57, 1940.
41. Wentz, F. M., Maier, A. W., and Orban, B.: Age Changes and Sex Differences in the Clinically "Normal" Gingiva, J. Periodont. **23**: 13, 1952.
42. Wermuth, J.: Beitrag zur Histologie der Gegend seitlich von der Papilla palatina (Histology of the Region Lateral to the Incisive Papilla), Deutsche Monatschr. f. Zahnh. **45**: 203, 1927.

Chapter X • SALIVARY GLANDS*

INTRODUCTION

The human salivary glands are compound merocrine glands. Their ducts open into the oral cavity. They perform many functions, of which the most extensively studied is the production of saliva. Saliva is the secretory product of the salivary glands, and among many other functions it assists in the mastication and deglutition of food and in the digestion of certain food elements. There are three pairs of large glands, which are often classified as major salivary glands or salivary glands proper. They are the parotid, the submandibular, and the sublingual glands. (Plate 3.) In addition, there are numerous small glands which are widely distributed in the mucosa and submucosa of the oral cavity. These are known as the minor salivary glands.

In this chapter, the classification of the salivary glands and their structure as seen with the light microscope using ordinary staining procedures will be presented first. The low resolving power of the light microscope is inadequate for the detailed study of certain tissue elements, and the ordinary staining procedures do not offer information on the chemical make-up of cellular and intercellular structures. In recent years the high resolving power of the electron microscope and the development of fine histochemical and cytochemical methods have given

---

*By George A. Krikos.

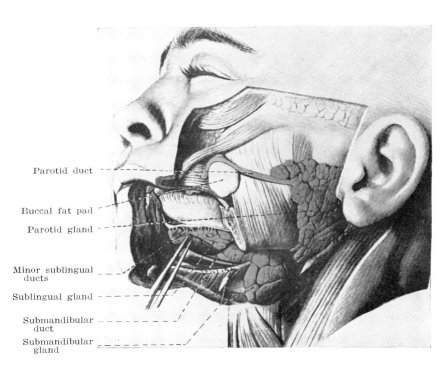

Parotid duct

Buccal fat pad

Parotid gland

Minor sublingual
ducts

Sublingual gland

Submandibular
duct

Submandibular
gland

Plate 3. Salivary glands of major secretion. Part of the mandible and mylohyoid muscle removed. (From Sicher, H., and Tandler, J.: Anatomie für Zahnärtze [Anatomy for Dentists],
Berlin, 1928, Julius Springer.)

us the opportunity to study with greater accuracy the structure and chemistry of tissue components. It is also becoming increasingly evident that alterations in functions are frequently accompanied by changes in structure at all levels of observation. The relations of structure and function are indeed at the heart of modern histology. For these reasons an attempt will be made to correlate the cytological, cytochemical, and biochemical observations on salivary glands. Finally, the functions of salivary glands and saliva and the contribution of the knowledge of the histology of the salivary glands to clinical practice will be discussed.

CLASSIFICATION OF SALIVARY GLANDS

The salivary glands of man can be classified in at least three ways: (1) according to the location of the glands, into glands of the vestibule and glands of the oral cavity proper; (2) according to size, into major and minor salivary glands; and (3) according to the nature of the substances that the secretory cells elaborate, into mucous, serous, and mixed glands. The secretory cells of the mucous glands elaborate a viscid secretion containing mucin. The secretory portions of the serous (albuminous) glands produce a watery secretion that is free of mucin. Finally, the mixed glands consist of both mucous and serous cells. The first two classifications are helpful in designating the size and location but are of little help in the functional analysis of the salivary gland in question. The third classification, initially proposed by Heidenhain,[19] has been of the greatest service because it has attempted to classify the salivary glands on a functional basis considering the nature of the secretory product.

It is preferable to use all classifications conjointly in order to designate simultaneously location and functional activity of the salivary gland in question.

The parotid gland of the adult is a pure serous gland. Glands with very few or no mucous cells are those of the vallate papillae. Glands in which both serous and mucous cells are present are referred to as predominantly serous or predominantly mucous depending upon the ratio of the cell types. Those with a few mucous cells include the submandibular gland and the parotid gland of the newborn. Those predominantly of mucous character include the labial glands, small buccal glands, anterior lingual glands, and the sublingual glands. In man, pure mucous glands are those at the base and border of the tongue, the glosso-palatine glands and the palatine glands. Following is a classification of the salivary glands according to location[83]:

A. Glands of the vestibule
    1. Labial glands
        (a) Superior labial glands
        (b) Inferior labial glands
    2. Buccal glands
        (a) Minor buccal glands
        (b) Parotid gland

B. Glands of the oral cavity proper (Plate 3)
    1. Glands of the floor of the mouth (alveololingual complex)
        (a) Submandibular gland
        (b) Major sublingual gland
        (c) Minor sublingual glands
        (d) Glossopalatine glands
    2. Glands of the tongue
        (a) Anterior lingual glands
        (b) Posterior lingual glands
            (1) Glands of the vallate papillae
            (2) Glands of the base of the tongue
    3. Palatine glands

STRUCTURAL ELEMENTS OF THE SALIVARY GLANDS

In general, the plan of organization of the salivary glands is similar to that of other exocrine glands. It consists of the following:

1. Connective tissue, which forms a capsule and extends as sheets or strands into the gland proper, dividing the gland into lobes and, on further subdivision, into lobules. It bears the ducts, blood vessels, lymphatics, and the nerves of the gland.

2. Ducts—in the connective tissue of the gland the larger ducts divide into ducts of progressively smaller caliber; in this way a complex duct system is formed. The smallest branches of this system are connected with the secretory or terminal portions of the gland.

3. Secretory cells—these cells are located in the terminal portions, which in turn lie in the lobules of the gland.

Detailed descriptions of the gross anatomy of salivary glands have been published by Sicher[68] and Carmalts.[8] The monographs by Stormont[77] and Zimmermann[83] describe the microscopic appearance of these glands.

Terminal portions (acini and tubules)

In general, a terminal portion consists of a layer of secretory cells lining a narrow lumen. These cells rest on a basement membrane that separates them from the underlying capillary bed. The shape of the terminal portions is not the same in all salivary glands. The pure mucous glands are compound tubular glands, the terminal portions usually being long, branching tubules. On the other hand, the serous and mixed salivary glands are compound tubuloacinous, their terminal portions being branched tubules with numerous outpocketings on the wall and on the blind ends.

Mucous and serous cells have certain structural characteristics. It must be emphasized, however, that it is not always possible to distinguish mucous from serous cells on the basis of morphology alone. The submandibular gland of the rabbit, for instance, has two types of secretory cells. One of these two types, known as "tropochrome cells," has an appearance very similar to mucous cells. However, these cells, when fixed in sublimate, do not exhibit some features be-

lieved to be characteristic of mucous cells; they do not stain red with mucicarmine, they are not metachromatic, and the secretion from this gland does not
contain mucin.[60, 77] These cells belong to the category of "special" serous cells,
and their functional significance is at present poorly understood.

Mucous cell. The appearance of mucous and serous cells varies with the state
of functional activity. When examined in the fresh state, the mucous cells are
seen to contain many droplets or granules of mucigen, the antecedent of mucin.
These droplets have a very low refractive index and are, therefore, very difficult
to see unless the optical equipment used is of high quality. They are also labile,
and for this reason they can be studied to best advantage if the fresh material
is examined in isotonic media. The mucous cell is usually so completely filled
with the droplets of mucigen that these droplets obscure the other elements. A
few granules, probably mitochondria, have been observed between the droplets,
but the nuclei are not visible in fresh material.[30]

In fixed preparations stained with hematoxylin and eosin, the mucous cells
have an entirely different appearance. The droplets of mucigen are destroyed by
the fixatives used, and the cell body assumes its classical clear, lightly stained
appearance, because it now contains a wide-meshed network. The spaces of this
network are not stained, while the trabeculae are slightly basophilic and are made
up of cytoplasm and precipitated mucigen. The trabeculae stain red with mucicarmine and are metachromatic. In such preparations the nucleus is angular in

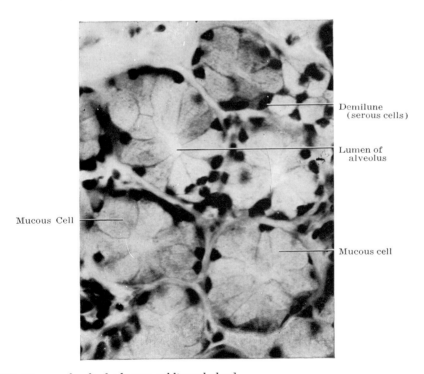

Demilune
(serous cells)

Lumen of
alveolus

Mucous Cell

Mucous cell

Fig. 214. Mucous alveoli of a human sublingual gland.

shape, stains deeply, and is located at the base of the cell. (Fig. 214.) There it is surrounded by a small accumulation of cytoplasm containing only small amounts of basophil material, which is so abundant in serous cells. However, when appropriate methods are used, such as freeze-drying, the droplets of mucigen are preserved, and the cells maintain characteristics similar to those seen in the fresh state. In such preparations, the mucous cells are found to contain large stainable granules that are separated from one another by thin partitions of protoplasm. Mucous cells are not associated with secretory capillaries. The lumina of mucous terminal portions are wider than those of serous terminal portions.

The previous description is that of a mucous cell in the "resting" state. The appearance changes with the state of functional activity. When the cell pours its secretion into the lumen, it becomes smaller, and only a few mucigen droplets remain which are confined near the free surface. The nucleus rises from the basal portion of the cell, becomes round, and one or more oxyphil nucleoli appear.

Serous cells. When examined in the fresh state, the serous cells are seen to contain a large number of highly refractile granules, known as secretion or zymogen granules. These are located primarily between the nucleus and the free surface of the cell and are less labile than the droplets of mucigen.

The secretion granules are easily destroyed by most fixatives, particularly those containing acetic acid. However, when appropriate fixatives are used, such as bichromates, they are preserved and can be stained by a number of methods, such as iron hematoxylin. These granules do not stain positively to mucicarmine and are not metachromatic. The nuclei of serous cells are round and are located in the basal third of the cell. The basal portion of the cytoplasm of serous cells contains large concentrations of a substance that stains strongly with basic dyes. This material has been known under a variety of names, such as basophil substance, chromophil substance, and ergastoplasm. In preparations fixed with acid fixatives, this material becomes arranged in parallel rods and filaments that give a vertical striation to the basal portion of the serous cell. This appearance is believed to be an artifact resulting from the precipitation of the basophil material by the acid fixative. The intense staining of the cytoplasmic constituents of the serous cells in sections stained with hematoxylin and eosin gives these cells a dark color that contrasts to the clear appearance of the mucous cells. Rod-shaped mitochondria are located in the cytoplasm at the basal portion of the cell, and a Golgi apparatus is located above the nucleus. Serous cells are always associated with secretory capillaries located between their lateral surfaces. The serous cells are roughly pyramidal in shape and line a small lumen. (Fig. 215.)

This is the appearance of a serous cell in the "resting" state. When the cell is stimulated to secrete, there is a decrease in the number of secretion granules, which are now confined close to the free surface. The volume of the cell decreases, and the intensity of the staining of the basophil material undergoes significant changes. The mitochondria increase in size and number, and the Golgi

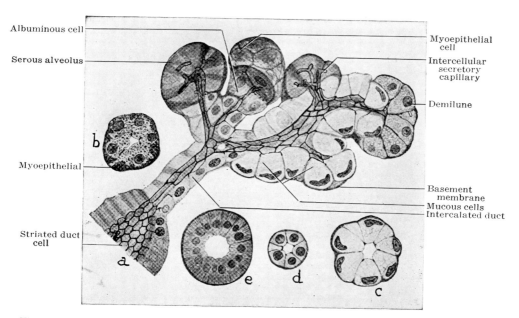

Albuminous cell
Serous alveolus
Myoepithelial
Striated duct cell

Myoepithelial cell
Intercellular secretory capillary
Demilune
Basement membrane
Mucous cells
Intercalated duct

Fig. 215. Reconstruction of a terminal portion and its duct of a salivary gland, **a. b,** Cross section through serous alveolus. **c,** Cross section through mucous alveolus. **d,** Cross section through intercalated duct. **e,** Cross section through striated duct. (From Maximow, A. A., and Bloom, W.: A Textbook of Histology, ed. 4, Philadelphia, 1942, W. B. Saunders Co.)

apparatus becomes larger. The nucleus increases in size, stains less intensely, and moves away from the base of the cell. The nucleolus becomes more prominent; it increases in size and stains more deeply. (Fig. 216.)

These descriptions point to certain differences between serous and mucous cells as seen in sections stained with hematoxylin and eosin. There are differences in the size, shape, location, and stainability of the nucleus, in the architecture of the cytoplasm, and in the intensity of the staining of the basophil material. It is also apparent that further differences can be observed when special methods of tissue preparation are employed. In such cases, droplets of mucigen, secretion granules, intercellular capillaries, and other structures can be observed and their chemical make-up studied. As previously mentioned, it is almost impossible in many cases to distinguish between mucous and serous cells on the basis of the morphologic characteristics alone. Furthermore, it must be emphasized that all mucous cells are not functionally identical. There are differences in the products elaborated by mucous cells of different glands in the same species, or by mucous cells of the same gland in different species. The same holds true for serous cells.

Arrangement of cells in mixed glands. Mixed glands consist of both mucous and serous cells. In these glands we can observe not only pure serous and pure mucous terminal portions but also terminal portions lined by both types of cells. In such mixed terminal portions the mucous and serous cells occupy different positions. The serous cells are located at the blind end of the terminal portion,

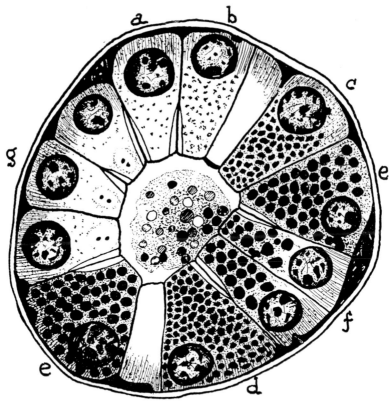

Fig. 216. Albuminous gland. Different functional stages of the cells. The secretory cycle is indicated by the letters **a** to **g**. (From Zimmermann, K. W.: Die Speicheldrüsen der Mundhöhle und die Bauchspeicheldrüse. In von Möllendorff, W. [editor]: Handbuch der mikroskopischen Anatomie des Menschen, vol. 5, pt. 1, Berlin, 1927, Julius Springer.)

whereas the mucous cells lie close to the excretory duct. In mixed glands in which the mucous cells predominate, the lumen of the mixed secretory portions is lined entirely by mucous cells, whereas the serous cells are arranged in small groups that in sections appear as crescents capping the blind ends of the mucous tubules. The serous cells of the crescents are connected with the lumen of the terminal portion by secretory capillaries that lie between the mucous cells. These crescents are known as demilunes of von Ebner or Giannuzzi, and they have all the previously mentioned characteristics of serous cells. (Figs. 215 and 224.)

Ducts

The duct system of the salivary glands is formed by the successive division within the connective tissue of the gland of larger ducts into ducts of progressively smaller caliber (Fig. 217). The ducts are named with reference to the gross architecture of the gland. We may distinguish intralobular, interlobular, lobar, and primary ducts. The necks or intercalated ducts and the striated or secretory

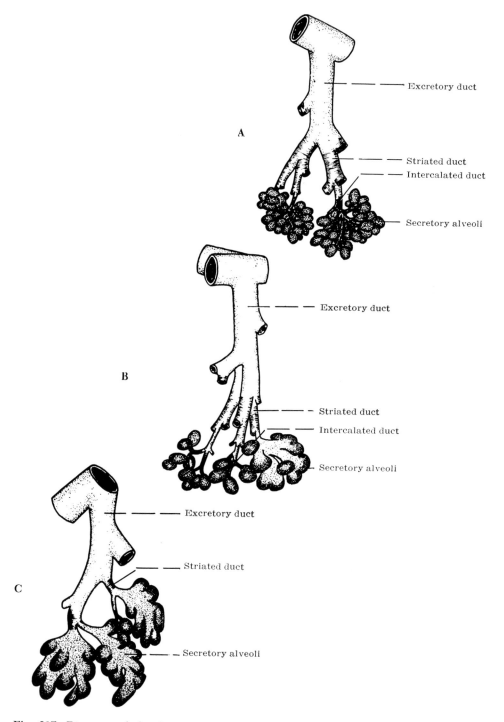

Fig. 217. Diagrams of the duct system and terminal secretory portions of salivary glands. **A**, Parotid. **B**, Submandibular. **C**, Sublingual. (Modified from Braus, H.: Anatomie des Menschen [Human Anatomy], vol. 2, ed. 2, Berlin, 1934, Julius Springer.)

ducts are the two orders of intralobular ducts; the intercalated and the striated ducts are not equally developed in all salivary glands.

Intercalated ducts. The intercalated ducts are thin, branching tubes of varying lengths that connect the terminal portions with the striated ducts. They are lined by a single layer of low cuboidal epithelial cells. The cytoplasm of these cells is relatively small in amount, stains faintly, and is free of granules. The nucleus is located in the center of the cell.[77] Whenever the intercalated ducts contain secretory cells, the transition between these ducts and the terminal portions is a gradual one. The proximal portion of the ducts consists of cells that resemble miniature acinous cells in having basophilic basal cytoplasm and secretory granules in their apical parts. The distal portion is lined by nonsecretory cells similar to those described previously. (Figs. 215 and 220.)

Striated ducts. The striated ducts are lined by a single layer of tall, columnar epithelial cells. Their nuclei are large and spherical and usually lie in the center of the cell. The cytoplasm is relatively large in amount, is eosinophilic, and, when appropriately fixed and stained, shows a pronounced striation at the basal portion of the cell perpendicular to the basal surface. This vertical striation is due in part to the presence of radially arranged mitochondria (Figs. 215, 218, and 220).

The larger excretory ducts have a pseudostratified columnar epithelium that may contain a few goblet cells. The epithelium of the main ducts gradually merges into the stratified squamous epithelium of the oral cavity.

In the terminal portions and in the ducts of the salivary glands several other

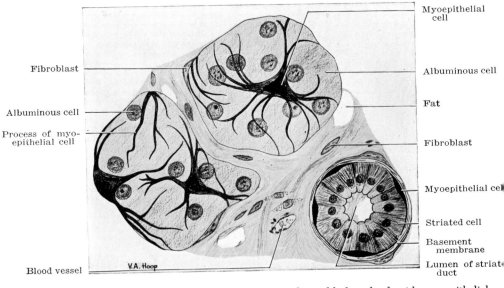

Fig. 218. Albuminous alveoli and striated duct of submandibular gland with myoepithelial cells. (Modified from Zimmermann, K. W.: Die Speicheldrüsen der Mundhöhle und die Bauchspeicheldrüse. In von Möllendorff, W. [editor]: Handbuch der mikroskopischen Anatomie des Menschen, vol. 5, pt. 1, Berlin, 1927, Julius Springer.)

cell types can be found in addition to the secretory cells and the ductal epithelium. The most important of these cells are the myoepithelial cells and the oncocytes.

Myoepithelial cells. The myoepithelial cells (basal cells, basket cells) form a syncytium of branched cells and lie between the basement membrane and the glandular or ductal epithelium. In cross section they are spindle-shaped. When viewed from the surface they exhibit a stellate body and numerous processes embracing the secretory portion or duct (Figs. 215 and 218).

The myoepithelial cells are most likely epithelial in nature. They are believed to be contractile and by their contraction to facilitate the movement of the secretion into the secretory ducts.

Oncocytes. The oncocytes are large cells having a small, centrally placed pyknotic nucleus and abundant, strongly eosinophilic cytoplasm. They are more frequently encountered in the parotid and submandibular glands of older individuals.

Interstitial connective tissue; blood, lymph, and nerve supply

The connective tissue may form a capsule around the gland and then extend into the gland proper, dividing it into lobes and lobules. This collagenous connective tissue is continuous with the reticular connective tissue of the lobules and the basement membrane, upon which rest the secretory cells and duct elements.

The salivary glands possess a rich blood supply. The larger arteries follow the course of the excretory ducts, giving off branches that accompany the divisions of the ducts to the lobules. The veins and the lymph vessels follow the arteries in reverse order to drain the gland.

The pattern of the vascular supply of acini and ducts within the microscopic lobule has not been adequately investigated. Kowalewsky[27] stated that in the submandibular gland of the cat there are two blood vessel systems: one system with capillaries in the walls of the ducts and another with capillaries between the alveoli. Presence of arteriovenous anastomoses has also been claimed.[57] Burgen and Seeman[6] stated that the findings of their radioisotope studies in the formation of saliva are not consistent with two separate systems of capillaries but, rather, with a series of continuous systems of capillaries that supply the ducts and acini and in which the direction of blood flow is opposite to that of the saliva (countercurrent portal system). It is obvious that there is a great need for the investigation of the intralobular blood supply of salivary glands, particularly if observations on the secretion of saliva are to be interpreted accurately.

The main branches of the nerves supplying the salivary glands also follow the course of the vessels to break up into terminal plexuses in the connective tissue adjacent to the alveoli. Both sympathetic and parasympathetic fibers pass through the basement membrane and end in budlike expansions between the secretory cells.

MAJOR SALIVARY GLANDS

The parotid, submandibular and sublingual glands are often classified as the major salivary glands. They are located at some distance from the oral cavity, with which they communicate by variably long ducts. A comparison of the anatomical features of the three large salivary glands is presented in Table 5.

Parotid gland. The parotid gland is the largest of the salivary glands. Its superficial portion is located in front of the external ear, while its deeper part fills the retromandibular fossa. The gland is enclosed within a well-formed capsule. The main excretory duct (Stensen's duct) of the parotid gland opens into the oral cavity on the mucosa of the cheek opposite the maxillary second molar. Usually a small papilla marks the opening. (Plate 3.)

Table 5. Comparison of the major salivary glands*

	Parotid	*Submandibular*	*Sublingual*
Size and shape	Largest; main and accessory parts both encapsulated; compound, branched, alveolar	Intermediate; well limited and encapsulated; compound, branched, alveolar, partly tubular	Smallest; major gland and several minor ones; no capsule; compound, branched, tubuloalveolar
Position	Around mandibular ramus anterior to ear	Beneath mandible	In floor of mouth
Ducts	Parotid (Stensen's) duct opens opposite second upper molar; double layer columnar cells on marked basement membrane	Submandibular (Wharton's) duct opens on either side of frenulum of tongue; structure same	Major sublingual (Bartholin's) duct opens near submandibular sometimes by common aperture, also several minor sublingual (Rivinian) ducts; structure same
Secretory ducts	Single layer very conspicuously striated columnar cells	Same but somewhat longer and may contain yellow pigment	Rare or absent
Intercalated ducts	Long, narrow, branching made of single layer of flattened cells	Much shorter but similar structure	Absent
Secretory epithelium	Serous alveoli, mucous alveoli rare (in newborn)	Serous alveoli predominate, some mucous alveoli have serous crescents	Major gland: mucous alveoli predominate; many serous crescents and alveoli. Minor glands all mucous
Interstitial tissue	Fat cells most abundant		Connective tissue septa most abundant
Nerve supply	Sensory: fifth nerve Secretory: (1) sympathetic, superior cervical ganglion (vasoconstriction); (2) parasympathetic, ninth nerve, otic ganglion (vasodilation)	Sensory: fifth nerve Secretory: (1) sympathetic, same; (2) parasympathetic, seventh nerve, chorda tympani, submandibular ganglion (vasodilation)	Sensory: fifth nerve Secretory: same as submandibular gland

*After Finerty, J. C., and Cowdry, E. V.: A Textbook of Histology, ed. 5, Philadelphia, 1960, Lea & Febiger.

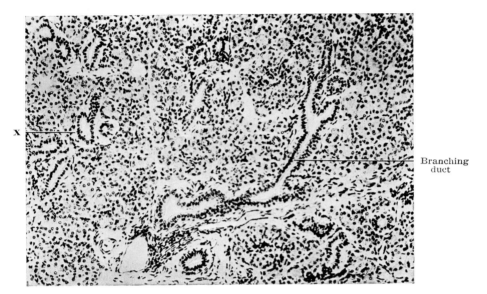

X

Branching
duct

Fig. 219. Section through a human parotid gland.

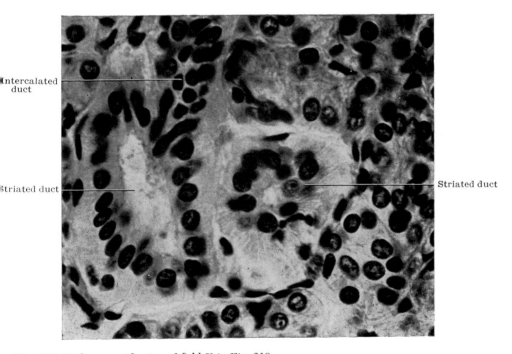

Intercalated
duct

Striated duct

Striated duct

Fig. 220. Higher magnification of field **X** in Fig. 219.

The parotid gland is a branched tubuloacinous gland. In the adult it is a
pure serous gland (Fig. 219), although occasional mucous acini can be found.
In the newborn, however, mucous acini are encountered with greater frequency.

The intercalated ducts are long and branching; the striated ducts are conspicuous (Figs. 217 and 220). In the parotid gland the connective tissue septa frequently contain fat cells, which increase in number with age.

Submandibular gland. The greater part of the submandibular gland is located in the submandibular triangle behind and below the free border of the mylohyoid muscle. A tonguelike extension of the gland usually lies above the mylohyoid muscle close to the sublingual glands. (Plate 3.) A well-formed capsule envelops the gland. The main excretory duct (Wharton's duct) opens by a narrow orifice on the summit of a small papilla, caruncula sublingualis, at the side of the lingual frenum at the floor of the mouth.

The submandibular gland is a compound tubuloacinous gland. It is of the mixed type, with the serous elements predominating. There are many serous terminal portions and only a few mucous terminal portions. The latter are capped by demilunes of serous cells. (Figs. 221 and 222.) The intercalated ducts are shorter but otherwise are similar in structure to those of the parotid gland. The striated ducts are also structurally similar to those of the parotid gland but are somewhat longer. (Figs. 217 and 222.)

Sublingual glands. The sublingual glands are located in the floor of the mouth in the sublingual fold (Plate 3). They are a composite of one larger and several smaller glands. The main secretory duct of the large sublingual gland (Bartholin's duct) opens into the oral cavity with or near, but independently from, the duct of the submandibular gland. The ducts of the smaller sublingual glands usually are 8 to 20 in number, and most of them open independently into the mouth on the sublingual fold.

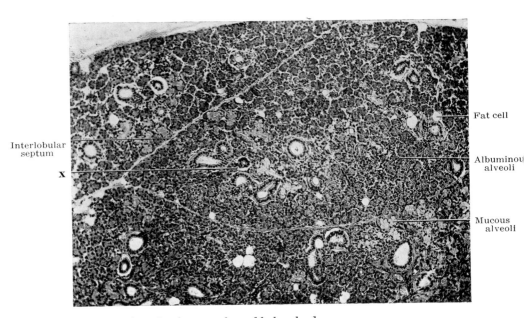

Fig. 221. Section through a human submandibular gland.

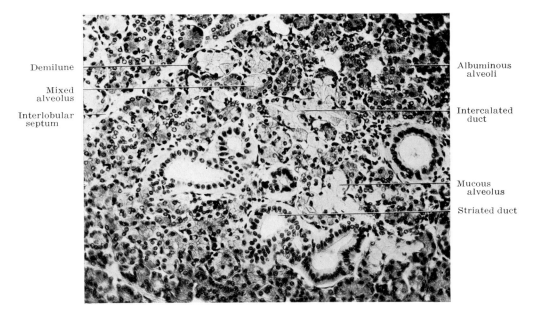

Demilune

Mixed
alveolus

Interlobular
septum

Albuminous
alveoli

Intercalated
duct

Mucous
alveolus

Striated duct

Fig. 222. Higher magnification of field **X** in Fig. 221.

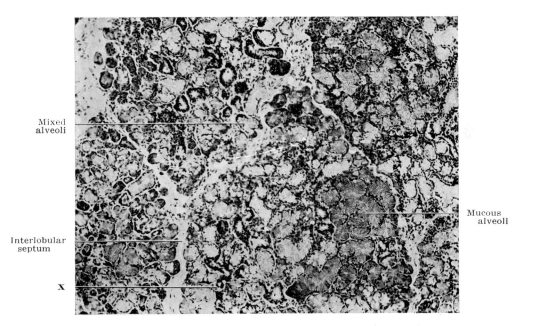

Mixed
alveoli

Interlobular
septum

Mucous
alveoli

X

Fig. 223. Section through a human major sublingual gland.

The major sublingual gland is a compound tubuloacinous gland. It is of the mixed type, but, in contrast to the submandibular gland, the mucous elements predominate. (Fig. 223.) There are numerous mucous terminal portions. The blind ends of some of them are capped by demilunes of serous cells. The majority

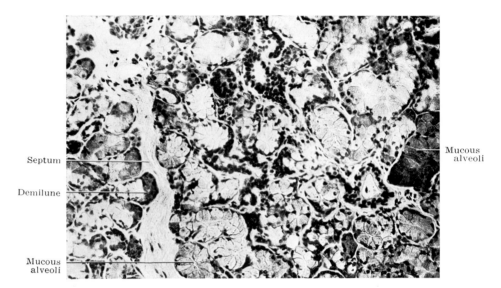

Fig. 224. Higher magnification of field **X** in Fig. 223.

of the mucous secretory portions do not possess demilunes. Pure serous alveoli are rare. (Fig. 224.) Striated and intercalated ducts, particularly the latter, are scarce or entirely absent. (Fig. 217.) The connective tissue septa separating the lobes and lobules are more pronounced in the sublingual than in either the parotid or the submandibular gland. However, the sublingual gland is practically devoid of an investing capsule. The smaller sublingual glands are mucous in character.

MINOR SALIVARY GLANDS

Labial glands. The labial glands, which are located near the inner surface of the lips, are of the mixed type. They are variable in size and are closely packed in the submucosa, where they may be easily palpated. They are not encapsulated. The terminal portions may contain both serous and mucous cells lining the same lumen, but more often typical demilunes are formed. A considerable number of the terminal portions may contain only mucous cells (Fig. 225). The cells have a distinct mucoalbuminous character; the intercalated ducts are short.

Minor buccal glands. The buccal glands, which are a continuation of the labial glands in the cheek, bear a marked resemblance to those of the lips. Those glands that lie in the immediate vicinity of the opening of the parotid duct and drain into the third molar region often are designated the molar glands. Buccal glands are found frequently on the outer surface of the buccinator muscle.

Glossopalatine glands. The glossopalatine glands are pure mucous glands; they are located in the isthmus region and are a continuation, posteriorly, of the lesser sublingual glands. They ascend in the mucosa of the glossopalatine fold. They may be confined to the anterior faucial pillar or may extend into the soft palate to fuse with the palatine glands proper. They may also be seen on the lingual side of the retromolar area of the mandible.

Palatine glands. The palatine glands, which occupy the roof of the oral cavity, can be topographically divided into glands of the hard palate and glands of the soft palate and uvula. They are composed of independent glandular aggregates numbering approximately 250 in the hard palate, 100 in the soft palate, and 12 in the uvula. In the posterior area of the hard palate, the glands lie between the mucous membrane and the periosteum, supported by a dense framework of connective tissue characteristic of this region. Continuing backward, the lateral groups become arranged into compact rows and take on considerable size. They merge with those of the soft palate and form a thick layer between the mucous membrane and palatal musculature (see Chapter IX).

The palatine glands are of the pure mucous type. The intercalated ducts are short; many undergo mucous transformation, in which case they function as part of the mucous terminal portion.

Glands of the tongue. The glands of the tongue are divided into anterior and posterior lingual glands. The anterior lingual gland (gland of Blandin-Nuhn) is embedded within the musculature of the inferior aspect of the tongue close to the midline near the apex. Approximately five small ducts open under the tongue near the lingual frenum. The anterior part of this gland is chiefly mucous in character. The posterior part consists of branching tubules lined with mucous cells and capped with demilunes of serous cells.

The posterior lingual glands are located at the base (root) of the tongue and in the vicinity of the vallate papillae. The glands of the base of the tongue

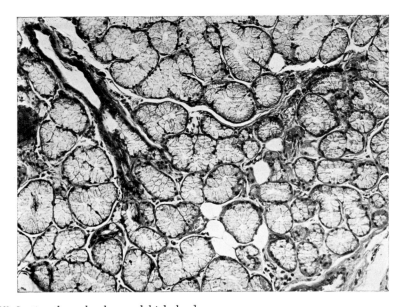

Fig. 225. Section through a human labial gland.

are of the pure mucous variety. The glands of the vallate papillae (von Ebner) are pure serous and open into the trough of the vallate papillae. Their secretion probably serves to wash out the furrows of the vallate papillae (see Chapter IX).

HISTOGENESIS

The salivary glands are formed during fetal life as solid buds of oral epithelium with club-shaped ends pushing into the subjacent mesenchyme. As the bud or primordium grows, it proliferates distally, forming cords of cells. The most distal portion forms the alveoli or functional elements of the gland. Cords and buds are at first solid and are later hollowed out to form ducts and alveoli.

The bud of the parotid salivary gland appears as a shelflike outgrowth of epithelium during the fourth week of fetal life at the angle between the maxillary process and the mandibular arch (sulcus buccalis); the bud of the submandibular gland appears in the sixth week, and that of the major sublingual gland appears during the eighth to ninth week from similar outgrowths located at the medial angle of the hollow between the tongue and the mandibular arch (sulcus sublingualis). The minor sublingual glands arise as independent proliferations in the alveololingual region, associated with the sulcus sublingualis at the lateral margin of the plica sublingualis. Accessory and secondary lobes of the parotid and the submandibular glands become visible during the eighth to ninth weeks as outgrowths arising from the cords of the respective glands. All the elements of the smaller sublingual, glossopalatine, and palatine groups develop from the primitive oral epithelium. The anterior lingual glands are noticeable for the first time at 10 weeks. They start as epithelial proliferations located on the ventral surface near the tip of the tongue on both sides of the median line. Development of the labial glands takes place simultaneously with the anterior lingual glands. Lymphoid tissue is found frequently in the fetal salivary glands; this is especially common in the parotid gland. Occasionally, remnants of lymphatic tissue are found in the adult.

CYTOLOGIC, CHEMICAL, AND PHYSIOLOGIC CORRELATIONS

Knowledge about the ultrastructure, chemistry, and biochemical activity of the cell components and the secretory products of salivary glands and about the role the cell components play in the production of the secretory products is most valuable for the understanding of the general economy of the gland and the secretory cells. The development of fine histochemical and cytochemical methods, the development of cell fractionation procedures, and the use of the electron microscope have been of great help in this respect. Significant studies have been done on various exocrine glands,[49] particularly the pancreas.[46] However, studies of this type on salivary glands are not numerous. The number of such studies on *human* salivary glands is exceedingly small. In the majority of cases, different procedures have been employed on different salivary glands of different animal species. We have already emphasized that there are significant differences from one salivary gland to another and from one species to another. This state of affairs makes correlation a difficult task.

The process of secretion consists of at least the following three steps[26]: (1) ingestion of raw material into the cell; (2) synthesis of complex molecules, which may then be stored in the form of granules, crystals, vacuoles, etc.; and (3) extrusion of the secretory product from the cell.

In the salivary glands we are particularly concerned with the synthesis of proteins or proteins combined with a variable amount of polysaccharides. The latter product is particularly important in the formation of mucin by the mucous cells.

Serous cell. In a recent electron microscopic study, Parks[50] observed that the acinous cell of the mouse parotid is very similar in structure to the exocrine cell of the pancreas.[73, 74] In the mouse parotid the endoplasmic reticulum appears as an extensive system of flattened membranous vesicles that are commonly known as cisternae.[47] These membranous structures reach their highest intra-

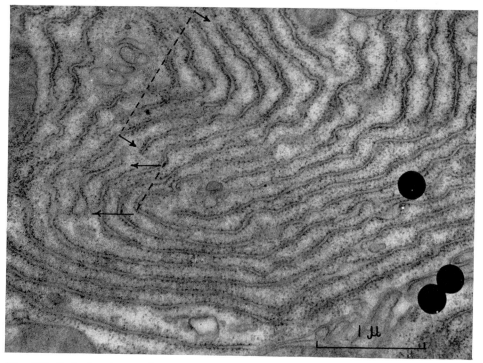

Fig. 226. Endoplasmic reticulum in parotid acinous cell of mouse. The endoplasmic reticulum consists mainly of flattened membranous vesicles or cisternae that present long, thin profiles when sectioned in a plane perpendicular to their broad surfaces. The cisternae appear in sections to begin and end blindly (arrows), but they are generally considered to be dilated parts of a continuous netlike membranous formation. The external surfaces of the cisternae have numerous tiny, dense ribonucleoprotein granules attached to them. These granules are believed to be importantly concerned in protein synthesis. Three small mitochondria are seen in the top of the field. (Courtesy Dr. Harold F. Parks.)

cellular concentration in the basal region of the acinous cell and are characteristically arranged parallel to one another; numerous dense particles are attached to their outer surface. Many particles of similar structure lie also free in the cytoplasm. (Fig. 226.) It has been demonstrated that these particles in the pancreatic acinous cell of the guinea pig are ribonucleoprotein (RNA) particles.[48] In the parotid of the mouse these particles have not as yet been isolated and analyzed, but there is good reason to assume that they, too, contain RNA. Caspersson and associates,[10] using ultraviolet microspectrophotometric methods, demonstrated high concentrations of RNA in the basal cytoplasm of serous cells of dog parotid and submandibular gland, and Noback and Montagna[42] showed that the intense basophilia of the basal cytoplasm of the serous cells of mouse parotid and submandibular glands is removable with the enzyme ribonuclease. It is thus apparent that the endoplasmic reticulum and RNA particles are identical with the basophil substance or ergastoplasm of the histologists.

There is a considerable body of evidence to suggest that the cytoplasmic RNA is associated with protein synthesis,[9, 10] and recent radioisotope studies have implicated the RNA particle as the probable site of this process.[71] It is, therefore, not surprising that in protein-producing cells, such as the serous cells of salivary glands, significant changes have been observed in the basophil substance during the various stages of their secretory activity. There is no unanimity, however, in the interpretation of the changes that occur. Noback and Montagna[42] found a decrease in the intensity of the ribonuclease-removable basophilia of the serous cells of mouse parotid and submandibular glands following pilocarpine injection. Caspersson and associates[10] had similar results also. On the other hand, Stormont[77] stated that "the chromophile material increases in amount while the cell is actively exporting its secretion, and again diminishes in amount when export ceases and the cell enters on a period of rest."[*] The histochemical methods employed in the experiments just mentioned indicate changes in the concentration of RNA in certain areas of the cell during the various stages of functional activity, but they do not give any information on the amount of RNA per cell. It is quite possible that the changes observed reflect an intracellular redistribution of RNA during secretion rather than a change in the total amount of RNA per cell. In this respect it is interesting to note that Hokin and Hokin,[22] using chemical analytical methods, did not find any significant change in RNA concentration in rabbit parotid slices stimulated in vitro by carbamylcholine.

Although protein synthesis is connected with the endoplasmic reticulum, the zymogen granule, which is the morphologically recognizable form of a secretory product (Figs. 227 and 228), makes its first appearance in the Golgi bodies (with the possible exception of the acinous cell of the guinea pig pancreas).[45] From the observation that the Golgi apparatus undergoes significant morphologic

---

[*]Stormont, D. L.: The Salivary Glands. In Cowdry, E. V. (editor): Special Cytology, New York, 1932, Paul B. Hoeber, Inc., vol. 1, pp. 153-196.

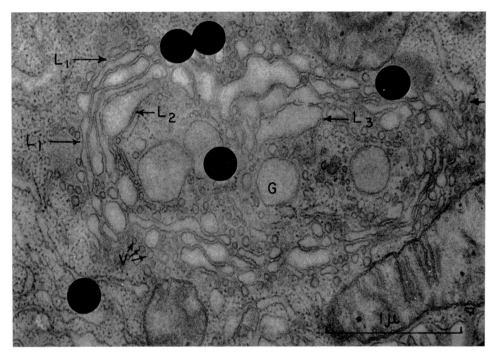

Fig. 227. Golgi apparatus in parotid acinous cell of mouse. This organelle consists of two membranous components: tiny spherical vesicles, **V**, and larger flattened vesicles or lamellae, **L**. The lamellae tend to be stacked in parallel groups. Four immature secretion granules, **G**, are seen in the space enclosed by the Golgi body. The impression is gained from examining lamellae that they swell up to form the secretion granules: that L_2 is thicker than L_1, and the contents of L_3 have taken on a texture like that of the secretion granules. The arrow at the right shows a nongranular diverticulum of a cisterna of the endoplasmic reticulum. This frequently seen configuration suggests that the small Golgi vesicles may arise by pinching off from the endoplasmic reticulum or that they coalesce with the endoplasmic reticulum and thus contribute to its substance. (Courtesy Dr. Harold F. Parks.)

changes during the secretory activity of the cell, many microscopists[2, 40] hypothesized that this apparatus is in some way connected with the production of secretory granules. Recent electron microscopic studies[74] have substantiated this hypothesis. In the acinous cell of the mouse parotid,[50, 52] the Golgi bodies consist of small spherical membranous structures, known as vesicles, and of lamellae, which are larger, flattened membranous vesicles arranged parallel to one another (Fig. 227). In this cell the zymogen granules appear to arise by a swelling and enspherulation of the Golgi lamellae (Fig. 227). The granules enlarge and mature and move toward the luminal surface of the cell.

Studies on the living gland[29] and of microscopic sections[77] have suggested that the secretory granules are extruded into the lumen, but the details of this extrusion process have been clarified only recently by the use of the electron microscope. In the acinous cell of the mouse parotid the membrane enclosing the granule fuses with the cell membrane. This fusion is followed by a perforation

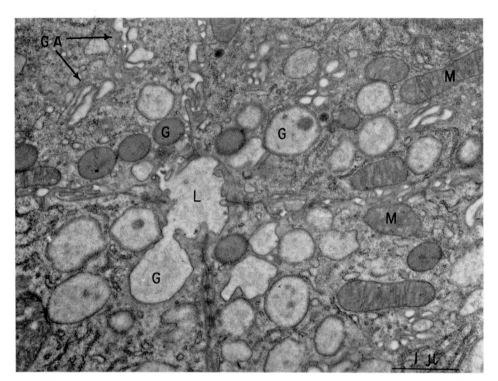

Fig. 228. Secretory activity in parotid acinus of mouse. The lumen, **L**, of an intercellular secretion canal is seen to be bordered by four cells. At its lower left, a secretion granule, **G**, has extruded its contents into the lumen, and the membrane that once surrounded the granule is now part of the cell membrane. Examples of secretion granules, **G**, Golgi apparatus, **GA**, and mitochondria, **M**, are labeled. (From Parks, Harold F.: J. Ultrastructure Res. 1962. (In press.)

at the site of the fusion, which allows the contents of the secretion granule to flow into the lumen.[51] (Fig. 228.) It is most interesting that the secretory granules are always separated from the cytoplasm by a membrane and that during extrusion the cell membrane does not lose its continuity. While the contents of the zymogen granules of the pancreas are reasonably well known,[70] the zymogen granules of salivary glands have not yet been isolated and analyzed. It may be assumed that, among other substances, they contain the enzymes found in saliva obtained directly from the main excretory ducts. In saliva thus obtained,[11, 20] numerous enzymes have been found and have been demonstrated histochemically in salivary glands.[7, 12] The zymogen granules are as a rule periodic acid-Schiff (PAS) positive,[26, 50] which suggests that they may contain polysaccharides.

Although much has been learned, much is still unknown. The process of protein synthesis, the transfer of the product from the site of synthesis (presumably the RNP particles) to the Golgi bodies, the aggregation of the zymogen molecules into granules, the mechanism of the movement of these granules from the Golgi region to the luminal surface of the cell, and the nature of the forces that eject the zymogen material into the lumen are all questions that need intensive investigation. There is evidence[52] to suggest that the Golgi vesicles may transfer the secretion antecedents from their site of synthesis to the Golgi lamellae.

The changes in the number and form of the mitochondria during the secretory cycle caused many histologists to suggest that these organelles participate in the process of secretion. Regaud and Mawas,[63] for instance, observed that in the discharged acinous cell of the parotid the mitochondria were abundant and distributed in the whole height of the cell, whereas in the charged state these organelles were represented by a few filaments that were exclusively localized at the base of the cells. The mitochondria contain the enzymes for the citric acid cycle, electron transport and oxidative phosphorylation.[18] They are, therefore, the centers of biologic oxidation and act as energy suppliers for the cell. Since there is evidence to suggest that aerobic oxidation is the source of energy for the secretory process in salivary glands, it is not surprising that the mitochondria undergo significant changes during the secretory cycle. Junqueira and his associates[25, 26, 62] observed that ligation of the main duct of the submandibular glands of mice and rats resulted in a diminution of cell and gland size, a reduction in the number of mitochondria, an abolition of secretion as evidenced by the disappearance of secretion granules, and a significant reduction of the amylase and protease activity of the gland. These changes in secretion were associated with a decrease in oxygen consumption, in cytochrome oxidase and succinic dehydrogenase activities, and in ATP content of the nonsecreting gland. Glycolysis remained unaltered. These findings indicate that energy for cell secretion is derived from aerobic oxidation. Similarly, Schneider and Person[64] found high cytochrome oxidase activity in the acini and ducts of submandibular glands.

In the acinous cell of the mouse parotid the mitochondria have the well-known structural characteristics[73] (Figs. 226 and 228) and frequently lie in close proximity to the basal or lateral cell membrane, with their long axes parallel.[50]

Mucous cell. In an electron microscope study of the salivary glands of the rat, Scott and Pease[66] observed that in the mucous cell of the sublingual gland the cytoplasm is located basally and is richly endowed with mitochondria and endoplasmic reticulum, while the mucoid mass occupies the center and apical portion of the cell. They also observed that the secretory product could be traced directly back to the Golgi bodies. It appears that Golgi lamellae become dilated by the accumulation of mucin. The secretory granules increase in size and coalesce.

Mucins are an important secretory product of the mucous cells. They represent a group of quite different chemical substances. As a group, the mucins are principally glycoproteins, i.e., large molecules consisting of a carbohydrate firmly bound to a protein. The composition of these two moieties varies from mucin to mucin. Certain mucins have strong acidic properties, and sialic acid, in the form of acylated derivatives, has been found in some of them.[58] Recently, Pigman and his associates[41, 81] purified and characterized mucins from bovine submandibular and sublingual glands and found them to contain sialic acid. In this connection, it is interesting to note that mucous cells of bovine submandibular glands are metachromatic and stain positively with Alcian blue, suggesting the presence of a substance or substances having available and appropriately arranged acidic groups. Digestion of the sections with sialidase, an enzyme that removes sialic acid, resulted in loss of these staining properties, indicating that they were due to the acidic groups of sialic acid.[61] Histochemical studies on the mucous cells of the sublingual gland of the mouse[76] showed similar results, indicating the presence within these cells of a sialic acid-containing mucin. In contrast, the mucin of the sublingual gland of the rat contains sialic acid, but the mucous cells are not metachromatic, and digestion of the sections with sialidase does not remove sialic acid. These histochemical differences between the sublingual gland of the rat and the mouse emphasize the fact that mucous cells, although morphologically similar, may not be functionally identical.

Intercalated ducts. Electron microscopic studies of intercalated ducts draining serous terminal portions have shown that secretory cells, when present, are similar to the serous cells in that they have large amounts of endoplasmic reticulum and contain secretion granules. The nonsecreting cells of these ducts are

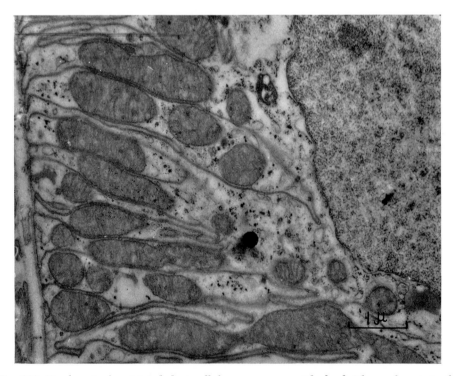

Fig. 229. Basal part of a striated duct cell from mouse parotid gland. The nucleus is in the upper right; the basal surface of the cell is at the left. It can be seen that the basal striations of these cells are due in part to the presence of radially arranged mitochondria and in part to numerous infoldings of the plasma membrane. (From Parks, Harold F.: Am. J. Anat. **108:** 303, 1961.)

free of secretion granules and are practically devoid of granular endoplasmic reticulum.[50]

Striated ducts. The most characteristic electron microscopic features of the epithelium of striated ducts are the presence of large numbers of radially arranged mitochondria and particularly the presence in the basal portions of the cells of numerous lateral branching cytoplasmic processes that interdigitate with similar processes of neighboring cells[50] (Fig. 229). Similar but not identical complex folding of the cell membrane has been observed also in cells noted for their water transport, such as epithelial cells of the kidney, choroid plexus, and ciliary body.[55] This folding increases to a significant extent the area of basal cell membrane available for the transfer of water and electrolytes and brings the cell membrane into close proximity with larger numbers of mitochondria.

There is good evidence to suggest that the ducts do not play a passive role but instead modify the secretion elaborated by the acinous cells. Striated ducts are present in parotid and submandibular glands which elaborate hypotonic secretions, and they are absent in sublingual glands and pancreas which produce isotonic secretions independent of rate of flow. Furthermore, the cytochrome oxidase activity of ducts of the submandibular glands is higher than that of their acini,[64] indicating that the ducts have a high metabolic activity. There is no unanimity in the specific physiologic actions of the ducts. It has been suggested that sodium and chlorides are absorbed in excess of water by the ducts, resulting in hypotonic saliva, particularly when the flow rate is low.[79] On the other hand, Burgen and Seeman[6] suggested that in the ducts potassium is reabsorbed and partly replaced by sodium ions diffusing in from the plasma. It appears that the secretion of sodium and potassium by the salivary glands is in part regulated by the adrenal cortical hormones.[17] Perhaps the only well-established physiologic action of the ducts is the demonstration by radioautographic methods that in certain animals the duct epithelium concentrates and secretes iodide and thiocyanate into the saliva.[34] It is obvious that the role of the salivary acini and ducts in the secretion of water and electrolytes and the mechanism of the transport of these elements by the cells need further intensive investigation.

Myoepithelial cells. Study of myoepithelial cells with the electron microscope[50] has shown that these cells resemble smooth muscle cells. Their cytoplasm shows faint longitudinal striations resembling myofibrils, and their cell membrane has "pinocytotic vesicles." These observations are consistent with the assumed contractile nature of the myoepithelial cells.

FUNCTIONS OF SALIVARY GLANDS

The production of saliva is the most extensively studied function of the salivary glands. Experimental studies conducted during the past fifteen years indicate that the salivary glands, in addition to producing saliva, play a significant role in iodine metabolism, store a factor that affects the growth and differentiation of the sympathetic nervous system, contain a substance that affects calcium metabolism, and are functionally related with various endocrine organs. Observations of this sort suggest that the salivary glands not only affect the oral cavity through the saliva but also have far-reaching effects on the whole organism.

Saliva. The secretion of proteins, electrolytes, and water by the salivary glands has been discussed in the previous section. For the average "resting" secretion in man, approximately 69 per cent seems to be derived from the submandibular glands, 26 per cent from the parotid glands, and 5 per cent from the sublingual glands. The minor salivary glands do not contribute significantly. Since the composition of saliva varies greatly from individual to individual, from one gland to another, and depends upon the nature and intensity of the stimuli causing its secretion, the designation of the percentages of its various constituents is meaningless unless the exact condition under which the saliva was collected is also described. It may suffice to say that saliva contains 0.3 to 0.7 per cent of solid matter. The latter consists of inorganic salts, such as bicarbonates, chlorides, and phosphates of calcium, sodium and potassium, and of organic substances, such as proteins, including mucins, enzymes, blood group substances and antibodies, lipids, vitamins, amino acids, and urea. In addition, dissolved gases, mostly carbon dioxide and oxygen, are also present.[56, 57]

The proteins are the principal organic constituents of saliva. Various electrophoretic methods have been employed for the separation of proteins and other charged macromolecules of human parotid and submandibular saliva.[54, 82] Each type of secretion contained 6 to 12 electrophoretically separable components at pH 6, 7, and 8.5, and considerable differences between samples from different individuals were apparent. Amylase was the first electrophoretic component to be identified.[53] Recently, Mandel and Ellison[36] eluted the electrophoretic components of parotid saliva and analyzed them chemically and immunochemically. In addition to amylase they identified a number of serum proteins, such as albumin and alpha, beta, and gamma globulins, and two glycoproteins. In contrast to the glycoproteins of the submandibular and sublingual glands,[41, 81] those of the parotid gland do not seem to contain acidic groups, such as sialic acid. These chemical findings are consistent with histochemical studies,[26, 50] indicating that the zymogen granules are periodic acid-Schiff positive and nonmetachromatic. It would be most interesting to know if these glycoproteins of salivary gland origin are also present in the organic matrix of calculus (see Clinical Considerations).

It must be emphasized that the saliva in the oral cavity is different from the saliva collected from the ducts. The latter is significantly modified in the oral cavity by the activities of microbes and of the oral tissues and by such other substances as may be taken into the mouth from time to time. For instance, in whole saliva, ammonia, urease, and hyaluronidase are entirely of microbial origin, whereas lysozyme is entirely of salivary gland origin. A host of other constituents of whole saliva, such as amino acids, vitamins, lipase, acid phosphatase, etc., are

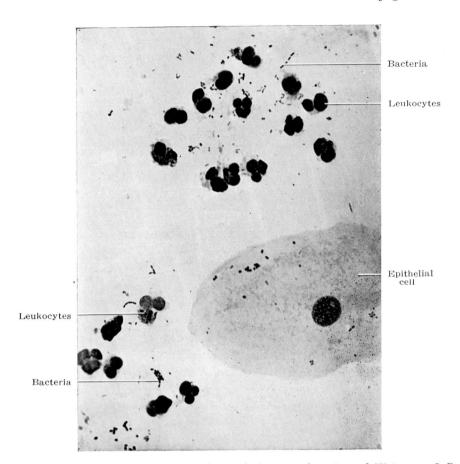

Fig. 230. Smear of human saliva (Wright's stain). (From Orban, B., and Weinmann, J. P.: J. A. D. A. 26: 2008, 1939.)

both of salivary and extrasalivary gland origin.[11, 56, 57] For this reason, in studies on the secretion of saliva and on the contribution of the salivary glands to oral health and disease, the pure secretions from the individual salivary glands must be used. The collection of these pure secretions is accomplished by the use of special devices.

The opacity of saliva is attributed mainly to the presence of desquamated epithelial cells and polymorphonuclear leukocytes, salivary corpuscles (Fig. 230). The epithelial cells are large and flat with oval nuclei. They may be round or irregular, with a granular cytoplasm. The salivary corpuscles are derived from the mucous membrane of the mouth, the tonsils, and the salivary glands. Corpuscle counts are high after a night's rest, low after meals. Their role is as yet imperfectly understood, but it is the opinion of some investigators that they are phagocytic.

The digestive function of saliva has mechanical and chemical aspects. From the mechanical standpoint, saliva brings food components into solution, thus facilitating chemical reactivity and the stimulation of the taste organs. Mucin aids in the lubrication of the bolus of food for deglutition. From the chemical standpoint, salivary amylase hydrolyzes starch components into mono-, di-, and trisaccharides. The role of salivary amylase in the breakdown of the starch of foodstuffs is not great since the foodstuffs remain in the oral cavity for only a short period of time, and amylase reactivity is destroyed shortly after the entrance of the bolus into the stomach. Most likely this enzyme acts as a cleansing agent by liquefying starchy foodstuffs that cling to the oral tissues.

Additional functions of saliva will be discussed under Clinical Considerations.

Iodine metabolism. The salivary glands play an important role in iodine metabolism.[39] In human beings and in certain animals, they possess a powerful mechanism for concentrating iodide.[14] The iodide concentration of human mixed saliva is usually over twenty times higher than in the blood plasma. Autoradiographic methods have shown that the iodide-concentrating mechanism is located in the cells of the striated ducts.[34] The accumulation of iodide in the salivary glands is not affected by thyrotrophic hormone,[78] which is known to produce hyperplasia and to stimulate the iodide-concentrating mechanism in the thyroid gland. In this connection, it is interesting to note that the salivary glands may control the level of thyroxin in the blood. Fawcett and Kirkwood[16] proposed that the salivary glands deiodinate thyroxin and recycle the iodide ion to the thyroid gland via the saliva and the gastrointestinal tract.

Endocrine interrelations. In 1940, Lacassagne[28] observed that there is a sexual dimorphism in the tubular portion of the mouse submandibular glands, this portion being more highly developed in the male than in the female mice. This observation suggested a relation between the salivary glands and the sex organs and stimulated a large number of studies that have shown that the salivary glands, at least in the experimental animal, are intimately associated with the endocrine organs. These studies have been reviewed recently by Shafer and Muhler.[67] It has been observed, for instance, that thyroidectomy causes a decrease in the size and number of the so-called granular tubules of the submandibular glands, a decrease in salivary flow, and an increase in the viscosity of saliva. It is most interesting that these structural and functional changes are accompanied by significant changes in the incidence of dental caries. In thyroidectomized animals, the incidence of dental caries is increased. In these animals, thyroxin replacement therapy causes a return of the structure of the salivary gland and of the salivary flow and viscosity back to control levels, and this is associated with a return of the caries scores to those of the control level. The interrelations between endocrine glands, salivary glands, saliva, and caries are still obscure, but here we have a well-controlled experimental model that may help solve some of the unexplained aspects of the problem of dental caries.

The sex organs and the hypophysis have also been shown to influence the salivary glands.[67]

In 1935, Ogata[43] presented a hypothesis that the salivary glands secrete a hormone acting on the mesenchymal tissues. Subsequently, an active principle was isolated from bovine parotid and submandibular glands and was named parotin. This substance lowers the serum calcium level and enhances the calcification of incisor dentin in rabbits and rats.[24] Although the Japanese workers claim that the salivary glands are endocrine organs, their studies are not convincing, and certainly more research is necessary before their endocrine role is established firmly.

CLINICAL CONSIDERATIONS

The salivary glands are the site of numerous pathologic conditions. On the other hand, the fact that the oral mucous membrane and the teeth are in continuous contact with the saliva would suggest that saliva could exert a profound influence on oral health and disease.

Dental caries. In a simplified form, the process of dental caries appears to depend on an interplay between tooth composition, diet, and oral microbial flora. In turn, each of these factors is influenced by a large number of other agents, saliva being only one of these. Salivary factors, such as the viscosity, pH, and buffering capacity of saliva and its content in various electrolytes and organic substances, such as enzymes and antibacterial factors, have been investigated as to their significance in dental caries. With few exceptions, none of the physical and chemical characteristics of saliva has been related consistently to human dental caries. This state of affairs is understood easily if we consider that experiments on human beings subsisting under different environmental conditions and eating different diets cannot be easily controlled. The variable under study is affected to different degrees in different individuals by factors having similar or opposite effects. The need to study the role of the various salivary factors on dental caries under well-controlled experimental conditions is obvious. Since all carious lesions are initiated under a dental plaque, well-controlled studies on the role of salivary factors on the formation, composition, and permeability of the dental plaque are of even greater significance.

In a few instances, the role of salivary factors on dental caries is reasonably well documented. A significant decrease in the rate of salivary flow, such as occurs in salivary gland extirpation, congenital aplasia, Mikulicz's disease, etc., is always associated with an increase in the incidence of dental caries.[13, 80] This is attributed to the absence of the cleansing action of saliva, resulting in protein and amino acid retention and in an increase in the number of microorganisms[65] After eruption and throughout the life span of the teeth, fluoride from saliva is taken up by the enamel surface, as shown by the observation that the fluoride content of the enamel surface of erupted teeth increases with age in individuals drinking water containing fluoride.[4] This is associated with a decrease in the incidence of dental caries. In experimental animals, diets high in phosphate cause a reduction in the incidence of dental caries. This reduction has been attributed to a decrease in the carbonate content of teeth, rendering them more resistant to acid attack. It is very likely that this alteration of tooth composition is brought about not only during tooth formation by the increased phosphate in the blood serum but also after eruption by the increased phosphate in the saliva acting on the enamel surface.[75] Finally, Fanning and his associates[15] observed that desalivation of rats at 21 days of age resulted in a much higher incidence of dental caries than desalivation at 61 days of age. These observations suggest that there is a decrease in caries susceptibility with advancing posteruptive age of teeth and that the normal flow of saliva has a critical effect on this increasing resistance of the teeth to dental caries. The nature of the salivary factor that contributes to this effect remains unknown.

Periodontal disease. Saliva may affect calculus formation and the oral microorganisms contributing to periodontal disease. However, there is no specific, well-documented information on the role of salivary factors on the microbes contributing to periodontal disease. There is a need for well-controlled experiments in this area.

Dental calculus is an important local factor in the etiology of periodontal disease. All elements found in calculus are also contained in saliva. Calculus formation begins with the formation of a bacterial mucinous plaque that later becomes calcified. There is very little information on the conditions controlling the formation of this plaque. It is reasonable to assume that the nature of the salivary proteins and mucoproteins and the pH and ionic strength of saliva may be of significance in the precipitation of these substances on the tooth surface. The calcification of this plaque is in part controlled by changes in the physiochemical properties of saliva. Changes in the salivary proteins and protein-carbohydrate complexes, which help maintain the supersaturated state of saliva with respect to calcium,[59] or a decrease in salivary pH, which usually results from the loss of carbon dioxide from saliva,[21, 31] will cause precipitation of calcium salts. There is also evidence to suggest that the nature of the carbohydrate-protein components of the bacterial plaque may play an important role in the calcification process, since it was observed that with the onset of calcification there were changes in the histochemical reactivity of these components of the plaque similar to those associated with calcification in other areas of the body.[35, 37] It is possible that the protein carbohydrate components of the plaque may chelate calcium and that this compound may act as a nucleus for the crystallization of hydroxyapatite. This possibility is strengthened by the observation that bovine submandibular mucoid has a specific action in binding calcium.[32] It is thus obvious that further studies on the nature of the salivary proteins and protein carbohydrate complexes and on the regulation of the carbon dioxide tension in saliva will help to a better understanding of calculus formation and possibly in finding methods for its prevention.

References

1. Babkin, B. P.: Secretion Mechanism of the Digestive Glands, New York 1950, Paul B. Hoeber, Inc.

2. Bowen, R. H.: On a Possible Relation Between the Golgi Apparatus and Secretory Products, Am. J. Anat. **33**: 197, 1924.
3. Braus, H.: Anatomie des Menschen, vol. 2, ed. 2, Berlin, 1934, Julius Springer.
4. Brudevold, F.: Inorganic and Organic Components of Tooth Structure, Ann. New York Acad. Sc. **85**: 110, 1960.
5. Brusilow, S. W., and Cooke, R. E.: Role of Parotid Ducts in Secretion of Hypotonic Saliva, Am. J. Physiol. **196**: 831, 1959.
6. Burgen, A. S. V., and Seeman, P.: The Role of the Salivary Duct System in the Formation of the Saliva, Canad. J. Biochem. Physiol. **36**: 119, 1958.
7. Burstone, M. S.: Esterase of the Salivary Glands, J. Histochem. & Cytochem. **4**: 130, 1956.
8. Carmalts, C.: Contribution to the Anatomy of the Adult Human Salivary Glands. In Studies in Cancer and Allied Subjects, vol. 4, New York, 1913, Columbia University Press.
9. Caspersson, T.: Cell Growth and Cell Function, New York, 1950, W. W. Norton Co., Inc.
10. Caspersson, T., Landstrom-Hyden, H., and Aquilonius, L.: Cytoplasma-nucleotide in Eiweissproduzierenden Drusenzellen, Chromosoma **2**: 111, 1941.
11. Chauncey, H. H., Lionetti, F., Winer, R. A., and Lisanti, V. F.: Enzymes of Human Saliva. I. The Determination, Distribution and Origin of Whole Saliva Enzymes, J. D. Res. **33**: 321, 1954.
12. Chauncey, H. H., and Quintarelli, G.: Histochemical Localization of Hydrolytic Enzymes in Human Salivary Glands, J. D. Res. **38**: 961, 1959.
13. Cheyne, V. D.: Effect of Salivary Gland Extirpation Upon Experimental Dental Caries in the Rat, Proc. Soc. Exper. Biol. & Med. **18**: 587, 1939.
14. Elmer, A. W.: Iodine Metabolism and Thyroid Function, London, 1938, Oxford University Press.
15. Fanning, R. J., et al.: Salivary Contribution to Enamel Maturation and Caries Resistance, J. A. D. A. **49**: 668, 1954.
16. Fawcett, D. M., and Kirkwood, S.: Role of the Salivary Glands in Extrathyroidal Iodine Metabolism, Science **120**: 547, 1954.
17. Godding, J. R., and Denton, D. A.: Adrenal Cortex and the Parotid Secretion of Sodium-Depleted Sheep, Science **123**: 986, 1956.
18. Green, D. E.: Mitochondrial Structure and Function. In Hayashi, T. (editor): Subcellular Particles, New York, 1959, The Ronald Press Co., p. 84.
19. Heidenhain, R.: Beiträge zur Lehre von der Speichelsecretion, Studien Physiol. Inst. Breslau **4**: 1, 1868.
20. Henriques, B. L., and Chauncey, H. H.: Comparative Enzyme Concentrations of Submaxillary and Parotid Salivas, J. D. Res. **38**: 733, 1959. (Abst.)
21. Hodge, H. C., and Leung, S. W.: Calculus Formation, J. Periodont. **21**: 211, 1950.
22. Hokin, L. E., and Hokin, M. R.: The Ribonucleic Acid Content of Pancreas and Parotid Glands During Enzyme Synthesis and Secretion in Vitro, Biochim. et. biophys. acta **13**: 236, 1954.
23. Holzlohner, E., and Niessing, C.: Ueber Kapillardrosselung bei vermehrter Organdurchblutung, Ztschr. f. Biol. **97**: 108, 1936.
24. Ito, Y.: Parotin: A Salivary Gland Hormone, Ann. New York Acad. Sc. **85**: 228, 1960.
25. Junqueira, L. C. U.: Cytological, Cytochemical and Biochemical Observations on Secreting and Resting Salivary Glands, Exper. Cell Res. **2**: 327, 1951.
26. Junqueira, L. C. U., and Hirsch, G. C.: Cell Secretion: A Study of Pancreas and Salivary Glands, Internat. Rev. Cytol. **5**: 323, 1956.
27. Kowalewsky, N.: Ueber das Blutgefäss-system der Speicheldrusen, Arch. Anat. & Physiol., p. 385, 1885.
28. Lacassagne, A.: Dimorphism sexuel de la glande sous-maxillaire chez la souris, Compt. rend. Soc. de biol. **133**: 180, 1940.
29. Langley, J. N.: On the Changes of Serous Cells During Secretion, J. Physiol. **2**: 261, 1879-1880.
30. Langley, J. N.: On the Histology of the Mucous Salivary Glands and on the Behavior of Their Mucous Constituents, J. Physiol. **10**: 433, 1889.
31. Leung, S. W.: Calculus Formation; Salivary Factors, Dental Clinics of North America, Philadelphia, November, 1960, W. B. Saunders Co.
32. Leung, S. W., and Draus, F. J.: Effect of Bovine Submaxillary Mucoid on Ultrafiltration of Calcium, preprinted Abstracts, Thirty-Ninth General Meeting of the International Association for Dental Research, March, 1961.

33. Levi-Montalcini, R., and Cohen, S.: Effects of the Extract of the Mouse Submaxillary Salivary Glands on the Sympathetic System of Mammals, Ann. New York Acad. Sc. **85:** 324, 1960.

34. Logothetopoulos, J. H., and Myant, N. B.: Concentration of Radio-Iodide and ^{35}S-Thiocyanate by the Salivary Glands, J. Physiol. **134:** 189, 1956.

35. Mandel, I. D.: Calculus Formation; the Role of Bacteria and Mucoprotein, Dental Clinics of North America, Philadelphia, November, 1960, W. B. Saunders Co.

36. Mandel, I. D., and Ellison, S. A.: Characterization of Salivary Components Separated by Paper Electrophoresis, Arch. Oral Biol. **3:** 77, 1961.

37. Mandel, I., et al.: Histochemistry of Calculus Formation, J. Periodont. **28:** 132, 1957.

38. Maximow, A. A., and Bloom, W.: A Textbook of Histology, Philadelphia, 1942, W. B. Saunders Co.

39. Myant, N. B.: Iodine Metabolism of Salivary Glands, Ann. New York Acad. Sc. **85:** 208, 1960.

40. Nassonov, D.: Das Golgische Binnennetz und seine Beziehungen zu der Sekretion, Arch. f. mikr. Anat. **100:** 433, 1924.

41. Nisizawa, K., and Pigman, W.: Purification of a Glycoprotein From Bovine Submaxillary Glands, Biochem. J. **75:** 293, 1960.

42. Noback, C. R., and Montagna, W.: Histochemical Studies of the Basophilia, Lipase and Phosphatases in the Mammalian Pancreas and Salivary Glands, Am. J. Anat. **81:** 343, 1947.

43. Ogata, T.: Internal Secretions of the Salivary Glands, Transactions Ninth Congress of Far East, Association of Tropical Medicine **2:** 709, 1935.

44. Orban, B., and Weinmann, J. P.: Cellular Elements of Saliva and Their Possible Role in Caries, J. A. D. A. **26:** 2008, 1939.

45. Palade, G. E.: Intracisternal Granules in the Exocrine Cells of the Pancreas, J. Biophys. & Biochem. Cytol. **2:** 417, 1956.

46. Palade, G. E.: Functional Changes in the Structure of Cell Components. In Hayashi, T. (editor): Subcellular Particles, New York, 1959, The Ronald Press Co., p. 64.

47. Palade, G. E., and Porter, K. R.: Studies on the Endoplasmic Reticulum. I. Its Identification in Situ, J. Exper. Med. **100:** 641, 1954.

48. Palade, G. E., and Siekevitz, P.: Pancreatic Microsomes, J. Biophys. & Biochem. Cytol. **2:** 671, 1956.

49. Palay, S. L.: The Morphology of Secretion. Frontiers of Cytology, New Haven, 1958, Yale University Press, pp. 305-336.

50. Parks, H. F.: On the Fine Structure of the Parotid Gland of the Mouse and Rat, Am. J. Anat. **108:** 303, 1961.

51. Parks, H. F., and Johansen, E.: Electronmicroscopic Study of Secretion of Parotid Gland in Mice and Rats, J. D. Res. **39:** 720, 1960. (Abst.)

52. Parks, H. F., and Johansen, E.: The Golgi Apparatus of Parotid Acinous Cells of the Mouse, preprinted Abstracts, International Association for Dental Research, Thirty-Ninth General Meeting, March, 1961, p. 8.

53. Patton, J. R., and Pigman, W.: Amylase in Electrophoretic and Ultracentrifugal Patterns of Human Parotid Saliva, Science **125:** 1292, 1957.

54. Patton, J. R., and Pigman, W.: Electrophoretic and Ultracentrifugal Components of Human Salivary Secretions, J. Am. Chem. Soc. **81:** 3035, 1959.

55. Pease, D. C.: Infolded Basal Plasma Membranes Found in Epithelia Noted for Their Water Transport, J. Biophys. & Biochem. Cytol. (supp.) **2:** 203, 1956.

56. Pigman, W.: Some Recent Developments in the Composition and Physiology of Human Saliva, J. A. D. A. **54:** 469, 1957.

57. Pigman, W., and Reid, A. J.: The Organic Compounds and Enzymes of Human Saliva, J. A. D. A. **45:** 325, 1952.

58. Pigman, W., and Tsuiki, S.: The Nature of Epithelial Mucins, Internat. D. J. **9:** 502, 1959.

59. Prinz, H.: The Origin of Salivary Calculus, D. Cosmos **63:** 231, 269, 503, 619, 1921.

60. Quintarelli, G., and Chauncey, H. H.: Metachromatic Reactivity of Mammalian Salivary Glands, Arch. Oral Biol. **2:** 162, 1960.

61. Quintarelli, G., et al.: Histochemical Studies of Bovine Salivary Gland Mucins, Biochem. & Biophys. Res. Com. **2:** 423, 1960.

62. Rabinowitch, M., et al.: Nucleic Acid Phosphorus in Submaxillary Glands of Mice After Duct Ligation, J. Biol. Chem. **194:** 835, 1952.

63. Regaud, C., and Mawas, J.: Sur les mitochondries des glandes salivaires chez les mammiferes, Compt. rend. de Soc. biol. **66:** 97, 1909.
64. Schneider, R. M., and Person, P.: Aerobic Oxidative Metabolism of Salivary Glands, Ann. New York Acad. Sc. **85:** 201, 1960.
65. Schwartz, A., and Weisberger, D.: Salivary Factors in Experimental Animal Caries. In Sognnaes, R. F. (editor): Advances in Experimental Caries Research, Washington, D. C., 1955, American Association for the Advancement of Science.
66. Scott, B. L., and Pease, D. C.: Electronmicroscopy of the Salivary and Lacrimal Glands of the Rat, Am. J. Anat. **104:** 115, 1959.
67. Shafer, W. G., and Muhler, J. C.: Endocrine Influences Upon the Salivary Glands, Ann. New York Acad. Sc. **85:** 215, 1960.
68. Sicher, H.: Oral Anatomy, St. Louis, 1960, The C. V. Mosby Co.
69. Sicher, H., and Tandler, J.: Anatomie für Zahnärzte, Berlin, 1928, Julius Springer.
70. Siekevitz, P., and Palade, G. E.: A Cytochemical Study of the Pancreas of the Guinea Pig. I. Isolation and Enzymatic Actvities of Cell Fractions, J. Biophys. & Biochem. Cytol. **4:** 203, 1958.
71. Siekevitz, P., and Palade, G. E.: A Cytochemical Study of the Pancreas of the Guinea Pig. III. In Vitro Incorporation of Leucine-l-C^{14} Into the Proteins of Cell Fractions, J. Biophys. & Biochem. Cytol. **4:** 557, 1958.
72. Simmons, N. S.: Studies on the Defense Mechanisms of the Mucous Membranes With Particular Reference to the Oral Cavity, Oral Surg., Oral Med., & Oral Path. **5:** 513, 1952.
73. Sjostrand, F. S., and Hanzon, V.: Membrane Structures of Cytoplasm and Mitochondria in Exocrine Cells of Mouse Pancreas as Revealed by High Resolution Electron Microscopy, Exper. Cell Res. **7:** 393, 1954.
74. Sjostrand, F. S., and Hanzon, V.: Ultrastructure of Golgi Apparatus of Exocrine Cells of Mouse Pancreas, Exper. Cell Res. **7:** 415, 1954.
75. Sobel, A. E.: Interrelationship of Tooth Composition, Body Fluids, Diet, and Caries Susceptibility, School of Aviation Medicine, Brooks Air Force Base (Texas), Report 60-50, August, 1960.
76. Spicer, S. S., and Warren, L.: The Histochemistry of Sialic Acid Containing Mucoproteins, J. Histochem. & Cytochem. **8:** 135, 1960.
77. Stormont, D. L.: The Salivary Glands. In Cowdry, E. V. (editor): Special Cytology, New York, 1932, Paul B. Hoeber, Inc., vol. 1, pp. 153-196.
78. Taurog, A., et al.: The Effect of Hypophysectomy and of TSH on the Mouse Submaxillary Iodine Pump, Endocrinology **64:** 1038, 1959.
79. Thaysen, J. H., et al.: Excretion of Sodium, Potassium, Chloride and Carbon Dioxide in Human Parotid Saliva, Am. J. Physiol. **178:** 155, 1954.
80. Trimble, H. C., et al.: Rate of Secretion and Incidence of Dental Caries, J. D. Res. **17:** 299, 1938.
81. Tsuiki, S., and Pigman, W.: The Mucin of Bovine Sublingual Glands, Arch. Oral Biol. **2:** 1, 1960.
82. Weinstein, E., et al.: An Improved Technique for the Paper Electrophoresis of Parotid Saliva, J. D. Res. **39:** 110, 1960.
83. Zimmermann, K. W.: Die Speicheldrüsen der Mundhöhle und die Bauchspeicheldrüse. In von Möllendorff, W. (editor): Handbuch der mikroskopischen Anatomie des Menschen, vol. 5, pt. 1, Berlin, 1927, Julius Springer.

Chapter XI • ERUPTION OF THE TEETH*

INTRODUCTION

The human teeth develop in the jaws and do not enter the oral cavity until the crown has matured. In the past the term eruption was generally applied only to the appearance of the teeth in the oral cavity. It is, however, known that the movements of the teeth do not cease when the teeth meet their antagonists.[6, 7] Movements of eruption begin at the time of root formation and continue throughout the life span of a tooth. The emergence through the gingiva is merely an incident in the process of eruption. The eruption of deciduous as well as of permanent teeth can be divided into a prefunctional and a functional phase. At the end of the prefunctional phase the teeth come into occlusion. In the functional phase the teeth continue to move to maintain a proper relation to the jaw and to each other.

Eruption is preceded by a period in which the developing and growing teeth move to adjust their position in the growing jaw.[3] A knowledge of the movements of the teeth during this pre-eruptive phase is necessary for a complete understanding of eruption. Thus, the movements of the teeth can be divided into the following phases: (1) pre-eruptive phase, (2) prefunctional eruptive phase, and (3) functional eruptive phase.

During these phases the teeth move in different directions.[20] These movements can be termed: (1) axial—occlusal movement in the direction of the long axis of the tooth; (2) drifting—bodily movement in a distal, mesial, lingual, or buccal direction; (3) tilting or tipping—movement around a tranverse axis; (4) rotating—movement around a longitudinal axis.

HISTOLOGY OF ERUPTION

Pre-eruptive phase. During the pre-eruptive phase the dental organ develops to its full size, and formation of the hard substances of the crown takes place. At this time the tooth germs are surrounded by the loose connective tissue of the dental sac and by the bone of the dental crypt.

---

*First draft submitted by Joseph P. Weinmann.

The development of the teeth and the growth of the jaw are simultaneous and interdependent processes. The microscopic picture of the growing jaw indicates that extensive growth takes place in that area of the jaws where the alveolar process will develop (Fig. 231). The tooth germs maintain their relation to the growing alveolar margin by moving occlusally and buccally.[1]

Two processes are responsible for the developing teeth attaining and maintaining their position in the growing jaw: bodily movement and excentric growth. *Bodily movement* is characterized by a shift of the entire tooth germ. It is recognized by apposition of bone behind the moving tooth and by resorption of bone in front of it. In *excentric growth* one part of the tooth germ remains stationary. Excentric growth leads to a shift of the center of the tooth germ. It is characterized by resorption of the bone at the surface toward which the tooth germ grows; no apposition takes place on the bony surfaces from which the tooth germ seems to move.

When the deciduous teeth develop and grow, upper and lower jaws grow in

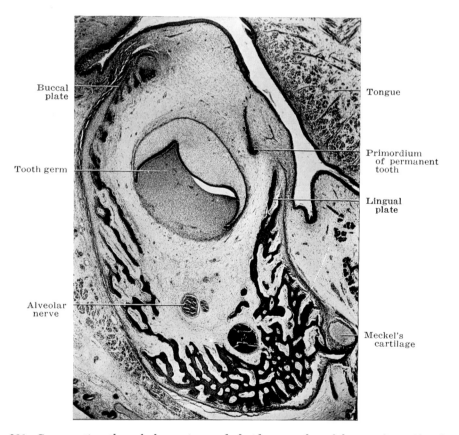

Fig. 231. Cross section through lower jaw and deciduous molar of human fetus (fourth month). Tooth germ moves buccally by excentric growth indicated by resorption at inner surface of buccal plate and lack of apposition at inner surface of lingual plate.

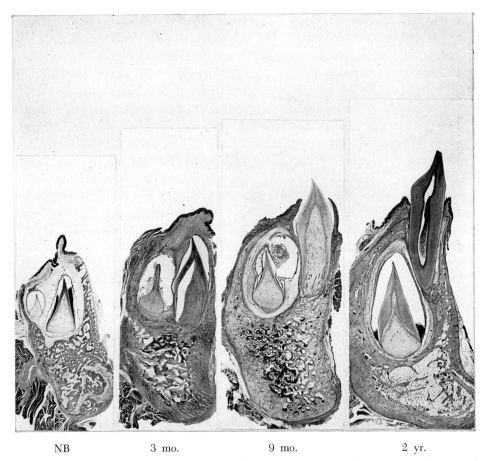

NB   3 mo.   9 mo.   2 yr.

Fig. 232. Buccolingual sections through deciduous and permanent lower central incisors of seven consecutive stages, from birth to 9 years of age.

length in the midline and at their posterior ends. Accordingly, the growing germs of the deciduous teeth shift in vestibular direction; at the same time the anterior teeth move mesially, the posterior teeth move distally, into the expanding alveolar arches.[19] These movements of the deciduous teeth are partly bodily movements, partly shifts by excentric growth. The deciduous tooth germ grows in length at about the same rate as the jaws grow in height. The deciduous teeth maintain, therefore, their superficial position throughout the pre-eruptive phase.

The permanent teeth that have temporary predecessors undergo an intricate movement before they reach the position from which they emerge. The permanent incisor (Fig. 232) and the canine develop at first lingual to the deciduous tooth germ at the level of its occlusal surface.[14] At the close of the pre-eruptive phase they are found lingual to the apical region of their deciduous predecessors. The permanent premolars (Fig. 233) begin their development lingual to, and at the level of, the occlusal plane of the deciduous molars.[13] Later, they are found

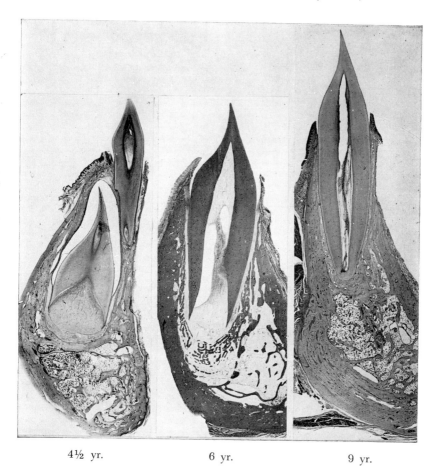

4½ yr.   6 yr.   9 yr.

Fig. 232 (cont'd). For legend see opposite page.

between the divergent roots and, at the end of the pre-eruptive phase, below the roots of the deciduous molars (see Chapter XII). The changes in axial relationship between deciduous and permanent teeth are due to the occlusal movement of the deciduous teeth and to the growth of the jaw in height. The germs of the premolars move by their buccally directed excentric growth into the interradicular space of the deciduous molars.

Prefunctional eruptive phase. The prefunctional phase of eruption begins with the formation of the root (Chapter II) and is completed when the teeth reach the occlusal plane. Until the tooth emerges into the oral cavity, its crown is covered by the reduced dental epithelium. While the crown moves toward the surface, the connective tissue between the dental epithelium and the oral epithelium disappears, probably by a desmolytic action of the cells of the dental epithelium. When the edge or the cusps of the crown approach the oral mucosa, oral epithelium and reduced dental epithelium fuse. In the center of the area

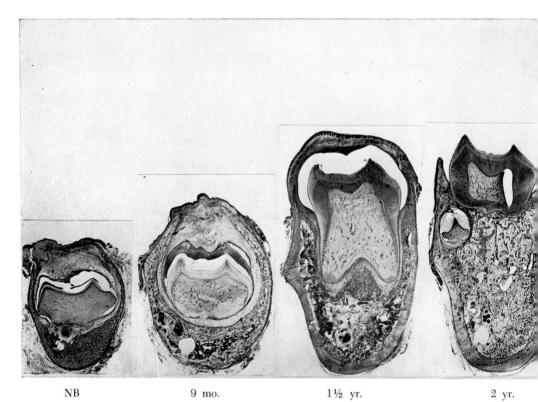

NB   9 mo.   1½ yr.   2 yr.

Fig. 233. Buccolingual sections through lower deciduous first molar and first permanent premolar of eight consecutive stages, from birth to 14 years.

of fusion the epithelium degenerates, and the incisal edge or the tip of a cusp emerges into the oral cavity. The gradual emergence of the crown is due to the occlusal movement of the tooth, active eruption, and also to the separation of the epithelium from the enamel, passive eruption. The reduced dental epithelium remains attached to that part of the crown which has not yet emerged (see Chapter IX, section on Dentogingival Junction). The growth of the root or roots of a tooth is initiated by simultaneous and correlated proliferation of Hertwig's epithelial root sheath and the connective tissue of the dental papilla. The proliferation of the epithelium takes place by mitotic division of the cells of the epithelial diaphragm. The proliferation of the connective tissue cells of the pulp is concentrated in the area above the diaphragm.

During the prefunctional phase of eruption, the primitive periodontal ligament, derived from the dental sac, is adapted to the relatively rapid movement of the teeth. Three layers of the periodontal ligament can be distinguished around the surface of the developing root: (1) adjacent to the surface of the root, dental fibers; (2) attached to the primitive alveolus, alveolar fibers; and (3) the intermediate plexus (Fig. 140). The intermediate plexus consists mainly of argyrophil fibers, whereas the alveolar and the dental fibers are mainly mature collagenous

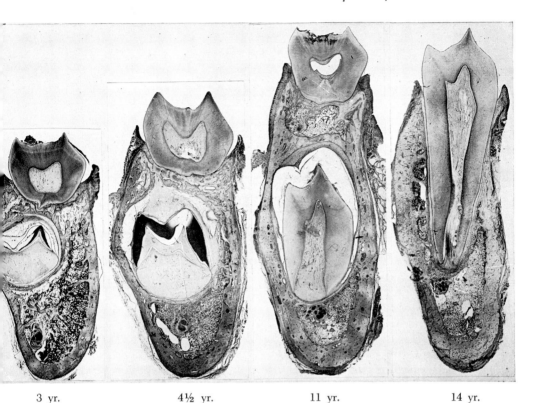

3 yr.   4½ yr.   11 yr.   14 yr.

Fig. 233 (cont'd). For legend see opposite page.

fibers. They can be traced into the intermediate plexus for a short distance. The intermediate plexus permits continuous readjustment of the periodontal ligament during the phase of rapid eruption.[16, 20]

In the region of the fundus, the dental sac differentiates into two layers: one, close to the bone, consists of loose connective tissue; the other, adjacent to the growing end of the tooth, consists of a network of rather thick fibers. These fibers are attached to the bone, curve as a strong ligament around the edge of the root and then divide into a network whose spaces are filled with fluid. This structure is designated as hammock or cushioned hammock ligament.[21] (Fig. 234.)

In the prefunctional phase of eruption the alveolar ridge of the jaws grows rapidly. To emerge from the growing jaws the primary teeth must move more rapidly than the ridge increases in height. Growth of the root is not always sufficient to meet these requirements. A rapid growth of bone begins at the alveolar fundus, where it is laid down in trabeculae parallel to the surface of the alveolar fundus[12] (Fig. 235). The number of trabeculae increases markedly during the prefunctional phase and varies in different teeth. The smallest number of trabeculae is found at the fundus of the molars. This variance in the number of

Dentin

Pulp

Proliferation
zone of pulp

Epithelial
diaphragm

Cushioned
hammock
ligament

Fig. 234. Cushioned hammock ligament. Root end of an erupting permanent lower canine. Proliferation zone of the pulp above the epithelial diaphragm. Note the numerous tissue spaces in the ligament. (From Sicher, H.: J. D. Res. 21: 201, 1942.)

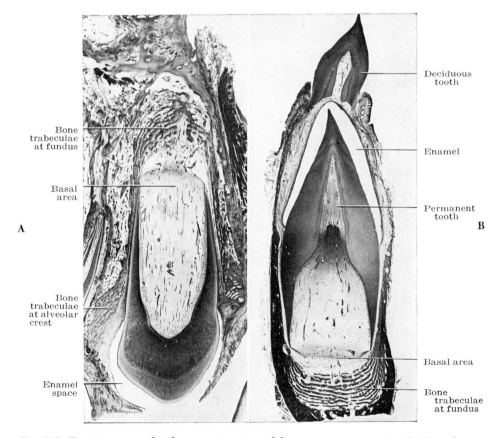

Bone
trabeculae
at fundus

Basal
area

A

Bone
trabeculae
at alveolar
crest

Enamel
space

Deciduous
tooth

Enamel

Permanent
tooth

B

Basal area

Bone
trabeculae
at fundus

Fig. 235. Erupting upper deciduous canine, A, and lower permanent canine, B. Note formation of numerous parallel bone trabeculae at alveolar fundus. Formation of bone trabeculae at the alveolar crest of deciduous canine, A, is a sign of rapid growth of the maxilla in height. (From Kronfeld, R.: D. Cosmos 74: 103, 1932.)

trabeculae seems to depend upon the distance that the teeth have to travel during this phase of tooth eruption.

The germs of most permanent teeth develop in a crowded position. They occupy, therefore, a position that differs markedly from their ultimate position after emergence. The molars are tilted; the occlusal surfaces of the upper molars, which develop in the maxillary tuberosity, are directed distally and downward. The occlusal surfaces of the lower molars, which develop in the base of the mandibular ramus, are directed mesially and upward. The long axis of the upper canines deviates mesially. The lower incisors are frequently rotated around their long axes. In the later stages of the prefunctional phase of eruption, these teeth undergo intricate movements to rectify their primary position. During these tilting or tipping and rotating movements, bone growth takes place in those areas

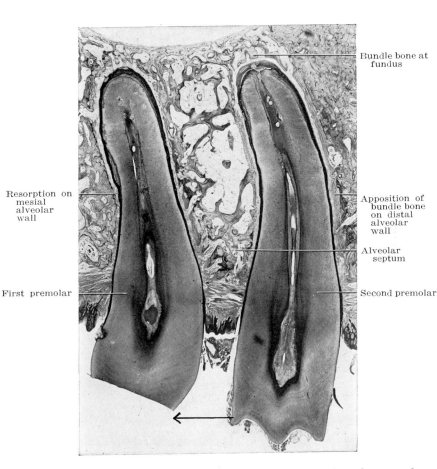

Fig. 236. Mesial drift and vertical eruption. Mesiodistal section through upper first and second premolars. Arrow indicates direction of drifting movement. Apposition of bundle bone at the distal surfaces, resorption of bone on the mesial surfaces of the alveoli. Apposition of bundle bone at the fundus and alveolar crest. (From Weinmann, J. P.: Angle Orthodontist **11:** 83, 1941.)

of the dental crypt from which the tooth moves; resorption occurs in the areas toward which the tooth moves. In all other details, the histologic changes correlated to eruption are identical in permanent and in deciduous teeth.

The histologic findings in erupting multirooted teeth present in later stages a characteristic picture. Bone growth occurs not only at the fundus of the socket but is also evident at the crest of the interradicular septum. The cementum in the bifurcation also shows signs of intensified growth.

Functional eruptive phase. For a long time it was believed that functioning teeth do not continue to erupt. However, clinical observations and histologic findings show unequivocally that the teeth continue to move throughout their life. The movements are in an occlusal as well as in a mesial direction.

Clinically, the continued active movement of teeth can be proved by an analysis of the so-called shortened and submerged teeth (see Chapter XII). Histologically, the changes in the alveolar bone furnish the evidence for the movements of the teeth during the functional period (Fig. 238) (see Chapter VIII).

During the period of growth, the occlusal movement of the teeth is fairly rapid. The bodies of the jaws grow in height almost exclusively at the alveolar crests, and the teeth have to move occlusally as fast as the jaws grow, in order to maintain their functional position. The eruptive movement in this period is masked by the simultaneous growth of the jaws.

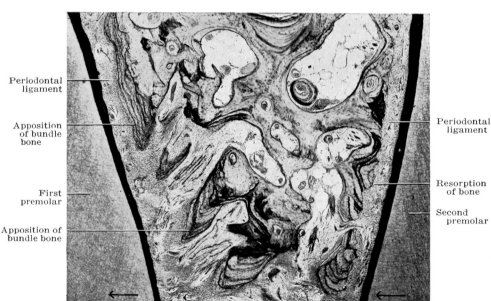

Fig. 237. Higher magnification of crest of interdental septum between first and second upper premolars of Fig. 236. Arrows indicate direction of movement. Apposition of bundle bone on surface of septum facing the first premolar and at alveolar crest, resorption of bone on surface of septum facing the second premolar. (From Weinmann, J. P.: Angle Orthodontist **11:** 83, 1941.)

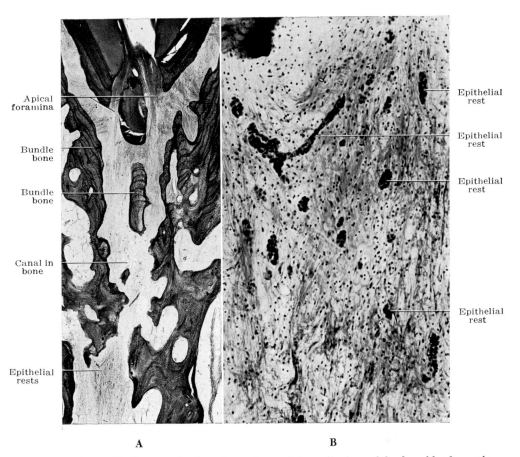

Fig. 238. A, Bundle bone at fundus of alveolus and in wall of canal leading blood vessels and nerves to apical foramina. Epithelial rests some distance from apex along blood vessels and nerves. B, High magnification of epithelial rests of A.

The continued vertical eruption also compensates for occlusal or incisal attrition. Only in this way can the occlusal plane and the distance between the jaws during mastication be maintained and a closing of the bite be prevented—conditions that are essential for the normal function of the masticatory muscles.

The masticatory or functional movements of the individual teeth lead to increasing wear at the contact areas. Sharp contact of the teeth is maintained despite the loss of substance at the contact surfaces by a continuous movement of the teeth toward the midline. This movement is termed physiologic mesial drift (Fig. 236).

Appositional growth of cementum continues along the entire surface of the root, but growth of bone is restricted principally to the fundus, alveolar crest, and distal wall of the socket (Fig. 237). The mesial wall of the socket shows resorption in wide areas. However, zones of reparative bone apposition can always be found on the mesial wall of the alveolus.

MECHANISM OF ERUPTION

The eruptive movements of a tooth are the effect of differential growth. One speaks of differential growth if two topographically related organs, or parts of an organ, grow at different rates of speed. Changes in the spatial relations of such organs, or of the parts of an organ, are the inevitable consequence of differential growth. The ontogenesis of almost any organ and of the whole embryo proves that differential growth is one of the most important factors of morphogenesis. In the jaws, it is the differential growth between tooth and bone that leads to the movement of a tooth.

The most obvious eruptive force is generated by the longitudinal growth of the dental pulp in the growing root. However, the different movements of an erupting tooth cannot be explained by the growth of its root alone. Some teeth, even while their roots develop, travel a distance that is longer than the fully developed root. An additional factor must account for the increased distance. Most teeth move during eruption also by tilting, rotating, drifting movements; the growth of the root can account only for the axial or vertical movement; other movements are caused by the growth of bone in the neighborhood of the tooth germ.

It is also a fact that the teeth move extensively after dentinal length of their roots has been fully established. The continued growth of the cementum covering the root and growth of the surrounding bone cause the movements of the tooth in this period.

Before the development of the root starts, the outer and the inner dental epithelia continue from the region of the future cementoenamel junction as a double epithelial layer, the epithelial diaphragm, which is bent into the roughly horizontal plane of the dental base. It forms a definite boundary between the coronal pulp of the tooth germ and the connective tissue between tooth germ and bony crypt. Thus, growth of the root is possible only by active proliferation of the pulpal tissue.

The growth of the pulpal tissue causes a slight increase of pressure in the confined space of the dental crypt. Resorption of bone at the fundus of the crypt is prevented by the suspension of the tooth germ by the hammock ligament, much in the same way as resorption of bone under masticatory forces is prevented by suspension of the functioning tooth by the periodontal ligament. It is important to realize that the rise in pressure within the crypt is the stimulus for the initiation of tissue changes that will reduce the pressure. Thus, pressure does not build up but acts in a wavelike fashion, rhythmically rising and falling. Because of its suspensory function, the hammock ligament is the fixed base or plane from which the tooth moves toward the oral surface.

Since the growth of the root alone cannot move a crown as far as is necessary to reach the occlusal plane, its vertical erupting movement is aided by growth of bone at the bottom of the crypt, lifting the growing tooth, with the hammock ligament, toward the surface. The growth of bone, preceded by a proliferation of the odontogenic connective tissue at the bottom of the crypt, occurs in different teeth at a different rate of speed. Where growth of bone is slow, new layers of bone are laid down upon the old bone, and a more or less compact bone results. Where growth of bone is rapid, spongy bone is formed in the shape of a framework of trabeculae (Fig. 235).

While the hammock ligament and the tooth are lifted toward the surface, the anchoring fibers of the hammock ligament have to be continually reconstructed. In other words, the hammock ligament has to shift its anchoring plane toward the surface of the jaws. Details of the mechanism of this shift are as yet not known, but they are, in all probability, comparable to the adjustment of the periodontal ligament during the functional phase of tooth eruption.

Enlargement of the root does not cease when its dentinal part is fully formed. By continual apposition of cementum, the root grows slightly in its transverse diameters and more rapidly in length. Cementum growth is not only increased in the apical area of roots but also at the furcation of multirooted teeth. Simultaneously, there is continuous growth of bone at the fundus of the socket and at the crests of the alveolar process. The bone apposition at the fundus and at the free border of the alveolar process is very rapid in youth, slows down in the thirties, but normally never ceases. Apposition at the alveolar crest, however, is found only when the tissues at the dentogingival junction are entirely normal. The frequency of inflammatory changes in this area accounts for the fact that this site of bone growth has been overlooked for a long time. There is also constant growth of bone on the distal wall of each socket, whereas the mesial wall shows resorption of bone alternating with reparative apposition.

Though the correlation of bone changes and movement of the teeth is self-evident, the question still must be raised whether the bone changes are primary and thus the cause of the movement of the teeth.

All available evidence points to the differential growth as the cause of the occlusomesial movements of the functioning teeth. Growth of cementum on the entire surface of the root, but intensified in apical and furcation areas, and growth of bone at the fundus and at the distal walls of the socket, as well as at the alveolar crests, are responsible for the movements of the tooth. Resorption at the mesial wall is secondary to the mesial component of the movement. The occlusal or vertical eruption and the mesial drift compensate for occlusal and contact wear and thus maintain the total integrity of the dentition.

During the occlusomesial movement of the functioning teeth, a continual rearrangement of the principal fibers of the periodontal ligament occurs in the intermediate plexus.

On the mesial surface, some principal fibers lose their attachment during the period of bone resorption and are then reattached or replaced by new fibers, which are anchored in the bone apposed during the periods of repair. Bone resorption does not occur at the same time on the entire extent of the mesial alveolar surface. Instead, at any given moment, areas of resorption alternate with areas of reparative apposition. Resorption occurs in restricted areas in one period and reconstruction occurs in the same areas, while the tooth, minutely tilting or rotating, causes resorption in another area. Only this can account for the fact that the functional integrity of the tooth is maintained in spite of its continued movements.

CLINICAL CONSIDERATIONS

The eruption of teeth is a part of general development and growth, and therefore the progress of tooth eruption may serve as an indicator of the physical condition of a growing individual. The time of emergence of a tooth is readily observed by clinical examination. Considerable work has been done in compiling data regarding this particular stage of eruption. Table 6 illustrates that the time of emergence of all teeth varies widely.[2, 5, 13] Only those cases that are not within the range of variation may be considered abnormal. Retarded eruption is by far more frequent than accelerated eruption, and it may have a local or a systemic cause.

Local causes, such as premature loss of deciduous teeth and closure of the space by a shift of the neighboring teeth, may retard the eruption of a permanent tooth. Severe acute trauma may result in an arrest of active tooth eruption during the functional phase if the periodontal ligament of the tooth has been injured. Resorption of the root may ensue, in which event deposition of bone in the spaces opened by resorption may lead to an ankylosis by fusion of alveolar bone and root.[6, 30] The movement of such a tooth is then arrested, while the other teeth continue to erupt. If this disturbance takes place in the permanent dentition, a so-called shortened tooth results. An ankylosed deciduous tooth may eventually be covered by the rapidly growing alveolar bone. Such teeth are called submerged teeth (see Chapter XII).

Generalized retardation of eruption can be caused by nutritional deficiencies, e.g., vitamin D deficiency, or by endocrine disturbances, e.g., hypopituitarism or hypothyroidism. In the latter cases one deals with a retardation of somatic growth. Since tooth eruption is but one facet of growth, delayed eruption under these conditions is to be expected.

The eruption of deciduous teeth is often preceded and accompanied by pain, slight fever, and general malaise. These symptoms cannot be considered as the consequence of a physiologic process but rather as accidents during this process. When a tooth is about to emerge into the oral cavity, pressure upon the covering tissue against sharp edges or cusps may cause slight injuries. If part of the crown is already exposed, a secondary infection may occur. Since the movement of the tooth into the oral cavity is quite rapid, these symptoms soon disappear. This is in contrast to pericoronal infections around an erupting lower third molar. Although they are caused by similar injuries they lead to long-lasting discomfort because of the slow or even arrested eruption of this tooth.

The movements of the teeth during eruption are intricate and are accom-

Table 6. Chronology of the human dentition*

Tooth			Formation enamel matrix and dentin begins	Amount of enamel matrix formed at birth	Enamel completed	Emergence into oral cavity	Root completed
Primary dentition	Maxillary	Central incisor	4 mo. in utero	Five-sixths	1½ mo.	7½ mo.	1½ yr.
		Lateral incisor	4½ mo. in utero	Two-thirds	2½ mo.	9 mo.	2 yr.
		Canine	5 mo. in utero	One-third	9 mo.	18 mo.	3¼ yr.
		First molar	5 mo. in utero	Cusps united	6 mo.	14 mo.	2½ yr.
		Second molar	6 mo. in utero	Cusp tips still isolated	11 mo.	24 mo.	3 yr.
	Mandibular	Central incisor	4½ mo. in utero	Three-fifths	2½ mo.	6 mo.	1½ yr.
		Lateral incisor	4½ mo. in utero	Three-fifths	3 mo.	7 mo.	1½ yr.
		Canine	5 mo. in utero	One-third	9 mo.	16 mo.	3¼ yr.
		First molar	5 mo. in utero	Cusps united	5½ mo.	12 mo.	2¼ yr.
		Second molar	6 mo. in utero	Cusp tips still isolated	10 mo.	20 mo.	3 yr.
Permanent dentition	Maxillary	Central incisor	3 - 4 mo.	---	4 - 5 yr.	7- 8 yr.	10 yr.
		Lateral incisor	10 -12 mo.	---	4 - 5 yr.	8- 9 yr.	11 yr.
		Canine	4 - 5 mo.	---	6 - 7 yr.	11-12 yr.	13-15 yr.
		First premolar	1½- 1¾ yr.	---	5 - 6 yr.	10-11 yr.	12-13 yr.
		Second premolar	2 - 2¼ yr.	---	6 - 7 yr.	10-12 yr.	12-14 yr.
		First molar	At birth	Sometimes a trace	2½- 3 yr.	6- 7 yr.	9-10 yr.
		Second molar	2½- 3 yr.	---	7 - 8 yr.	12-13 yr.	14-16 yr.
		Third molar	7 - 9 yr.	---	12 -16 yr.	17-21 yr.	18-25 yr.
	Mandibular	Central incisor	3 - 4 mo.	---	4 - 5 yr.	6- 7 yr.	9 yr.
		Lateral incisor	3 - 4 mo.	---	4 - 5 yr.	7- 8 yr.	10 yr.
		Canine	4 - 5 mo.	---	6 - 7 yr.	9-10 yr.	12-14 yr.
		First premolar	1¾- 2 yr.	---	5 - 6 yr.	10-12 yr.	12-13 yr.
		Second premolar	2¼- 2½ yr.	---	6 - 7 yr.	11-12 yr.	13-14 yr.
		First molar	At birth	Sometimes a trace	2½- 3 yr.	6- 7 yr.	9-10 yr.
		Second molar	2½- 3 yr.	---	7 - 8 yr.	11-13 yr.	14-15 yr.
		Third molar	8 -10 yr.	---	12 -16 yr.	17-21 yr.	18-25 yr.

*From Logan, W. H. G., and Kronfeld, R.: Development of the Human Jaws and Surrounding Structures From Birth to the Age of Fifteen Years, J. A. D. A. **20:** 379, 1933; slightly modified by McCall and Schour.

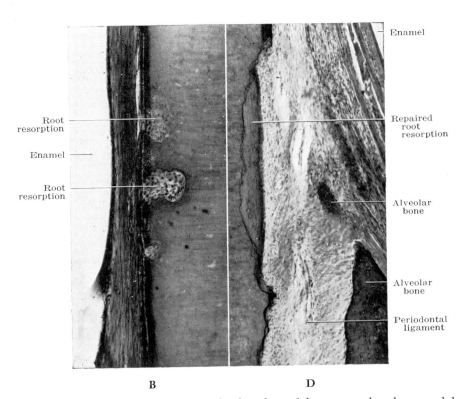

Enamel

Root resorption

Enamel

Root resorption

Repaired root resorption

Alveolar bone

Alveolar bone

Periodontal ligament

A   C

B   D

Fig. 239. Root resorption and repair on distal surface of lower second molar caused by pressure of erupting third molar. **A,** Relation of germ of third molar to second molar at the beginning of prefunctional phase of eruption. Note oblique position of crown of third molar. **B,** Area of contact between tooth germ of third molar and root of second molar in high magnification. Resorption reaching into dentin. **C,** Relation of lower second and third molars after third molar has attained its upright position. **D,** High magnification of alveolar crest. Resorption on distal root surface is partly repaired by apposition of cementum. (From Orban, B.: Arch. Clin. Path. 4: 187, 1940.)

plished by minute coordination of growth of the tooth, growth of the alveolar bone, and growth of the jaws. Any break in this correlation may affect the direction of the movements; this in turn may lead to an impaction or embedding of a tooth. At the time the third molars develop, the jaw has not reached its full length. Normally, the occlusal surface of a lower third molar turns anteriorly and upward. It is frequently prevented from straightening out because of a lack of correlation between growth in length of the lower jaw and tooth development. In such cases, the eruption of the lower third molar is arrested because its crown comes in contact with the roots of the second molar. If, at this time, the roots of the third molar are not as yet fully developed, they will grow into the bone and may become deformed. Canines, sometimes found in an oblique or horizontal position because of crowding of the teeth, may also fail to correct this position and remain embedded.

Erupting teeth may cause resorption on the roots of neighboring teeth.[16] This has been observed frequently on the lower second molars, due to the oblique position of the erupting third molar. (Fig. 239.) This tooth turns its occlusal surface mesially and upward and attains its upright position only in the later stages of eruption. Therefore, its crown comes into close relation to the distal surface of the distal root of the second molar and exerts pressure leading to resorption of cementum and dentin to a varying depth; it can be so extensive that the pulp may be exposed. When the pressure is relieved during the normal movement of the third molar, repair by apposition of cementum may follow. Such resorption was observed in about two-thirds of investigated jaws. A horizontal position of the lower third molar might lead to impaction. In such cases, the destruction on the root of the second molar may be severe.

Impacted or embedded upper third molars may cause similar resorption of the root of the second molar. Embedded upper canines may exert pressure on the root of the lateral incisor. During the time of eruption of teeth, the reduced or united dental epithelium may undergo changes which result in cyst formation. Such a cyst forms around the crown of the developing tooth and is known as a dentigerous cyst. Those which arise late may cause a noticeable swelling on the surface and are sometimes known as eruptive cysts, although they are simply a variation of dentigerous cysts.

References

1. Brash, J. C.: The Growth of the Alveolar Bone and Its Relation to the Movements of the Teeth, Including Eruption, Internat. J. Orthodont., Oral Surg. & Radiog. 14: 196, 283, 398, 487, 1928.
2. Brauer, J. C., and Bahador, M. A.: Variations in Calcification and Eruption of the Deciduous and Permanent Teeth, J. A. D. A. 29: 1373, 1942.
3. Brodie, A. G.: Present Status of Our Knowledge Concerning Movement of the Tooth Germ Through the Jaw, J. A. D. A. 24: 1830, 1934.
4. Brodie, A. G.: The Growth of Alveolar Bone and the Eruption of the Teeth, Oral Surg., Oral Med., & Oral Path. 1: 342, 1948.
5. Cattell, P.: The Eruption and Growth of the Permanent Teeth, J. D. Res. 8: 279, 1928.

6. Gottlieb, B.: Scheinbare Verkürzung eines oberen Schneidezahnes (So-called Shortening of an Upper Lateral Incisor), Ztschr. f. Stomatol. **22**: 501, 1924.
7. Gottlieb, B., Orban, B., and Diamond, M.: Biology and Pathology of the Tooth and Its Supporting Mechanism, New York, 1938, The Macmillan Co.
8. Gross, H.: Histologische Untersuchungen über das Wachstum der Kieferknochen beim Menschen (Histologic Investigations of the Growth of the Human Jaw Bone), Deutsche Zahnheilk. **89**: 1934.
9. Herzberg, F., and Schour, I.: Effects of the Removal of Pulp and Hertwig's Sheath on the Eruption of Incisors in the Albino Rat, J. D. Res. **20**: 264, 1941.
10. Hoffman, M. M.: Experimental Alterations in the Rate of Eruption of the Rat Incisor; Master's Thesis, University of Illinois Graduate School, 1939.
11. Hoffman, M. M., and Schour, I.: Quantitative Studies in the Development of the Rat Molar. II. Alveolar Bone, Cementum, and Eruption (From Birth to 500 Days), Am. J. Orthodont. & Oral Surg. **26**: 856, 1940.
12. Kronfeld, R.: The Resorption of the Roots of Deciduous Teeth, D. Cosmos **74**: 103, 1932.
13. Logan, W. H. G., and Kronfeld, R.: Development of the Human Jaws and Surrounding Structures From Birth to the Age of Fifteen Years, J. A. D. A. **20**: 379, 1933.
14. Logan, W. H. G.: A Histologic Study of the Anatomic Structures Forming the Oral Cavity, J. A. D. A. **22**: 3, 1935.
15. Massler, M., and Schour, I.: Studies in Tooth Development: Theories of Eruption, Am. J. Orthodont. & Oral Surg. **27**: 552, 1941.
16. Orban, B.: Growth and Movement of the Tooth Germs and Teeth, J. A. D. A. **15**: 1004, 1928.
17. Orban, B.: Resorption of Roots Due to Pressure From Erupting and Impacted Teeth, Arch. Clin. Path. **4**: 187, 1940.
18. Orban, B.: Epithelial Rests in the Teeth and Their Supporting Structures, Proc. Am. Assoc. D. Schools, 1928, p. 121.
19. Reichborn-Kjennerud: Ueber die Mechanik des Durchbruches der bleibenden Zähne beim Menschen (Mechanism of the Eruption of the Permanent Teeth in Man), Berlin, 1934, Hermann Meusser.
20. Sicher, H.: Tooth Eruption: The Axial Movement of Continuously Growing Teeth, J. D. Res. **21**: 201, 1942.
21. Sicher, H.: Tooth Eruption: The Axial Movement of Teeth With Limited Growth, J. D. Res. **21**: 395, 1942.
22. Sicher, H.: Oral Anatomy, ed. 2, St. Louis, 1952, The C. V. Mosby Co.
23. Sicher, H., and Weinmann, J. P.: Bone Growth and Physiologic Tooth Movement, Am. J. Orthodont. & Oral Surg. **30**: 109, 1944.
24. Stein, G., and Weinmann, J. P.: Die physiologische Wanderung der Zähne (The Physiologic Drift of the Teeth), Ztschr. f. Stomatol. **23**: 733, 1925.
25. Wasserfallen, P.: Movements of Dental Follicles in Human Fetal Mandible, Schweiz. Msch. f. Zhkde **64**: 551, 1954.
26. Wassermann, F.: Personal communication.
27. Weinmann, J. P.: Das Knochenbild bei Störungen der physiologischen Wanderung der Zähne (The Bone Picture in Cases of Disturbances of the Physiologic Movement of Teeth), Ztschr. f. Stomatol. **24**: 397, 1926.
28. Weinmann, J. P.: Bone Changes Related to Eruption of the Teeth, Angle Orthodontist **11**: 83, 1941.
29. Weinmann, J. P., and Sicher, H.: Correlation of Active and Passive Eruption, Bur **46**: 3, 1946.
30. Willman, W.: An Apparent Shortening of an Upper Incisor, J. A. D. A. **17**: 444, 1930.

Chapter XII • SHEDDING OF THE DECIDUOUS TEETH*

INTRODUCTION AND DEFINITION

Human teeth, as those of most mammals, develop in two generations known as the deciduous and the permanent dentitions. The deciduous teeth are adapted in their number, size, and pattern to the small jaw of the early years of life. The size of their roots and, therefore, the strength of the periodontal ligament are in accordance with the developmental stage of the masticatory muscles. They are replaced by the permanent teeth, which are larger, more numerous, and possess a stronger suspensory ligament. The physiologic elimination of deciduous teeth, prior to the replacement by their permanent successors, is called shedding.

PROCESS OF SHEDDING

The elimination of deciduous teeth is the result of the progressive resorption of their roots by osteoclasts. In this process both cementum and dentin are attacked. (Fig. 240.) The osteoclasts differentiate from the cells of the loose connective tissue in response to the pressure exerted by the growing and erupting permanent tooth germ. Resorption of a deciduous tooth can, however, occur in the absence of its successor. At first, pressure is directed against the bone separating the alveolus of the deciduous tooth and the crypt of its permanent successor; later it is directed against the root surface of the deciduous tooth itself. (Fig. 241.) Because of the position of the permanent tooth germ, the resorption of the roots of the deciduous incisors and canines starts at the lingual surface in the apical third (Fig. 242). The movement of the permanent germ at this time proceeds in an occlusal and vestibular direction. In later stages, the germ of the permanent tooth is frequently found directly apical to the deciduous tooth (Fig. 240, A). In such cases the resorption of the deciduous root proceeds in transverse planes, thus allowing the permanent tooth to erupt later in the position of the deciduous tooth. However, movement in a vestibular direction is frequently not complete when the crown of the permanent tooth emerges through the gingiva. In such cases, the permanent tooth appears lingual to its deciduous predecessor.

---

*First draft submitted by Myron S. Aisenberg.

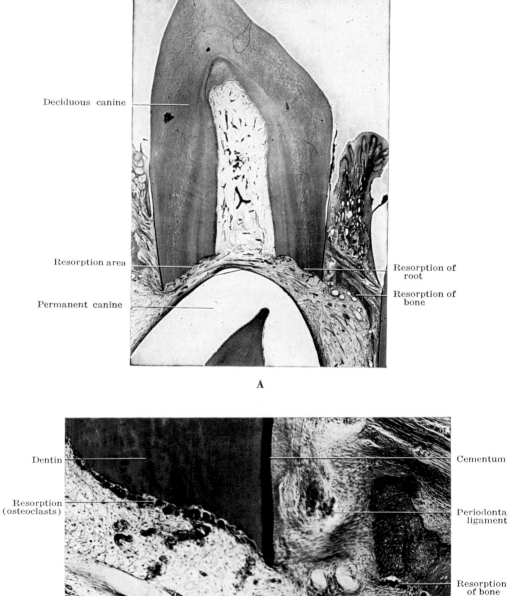

Fig. 240. Resorption of root of deciduous canine during eruption of permanent successor. A, General view. B, Lingual resorption area in higher magnification. (From Kronfeld, R.: D. Cosmos 74: 103, 1932.)

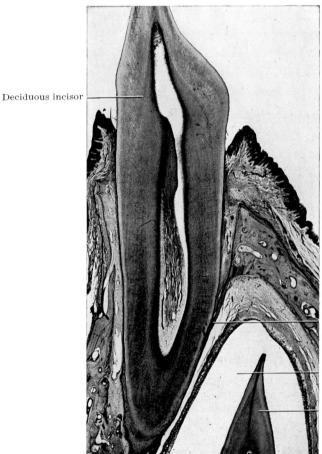

Deciduous incisor

Bone between deciduous tooth and successor

Enamel of permanent incisor

Dentin

Fig. 241. A thin lamella of bone separates permanent tooth germ from its predecessor.

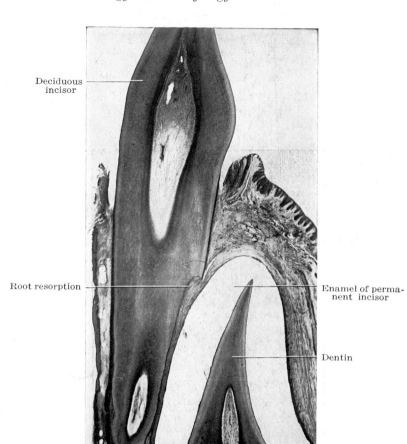

Deciduous
incisor

Root resorption

Enamel of perma-
nent incisor

Dentin

Fig. 242. Resorption of root of deciduous incisor due to pressure of erupting successor.

(Fig. 242.) In the first-described alternative, the deciduous tooth is lost before the permanent tooth erupts, whereas in the latter the permanent tooth may erupt while the deciduous tooth is still in its place.

Usually, resorption of the roots of the deciduous molars begins on the surfaces of the root facing the interradicular septum. This is due to the fact that the germs of the premolars are at first found between the roots of the deciduous molars. (Fig. 243.) Resorption of the roots can then be observed long before actual shedding. However, during their continued active eruption the deciduous teeth move away from the growing permanent tooth germs, which, for the most part, soon come to lie apical to the deciduous molars (Fig. 244). This change in position allows the growing premolar adequate space for its development. The areas of early resorption on the deciduous molar are then repaired by the apposition of new cementum, and the alveolar bone regenerates[7] (Fig. 245). In later stages, however, the erupting premolars again overtake the deciduous molars, and in most cases their roots are entirely resorbed (Fig. 246). The resorption may even proceed far up into the coronal dentin; occasionally some areas of the enamel may be destroyed. The premolars appear with the tips of their crowns in the place of the deciduous teeth.

Under normal conditions osteoclastic resorption is initiated by the pressure of the permanent tooth and leads to the elimination of the deciduous tooth. Two auxiliary factors have to be taken into consideration. They are as follows:

1. The weakening of the supporting tissues of the deciduous tooth because of resorption of parts of its roots and its continued active and passive eruption, which seems to be accelerated during the period of shedding. The epithelial attachment of the deciduous tooth grows down along the cementum at this time, causing the clinical crown of the tooth to be enlarged and the clinical root, to which the principal fibers are anchored, to be shortened.

2. The masticatory forces increase during this period as a result of the growth of the masticatory muscles, but they act upon a tooth, weakened by resorption

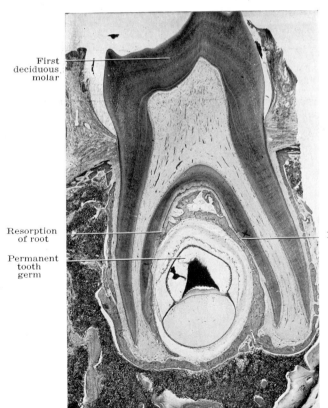

Fig. 243. Germ of lower first permanent premolar between the roots of lower first deciduous molar. Repaired resorption on the roots of the deciduous tooth (see Fig. 245).

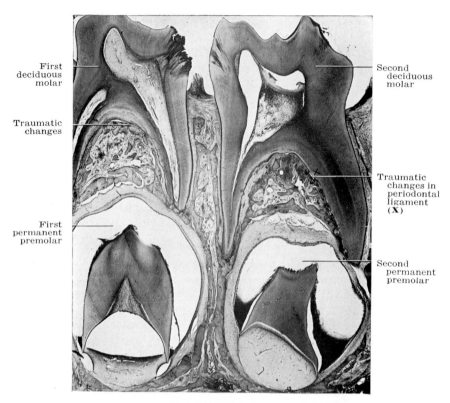

First
deciduous
molar

Second
deciduous
molar

Traumatic
changes

Traumatic
changes in
periodontal
ligament
(**X**)

First
permanent
premolar

Second
permanent
premolar

Fig. 244. Germs of permanent premolars below roots of deciduous molars. Traumatic changes in the periodontal ligament of the deciduous teeth. **X,** See Fig. 247.

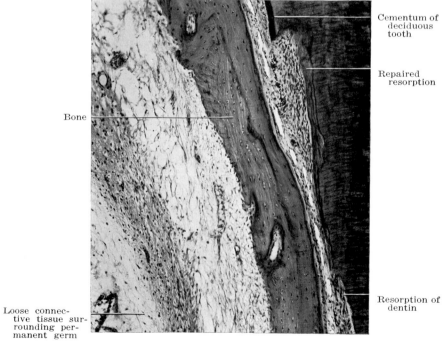

Cementum of
deciduous
tooth

Repaired
resorption

Bone

Loose connec-
tive tissue sur-
rounding per-
manent germ

Resorption of
dentin

Fig. 245. High magnification of a repaired resorption from area **X** of Fig. 243. New bone formed during rest period.

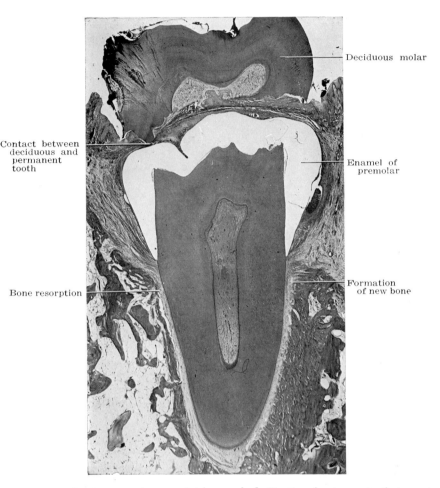

Deciduous molar

Contact between
deciduous and
permanent
tooth

Enamel of
premolar

Bone resorption

Formation
of new bone

Fig. 246. Roots of primary molar completely resorbed. Dentin of primary tooth in contact with enamel of the premolar. Resorption of bone on one side, formation of new bone on the opposite side of the premolar due to transmitted excentric pressure to the premolar. (From Grimmer, E. A.: J. D. Res. **18:** 267, 1939.)

of its root and by its progressive axial eruption, as a traumatic force.[5, 7, 10] Because of the loss of large parts of the suspensory apparatus, the masticatory forces are transmitted to the alveolar bone not as tension but as pressure. This leads to compression and injury of the periodontal ligament, with subsequent bleeding, thrombosis, and necrosis. (Fig. 247.) These changes are most frequently found in the furcation and on interradicular surfaces of deciduous molars. Resorption of bone and tooth substance, therefore, occurs most rapidly in such areas, thus relieving pressure. Repair of resorbed areas may be excessive and may even lead to ankylosis between bone and tooth. (Fig. 248.)

The process of shedding is not continuous. Periods of great resorptive activity alternate with periods of relative rest.[7] During the rest periods resorption not only ceases but repair may occur by apposition of cementum or bone upon the

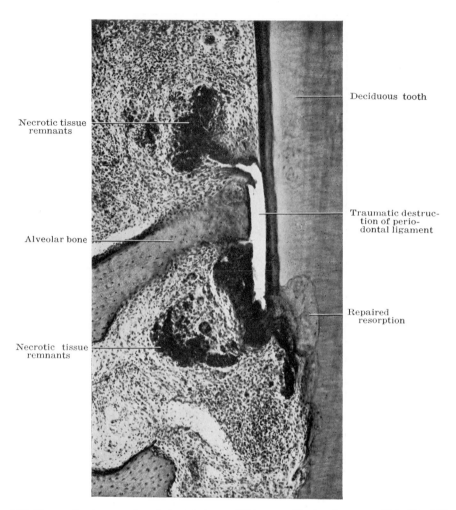

Deciduous tooth

Necrotic tissue
remnants

Traumatic destruc-
tion of perio-
dontal ligament

Alveolar bone

Repaired
resorption

Necrotic tissue
remnants

Fig. 247. Traumatic changes of periodontal tissues. High magnification from area **X** in Fig. 244.

resorbed surface of cementum or dentin. Even repair of resorbed alveolar bone may take place during rest periods (Fig. 245). The periods of rest and repair are probably lengthened by the continued axial eruption of the deciduous tooth.

The pulp of the deciduous teeth plays a passive role during shedding. Even in late stages the occlusal parts of the pulp may appear almost normal, with functioning odontoblasts. (Fig. 249.) However, since the cellular elements of the pulp are identical with those of loose connective tissue, resorption of the dentin may occur at the pulpal surface by the differentiation of osteoclasts from the cells of the pulp. The persistence of the pulpal tissue and its organic connection with the underlying connective tissue explain the fact that deciduous teeth show, to the last, a fairly strong attachment even after total loss of their root (Fig. 246). In such cases shedding may be unduly retarded, and the erupting permanent

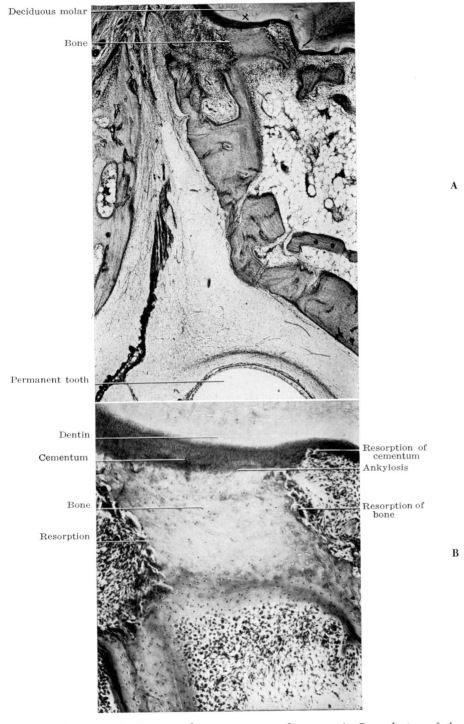

Deciduous molar

Bone

A

Permanent tooth

Dentin

Cementum

Resorption of cementum

Ankylosis

Bone

Resorption of bone

Resorption

B

Fig. 248. Ankylosis of deciduous tooth as a sequence of trauma. **A,** General view of the furcation of deciduous molar sectioned buccolingually. **B,** High magnification of area **X** in **A.**

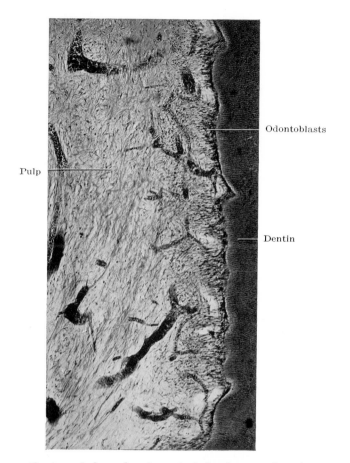

Fig. 249. High magnification of the pulp of resorbed deciduous molar of Fig. 246. Pulp of normal structure with odontoblasts.

tooth may actually come into contact with the deciduous tooth. The masticatory forces are then transmitted to the permanent tooth[2] before its suspensory ligament is fully developed and may cause traumatic injuries in the periodontal ligament of the permanent tooth. (Fig. 246.)

CLINICAL CONSIDERATIONS

Remnants of deciduous teeth. Parts of the roots of deciduous teeth which are not in the path of erupting permanent teeth may escape resorption. Such remnants of roots, consisting of dentin and cementum, may remain in the jaw for a considerable time.[3, 8] Most frequently, such remnants are found along the permanent premolars, especially in the region of the lower second premolars. (Fig. 250.) This can be explained by the fact that the roots of the lower second deciduous molar are strongly curved or divergent. The mesiodistal diameter of the second premolars is much smaller than the greatest distance between the roots of the

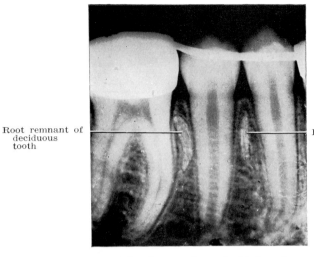

Root remnant of
deciduous
tooth

Root remnant of
deciduous tooth

Fig. 250. Remnants of roots of deciduous molar embedded in the interdental septa. (Courtesy Dr. G. M. Fitzgerald, University of California.)

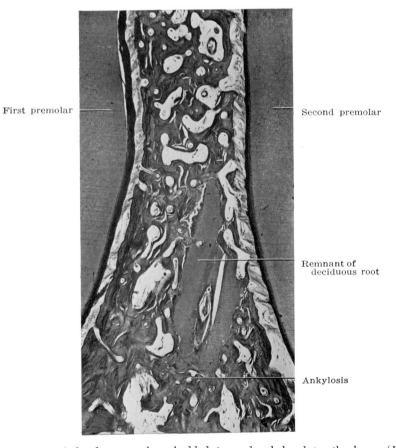

First premolar

Second premolar

Remnant of
deciduous root

Ankylosis

Fig. 251. Remnant of deciduous tooth embedded in, and ankylosed to, the bone. (From Schoenbauer, F.: Ztschr. f. Stomatol. 29: 892, 1931.)

deciduous molar. Root remnants may later be found deep in the bone, completely surrounded by, and ankylosed to, the bone (Fig. 251). Frequently they are encased in heavy layers of cellular cementum. In cases in which the remnants are close to the surface of the jaw (Fig. 252), they may ultimately be exfoliated. Progressive resorption of the root remnants and replacement by bone may cause the disappearance of these remnants.

Retained deciduous teeth. Deciduous teeth may be retained for a long time if the permanent tooth is congenitally missing.[1] This involves most frequently the upper lateral incisor (Fig. 253, *A*), less frequently the second permanent premolar, especially in the mandible (Fig. 253, *B*), and, rarely, the lower central incisor (Fig. 253, *C*). If a permanent tooth is embedded, its deciduous predecessor may also be retained (Fig. 253, *D*). This involves most often the deciduous upper canine in an impaction of the permanent canine.

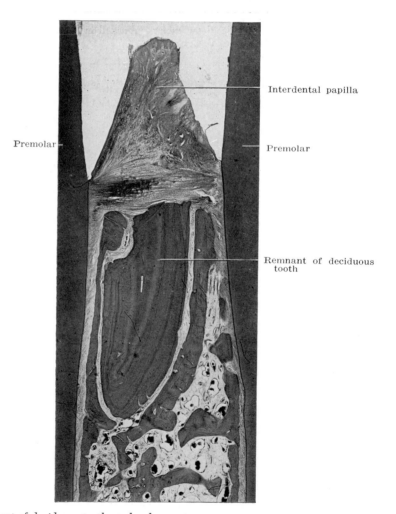

Interdental papilla

Premolar

Premolar

Remnant of deciduous tooth

Fig. 252. Remnant of deciduous tooth at alveolar crest.

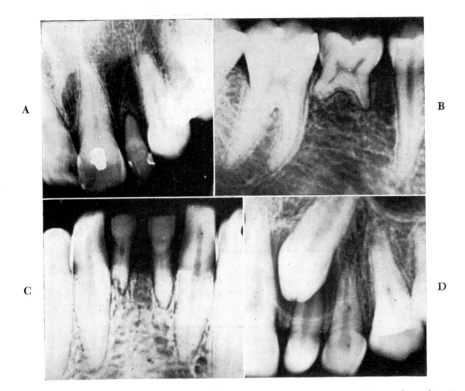

Fig. 253. Roentgenograms of retained deciduous teeth. **A,** Upper permanent lateral incisor missing, deciduous tooth retained (age 56). **B,** Lower second premolar missing, deciduous molar retained. Roots partly resorbed. **C,** Permanent lower central incisors missing, deciduous teeth retained. **D,** Upper permanent canine embedded, deciduous canine retained. (**A** and **B,** Courtesy Dr. M. K. Hine, University of Indiana; **C** and **D,** courtesy Dr. Rowe Smith, Texarkana, Ark.)

The fate of retained deciduous teeth varies. In some cases they persist for many years in good functional condition (Fig. 253, *A*); more often, however, resorption of the roots and continued active eruption and passive exposure cause their loosening and final loss (Fig. 253, *B*). The loss of retained deciduous teeth has been explained by the assumption that such teeth may undergo regressive age changes in their pulp, dentin, cementum, and periodontal ligament, thus losing those faculties that are necessary to compensate for the maintenance of functional integrity.[2] It is, however, more probable that such teeth, because of their smaller size, are not adapted to the strength of the masticatory forces in adult life. The roots are narrow and short, thus rendering the area available for attachment of principal fibers inadequate. Their loss is then due to occlusal trauma.

If the permanent lateral incisor is missing, the deciduous tooth is often resorbed under the pressure of the erupting permanent canine. This resorption may be simultaneous with that of the deciduous canine. (Fig. 254.) Sometimes the permanent canine causes resorption of the deciduous lateral incisor only and

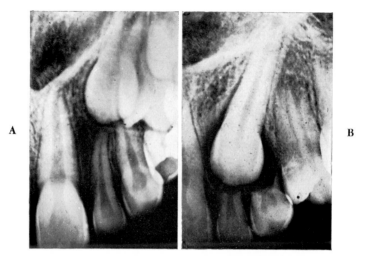

Fig. 254. Upper permanent lateral incisor missing. Deciduous lateral incisor and deciduous canine are resorbed due to pressure of erupting permanent canine. **A,** At the age of 11 years. **B,** At the age of 13 years.

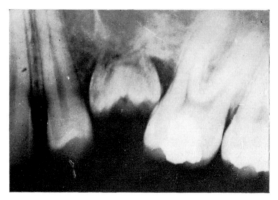

Fig. 255. Submerging deciduous lower second molar. Second premolar missing. (Courtesy Dr. M. K. Hine, University of Indiana.)

erupts in its place. In such cases, the deciduous canine may be retained distally to the permanent canine. A supernumerary tooth or an odontogenic tumor may occasionally prevent the eruption of a permanent tooth or teeth. In such cases, an ankylosis of the deciduous tooth may develop after traumatic injury .

Submerged deciduous teeth. Traumatic lesions, on the other hand, may lead to ankylosis of a deciduous tooth rather than its loss. The active eruption of an ankylosed tooth ceases, and therefore the tooth later appears "shortened" (Fig. 255) because of continued eruption of its neighbors. While the alveolar bone continues to grow, the tooth may become submerged in the alveolar bone.[6] The roots and crowns of such teeth show extensive resorption and formation of bone in the tortuous cavities of the dentin. Submerged deciduous teeth prevent the eruption of their permanent successors or force them from their position. Submerged deciduous teeth should, therefore, be removed as soon as possible.

References

1. Aisenberg, M. S.: Studies of Retained Deciduous Teeth, Am. J. Orthodont. & Oral Surg. **27:** 179, 1941.
2. Grimmer, E. A.: Trauma in an Erupting Premolar, J. D. Res. **18:** 267, 1939.
3. Kotanyi, E.: Histologische Befunde au Milchzahnreste (Histologic Findings on Deciduous Tooth Remnants), Ztschr. f. Stomatol. **23:** 516, 1925.
4. Kronfeld, R.: The Resorption of the Roots of Deciduous Teeth, D. Cosmos **74:** 103, 1932.
5. Kronfeld, R., and Weinmann, J. P.: Traumatic Changes in the Periodontal Tissues of Deciduous Teeth, J. D. Res. **19:** 441, 1940.
6. Noyes, F. B.: Submerging Deciduous Molars, Angle Orthodontist **2:** 77, 1932.
7. Oppenheim, A.: Histologische Befunde beim Zahnwechsel (Histologic Findings in the Shedding of Teeth), Ztschr. f. Stomatol. **20:** 543, 1922.
8. Schoenbauer, F.: Knöchern eingeheilte Milchzahnreste bei älteren Individuen (Ankylosed Deciduous Teeth Remnants in Adults), Ztschr. f. Stomatol. **29:** 892,1931.
9. Stafne, E. C.: Possible Role of Retained Deciduous Roots in the Etiology of Cysts of the Jaw, J. A. D. A. **24:** 1489, 1937.
10. Weinmann, J. P., and Kronfeld, R.: Traumatic Injuries in the Jaws of Infants, J. D. Res. **19:** 357, 1940.

Chapter XIII • TEMPOROMANDIBULAR JOINT*

ANATOMIC REMARKS

The mandibular articulation, temporomandibular or craniomandibular joint, is a bilateral diarthrosis between the articular tubercles of the temporal bone and the condyles, capitula, of the mandible. A fibrous plate, the articular disc, intervenes on either side between the articulating bones.

The interarticular surface of the temporal bone is concave in its posterior part, convex in its anterior part. The articular fossa extends from the squamo-tympanic and petrotympanic fissures in the back to the convex articular tubercle in front. The latter is strongly convex in a sagittal plane and slightly concave in a frontal plane. The convexity varies considerably, the radius ranging from 5 to 15 mm. The long axes of the articular tubercles are directed medially and slightly posteriorly. The articular surfaces of the mandibular condyles are approximately part of a cylinder, their axes placed in the same direction as those of the articular tubercles on the temporal bone. The articulating parts of the temporomandibular joint are covered by a fibrous or fibrocartilaginous tissue and not by hyalin cartilage, as in most other articulations of the human body. The hyalin cartilage *in* the mandibular condyle that is present during its growth period does not reach the surface, but remnants of this cartilage may persist in the adult.

The articular disc is an oval fibrous plate that fuses at its anterior margin with the fibrous capsule. Its posterior border is connected to the capsule by loose connective tissue, which gives it the necessary mobility (Fig. 256); its medial and lateral corners are directly attached to the poles of the condyle. The articular space is divided into two compartments: a lower, between condyle and disc, and an upper, between disc and temporal bone. The disc appears biconcave in sagittal section. Its central part is thin; the anterior and especially the posterior borders are thickened (Fig. 257). Fibers of the lateral pterygoid muscle are attached to its anterior border. The discs are the movable socket for the mandibular condyles.

---

*First draft submitted by Donald A. Kerr.

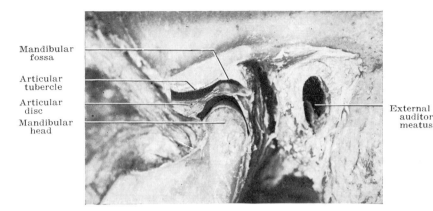

Mandibular
fossa

Articular
tubercle

Articular
disc

Mandibular
head

External
auditory
meatus

Fig. 256. Sagittal section through the temporomandibular joint. (From Bauer, W.: Ztschr. f. Stomatol. **30:** 1136, 1932.)

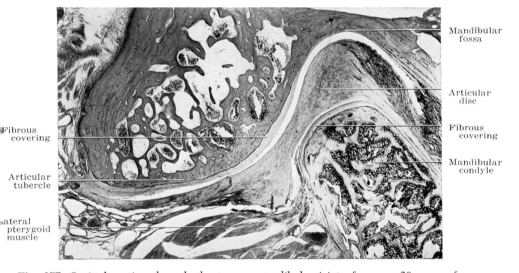

Mandibular
fossa

Articular
disc

Fibrous
covering

Mandibular
condyle

Fibrous
covering

Articular
tubercle

Lateral
pterygoid
muscle

Fig. 257. Sagittal section through the temporomandibular joint of a man 28 years of age. (Courtesy Dr. S. W. Chase, Western Reserve University.)

The articular capsule consists of an outer fibrous sac, which is loose. It is strengthened on its lateral side by the temporomandibular ligament. An inner layer, the synovial membrane, lines the fibrous capsule but not the surfaces of the disc, articular tubercle, or condyle. It is especially well developed on the upper and lower surfaces of the loose connective tissue between the disc and the posterior wall of the capsule.

HISTOLOGY

Bony structures. The condyle of the mandible is composed of cancellous bone covered by a thin layer of compact bone (Fig. 257). The trabeculae are grouped in such a way that they radiate from the neck of the mandible and reach the cortex at right angles, thus giving maximal strength to the condyle. The large marrow spaces decrease in size with progressing age by a marked thickening of the trabeculae. The red marrow in the condyle is of the myeloid or cellular type; in older individuals it is sometimes replaced by fatty marrow.

During the period of growth, a layer of hyalin cartilage lies underneath the fibrous covering of the condyle. This cartilaginous plate grows by apposition from

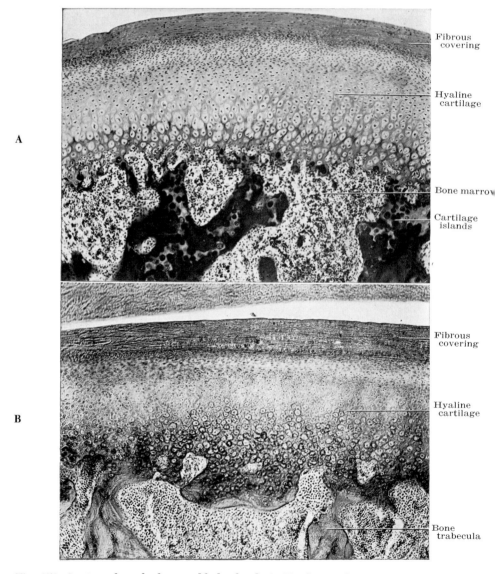

Fig. 258. Sections through the mandibular head. **A,** Newborn infant. **B,** Young adult. Note the transitional zone between the fibrous covering and the hyalin cartilage, characteristic for appositional growth of cartilage.

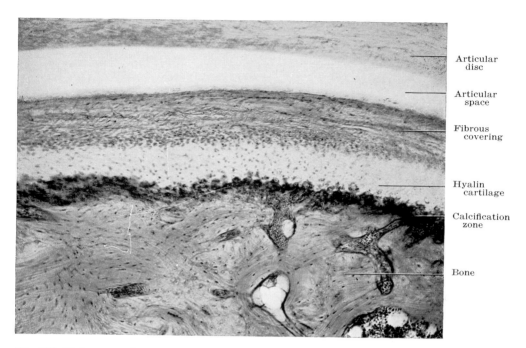

Fig. 259. Higher magnification of part of the mandibular condyle of Fig. 257.

the deepest layers of the covering connective tissue. At the same time, it is destroyed at its deep surface and replaced by bone (Fig. 258). Remnants of this cartilage may persist into old age (Fig. 259).

The bone of the mandibular fossa (Fig. 257) consists of a thin compact layer; the articular tubercle is composed of spongy bone covered with a thin layer of compact bone. In rare cases islands of hyalin cartilage are found in the articular tubercle.

Articular fibrous covering. The condyle, as well as the articular tubercle, is covered by a rather thick layer of fibrous tissue containing a variable number of cartilage cells. The fibrous covering of the mandibular condyle is of fairly even thickness (Fig. 259). Its superficial layers consist of a network of strong collagenous fibers. Cartilage cells or chondrocytes may be present, and they have a tendency to increase in number with age. They can be recognized by their thin capsule, which stains heavily with basic dyes. The deepest layer of the fibrocartilage is rich in chondroid cells as long as hyalin cartilage is present in the condyle; it contains only a few thin collagenous fibers. In this zone the appositional growth of the hyalin cartilage of the condyle takes place during the period of growth.

The fibrous layer covering the articulating surface of the temporal bone (Fig. 260) is thin in the articular fossa and thickens rapidly on the posterior slope of the articular tubercle (Fig. 257). In this region the fibrous tissue shows a definite

Bone

Calcific
zone

Inner fi
layer

Outer f
laye

Articul
spac

Articu
disc

Fig. 260. Higher magnification of articular tubercle of Fig. 257.

arrangement in two layers, with a small transitional zone between them; the two layers are characterized by the different course of the constituent fibrous bundles. In the inner zone the fibers are at right angles to the bony surface; in the outer zone they run parallel to that surface. As in the fibrous covering of the mandibular condyle, a variable number of chondrocytes is also found in the tissue on the temporal surface. In adults the deepest layer shows a thin zone of calcification.

There is no continuous cellular lining on the free surface of the fibrocartilage. Only isolated fibroblasts are situated on the surface itself; they are characterized by the formation of long, flat cytoplasmic processes.

Articular disc. In young individuals the articular disc is composed of dense fibrous tissue; the fibers are straight and tightly packed (Fig. 261). Elastic fibers are found only in relatively small numbers. The fibroblasts in the disc are elongated and send flat cytoplasmic winglike processes into the interstices between the adjacent bundles.

With advancing age some of the fibroblasts develop into chondroid cells, which later may differentiate into true chondrocytes. Even small islands of hyalin cartilage may be found in the discs of older persons. Chondroid cells, true cartilage cells, and hyalin ground substance develop in situ by differentiation of the fibroblasts. In the disc as well as in the fibrous tissue covering the articular surfaces, this cellular change seems to be dependent upon mechanical influences.

The presence of chondrocytes may increase the resistance and resilience of the fibrous tissue.

The fibrous tissue covering the articular eminence and mandibular condyle, as well as the large central area of the disc, is devoid of blood vessels[7] and nerves. They are adapted to resist considerable pressure.

Articular capsule. As in all other joints, the articular capsule consists of an outer fibrous layer that is strengthened on the lateral surface to form the temporomandibular ligament. The inner or synovial layer is a thin layer of connective tissue. It contains numerous blood vessels that form a capillary network close to its surface. From its surface folds or fingerlike processes, synovial folds and villi, protrude into the articular cavity (Fig. 262). A few fibroblasts of the synovial membrane reach the surface and, with some histiocytes and lymphatic wandering cells, form an incomplete lining of the synovial membrane.

A small amount of a clear, straw-colored viscous fluid, synovial fluid, is found in the articular spaces. It is a lubricant and also a nutrient fluid for the avascular

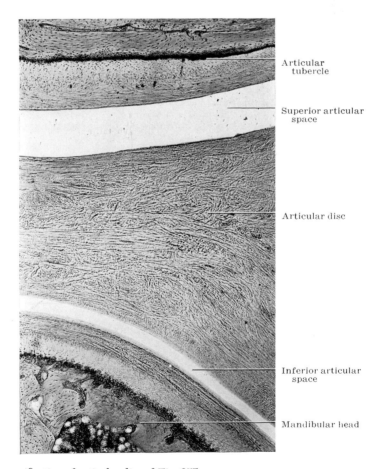

Articular tubercle

Superior articular space

Articular disc

Inferior articular space

Mandibular head

Fig. 261. Higher magnification of articular disc of Fig. 257.

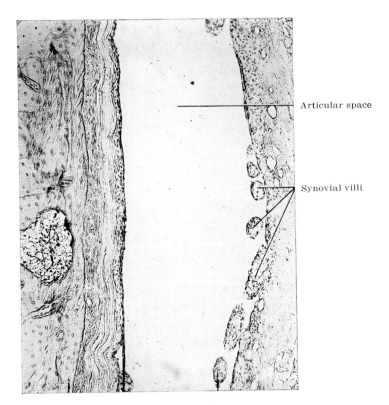

Articular space

Synovial villi

Fig. 262. Villi on the synovial capsule of temporomandibular joint.

tissues covering the condyle and the articular tubercle and for the disc. It is elaborated by diffusion from the rich capillary network of the synovial membrane, augmented by mucin possibly secreted by the cells of the synovial membrane.

CLINICAL CONSIDERATIONS

The thinness of the bone in the articular fossa is responsible for fractures if the mandibular head is driven into the fossa by a heavy blow. In such cases injuries of the dura mater and the brain have been reported.

The finer structure of the bone and its fibrocartilaginous covering depends upon mechanical influences. A change in force or direction of stress, occurring especially after loss of posterior teeth, may cause structural changes. These are characterized by degeneration of the fibrous covering of the articulating surfaces and of the disc.[21] Resorption of the underlying bone may lead to a flattening of the condyle and the articular tubercle. The function of the joint is then severely impaired.

There is considerable literature on the disturbances after loss of teeth or tooth substance due to changes in the mandibular articulation.[16] The clinical symptoms are said to be impaired hearing, tinnitus (ear buzzing), and pain localized to the temporomandibular joint or irradiating into the region of the ear or the tongue. Many explanations have been advanced for these variable symptoms: pressure on the external auditory meatus exerted by the mandibular condyle, which is driven deeply into the articular fossa; compression of the auriculotemporal nerve; compression of the chorda tympani; compression of the auditory tube; impaired function of the tensor palati muscle. Anatomic findings do not substantiate any one of these explanations.

References

1. Bauer, W.: Anatomische und mikroskopische Untersuchungen über das Kiefergelenk (Anatomical and Microscopic Investigations on the Temporo-Mandibular Joint), Ztschr. f. Stomatol. **30:** 1136, 1932.
2. Bauer, W. H.: Osteo-Arthritis Deformans of the Temporo-Mandibular Joint, Am. J. Path. **17:** 129, 1941.
3. Baecker, R.: Zur Histologie des Kiefergelenkmeniskus des Menschen und der Säuger (Histology of the Temporo-Mandibular Disc in Man and Mammals), Ztschr. f. mikr.-anat. Forsch. **26:** 223, 1931.
4. Breitner, C.: Bone Changes Resulting From Experimental Orthodontic Treatment, Am. J. Orthodontics **26:** 521, 1940.
5. Cabrini, R., and Erausquin, J.: La Articulacion Temporomaxilar de la Rata (Temporo-Mandibular Joint of the Rat), Rev. Odont. de Buenos Aires, 1941.
6. Choukas, N. C., and Sicher, H.: The Structure of the Temporo-Mandibular Joint, Oral Surg., Oral Med., & Oral Path. **13:** 1263, 1960.
7. Cohen, D. W.: The Vascularity of the Articular Disc of the Temporo-Mandibular Joint, Alpha Omegan, September, 1955.
8. Cowdry, E. V.: Special Cytology, ed. 2, New York, 1932, Paul B. Hoeber, Inc., pp. 981-989, 1055-1075.
9. Hammar, J. Aug.: Ueber den feineren Bau der Gelenke (The Microscopic Architecture of the Joints), Arch. f. mikr. Anat. **43:** 266, 1894.
10. Marquart, W.: Zur Histologie der Synovialmembran (Histology of the Synovial Membrane), Ztschr. f. Zellforsch. u. mikr. Anat. **12:** 34, 1931.
11. Peterson, H.: Die Organe des Skeletsystems (Organs of the Skeletal System) In von Möllendorff, W. (editor): Handbuch der mikroskopischen Anatomie des Menschen, vol. 2, pt. 2, Berlin, 1930, Julius Springer.
12. Sarnat, B. G.: The Temporomandibular Joint, Springfield, Ill., 1951, Charles C Thomas, Publisher.
13. Schaeffer, J. P.: Morris' Human Anatomy, ed. 10, Philadelphia, 1942, The Blakiston Co.
14. Schaffer, J.: Ueber den feineren Bau und die Entwicklung des Knorpelgewebes und über verwandte Formen der Stützsubstanz (On the Microscopic Structure and Development of Cartilage and Related Forms of Supporting Tissue), Ztschr. f. wissensch. Zool. **80:** 155, 1905.
15. Schaffer, J.: Die Stützgewebe (Supporting Tissues) In von Möllendorff, W. (editor): Handbuch der mikroskopischen Anatomie des Menschen, vol. 2, pt. 2, Berlin, 1930, Julius Springer.
16. Shapiro, H. H., and Truex, R. C.: The Temporo-Mandibular Joint and the Auditory Function, J. A. D. A. **30:** 1147, 1943.
17. Sicher, Harry: Temporomandibular Articulation in Mandibular Overclosure, J. A. D. A. **36:** 131, 1948.
18. Sicher, Harry: Some Aspects of the Anatomy and Pathology of the Temporomandibular Articulation, New York State D. J. **14:** 451, 1948.
19. Sicher, H.: Positions and Movements of the Mandible, J. A. D. A. **48:** 620, 1954.
20. Sicher, H.: Structural and Functional Basis for Disorders of the Temporomandibular Articulation, J. Oral Surg. **13:** 275, 1955.
21. Steinhardt, G.: Die Beanspruchung der Gelenkflächen bei verschiedenen Bissarten (Investigations on the Stresses in the Mandibular Articulation and Their Structural Consequences), Deutsche Zahnh. in Vortr. **91:** 1, 1934.

Chapter XIV • MAXILLARY SINUS*

INTRODUCTION

The relation of the maxillary sinus to the dentition was first recognized by Nathaniel Highmore. In his work *Corporis Humani Disquisitio Anatomica* (1651), he described the adult state of the maxillary sinus in detail and pointed out that his attention had been called to it because a patient had an abscess there which was drained by the extraction of a canine tooth. This proved to be one of those misleading first observations. It is now known that the canine root seldom is related to this space in such a way that its simple extraction would drain it. However, the erroneous idea still persists that this relation is generally true. The molar roots most often, and the premolar roots less frequently, are the dental structures that lie closest to the sinus (Fig. 265, *B*). Individual variations are great and can be determined only by careful interpretation of good roentgenograms.[4]

DEVELOPMENT

The maxillary sinus begins its development in the third month of fetal life. It arises by a lateral evagination of the mucous membrane of the middle nasal meatus, forming a slitlike space. In the newborn infant its measurements are about 8 by 4 by 6 mm. (Fig. 263); thereafter, it gradually expands by pneumatization of the body of the maxilla. The sinus is well developed when the permanent dentition has erupted, but it may continue to expand, probably throughout life.[8]

ANATOMIC REMARKS

The maxillary sinus, or antrum of Highmore, is situated in the body of the maxilla. It is pyramidal in shape; the base of the pyramid is formed by the lateral wall of the nasal cavity; the apex extends into the zygomatic process; the anterior wall corresponds to the facial surface of the body of the maxilla, and the roof corresponds to its orbital surface. The posterior wall is formed by the infratemporal surface of the maxilla; the floor often reaches into the alveolar process.

---

*First draft submitted by Paul C. Kitchin in collaboration with L. F. Edwards, Department of Anatomy, Ohio State University. Rewritten by Dorothy Permar.

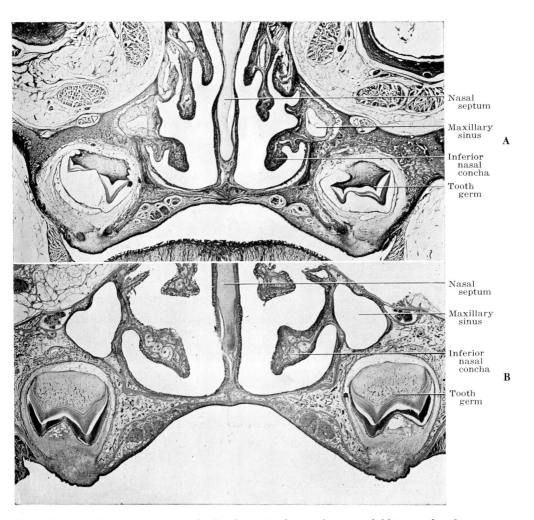

Nasal
septum

Maxillary
sinus

A

Inferior
nasal
concha

Tooth
germ

Nasal
septum

Maxillary
sinus

Inferior
nasal
concha

B

Tooth
germ

Fig. 263. Frontal sections through the head. **A**, Newborn infant. **B**, Child 9 months of age. Compare the size of the maxillary sinus.

The maxillary sinus communicates with a recess of the middle meatus of the nasal cavity (semilunar hiatus) by means of an aperture, the ostium maxillare, that is located high on the nasal or medial wall of the sinus and is therefore unfavorably situated for drainage (Fig. 265, A). An accessory ostium may occur that is lower and slightly more advantageously placed for drainage than the normal ostium.

There is a wide variation in size, shape, and position of the maxillary sinus,[10] not only in different individuals but also on the two sides of the same individual. Its average capacity in the adult is about 15 ml., and the average dimensions are as follows: anteroposteriorly, 3.4 cm.; transversely, 2.3 cm.; and vertically, 3.35 cm.

Variations in the size of the maxillary sinus are partially accounted for by differences in the extent of pneumatization of the body of the maxilla, i.e., the hollowing out by an air-filled pouch of the nasal cavity. In general, the greater the pneumatization the thinner the walls of the sinus, since pneumatization occurs at the expense of bone tissue. The sinus walls may vary from thick walls of 5 to 8 mm. to walls that are nearly paper thin.

Enlargement of the maxillary sinus may also result from its extension into the frontal process, extension into the zygomatic process and even into the zygomatic bone, extension into the maxillary tuberosity, and extension into the alveolar process. The extension of the floor of the maxillary sinus into the alveolar process may place the sinus floor not only between the roots of adjacent teeth but also between the roots of an individual tooth, so that the root apices protrude into the sinus cavity. Usually the bone of the sinus floor is elevated in spots to accommodate the protruding roots, so that bone completely covers the roots (Fig. 264). Sometimes, however, there are openings in the bone of the sinus floor (Fig.

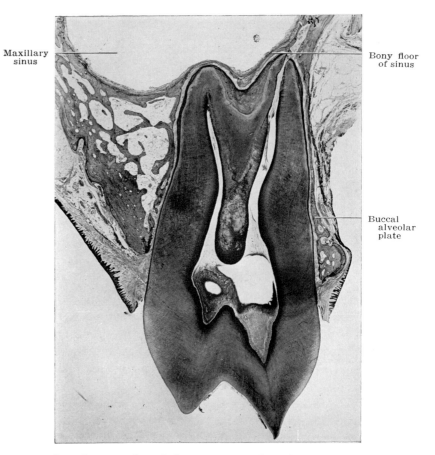

Maxillary sinus

Bony floor of sinus

Buccal alveolar plate

Fig. 264. Buccolingual section through first upper premolar. The apex is separated from the sinus by a thin plate of bone.

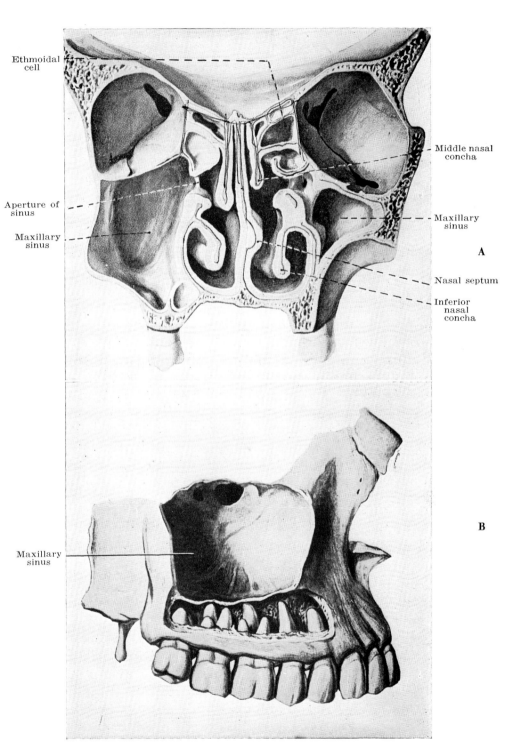

Ethmoidal
cell

Middle nasal
concha

Aperture of
sinus

Maxillary
sinus

Maxillary
sinus

Nasal septum

Inferior
nasal
concha

A

B

Maxillary
sinus

Fig. 265. Relation of the maxillary sinus and its opening into the nasal cavity. **A,** Frontal section showing marked asymmetry between right and left sinus. **B,** Relation of sinus to root apices.

266, *A*), and the roots protrude through the openings into the sinus cavity. Here they are covered only by a soft tissue composed of a combination of the periodontal membrane that surrounds the tooth root and the mucous membrane that lines the sinus cavity. The number of teeth the apices of which produce elevations in the floor of the sinus depends upon the degree and shape of pneumatization. Elevations of the sinus floor are produced most frequently by roots of the maxillary molars and less frequently by those of the premolars.

When enlargement of the sinus has placed the sinus floor deep in the alveolar process, the floor of the sinus may occupy a position lower than that of the floor of the nasal cavity. When the sinus is not so much enlarged and the bone apical to the tooth roots is comparatively thick, the floor of the sinus may be in a position that is higher than the floor of the nasal cavity. Sometimes the two floors are on the same level. The hard palate does not enter into the formation of the floor of the sinus; it forms the floor of the nasal fossae. The sinus floor is lateral to the hard palate.

The walls of the maxillary sinus may have septa that partially divide the sinus into compartments, and the placement of such septa may at times interfere with sinus drainage. Again, there may be present a septum that produces a complete division of the sinus into two separate cavities, each cavity having an independent opening into the nasal fossa. Such a septum usually is placed in such a way as to form a ventral and a dorsal compartment, but it may be placed in such a way as to form an inferior and a superior compartment.[8]

Unilateral supplemental maxillary sinuses have been observed.[8] They usually occur dorsal to the sinus proper and are, from the standpoint of origin, overdeveloped posterior ethmoid cells. Clinically they must be considered as maxillary sinuses.

HISTOLOGY

The maxillary sinus is lined by a mucous membrane that is thinner and more delicate than that of the nasal cavity.

The lamina propria of the sinus mucosa is fused with the periosteum of the underlying bone and consists of loose bundles of collagenous fibers with very few elastic fibers. It is only moderately vascular (Fig. 266, *A*). Glands of the mucous and serous types are present and are confined largely to that part of the lamina propria that is located around the opening or openings into the nasal cavity.

The epithelium of the sinus mucosa is typical of the epithelium of the respiratory passage: it is pseudostratified ciliated columnar, rich in goblet cells (Fig. 266, *B*). The goblet cells secrete mucus that moistens the surface of the sinus mucosa. The cilia beat in such a way as to convey any surface material toward the opening that communicates with the nasal cavity, and hence they act to clear the sinus cavity of inhaled substances and of mucus. A study of the ciliary movement has been made by Kohsaka.[6]

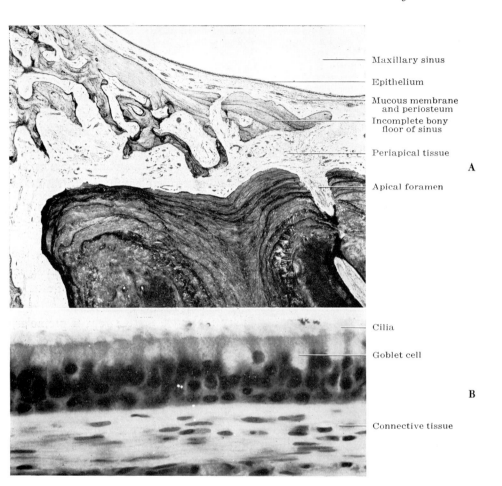

Maxillary sinus

Epithelium

Mucous membrane
and periosteum

Incomplete bony
floor of sinus

Periapical tissue

A

Apical foramen

Cilia

Goblet cell

B

Connective tissue

Fig. 266. Mucous membrane and epithelium of maxillary sinus. **A,** Apical region of a second premolar. The lining of the sinus is continuous with the periapical tissue through openings in the bony floor of the sinus. **B,** High magnification of the epithelium of the maxillary sinus. (From Bauer, W. H.: Am. J. Orthodont. & Oral Surg. **29:** 133, 1943.)

FUNCTION

Various functions have been ascribed to the maxillary sinus and to the other accessory nasal sinuses. It has been claimed by some, for instance, that the maxillary sinuses aid in warming and moistening inhaled air, or that they play an important role in vocalization.

The most probable explanation for the development of all nasal sinuses is that the maintenance of bone tissue depends largely on its mechanical function. Bone tissue that has lost its mechanical function is resorbed. An example of such bone resorption in response to loss of function is seen in the formation of the marrow cavities in long bones where fatty tissue develops in place of the disappearing bone tissue. The disappearance of nonfunctioning bone tissue in the neighborhood of the air-filled nasal cavity leads to the development of air-filled pouches in the bone. The supporting function of bone is maintained with a minimum of material.

CLINICAL CONSIDERATIONS

Periapical infection in teeth the root apices of which are in close approximation to the floor of the maxillary sinus can be a cause of sinus infection.[2, 5, 7]

Disease of the maxillary sinus can produce dental pain. The superior alveolar nerves run in narrow canals in the thin wall of the sinus. Sometimes these canals are partly open toward the sinus, and the nerves which supply the teeth are in contact with the sinus mucosa, where they may become involved in an inflammation of the mucoperiosteum. The resulting pain resembles pulpal pain, but it involves a group of teeth or even all of the teeth in one maxilla.

Because of its proximity to the roots of the maxillary posterior teeth, the maxillary sinus may easily become involved during oral surgical procedures.

If the bone of the floor of the maxillary sinus is thin, in the course of a tooth extraction a root may accidentally be forced into the maxillary sinus.

Following the loss of a single maxillary molar or, more rarely, a premolar, modification of the floor of the sinus frequently results in an extension of the floor down between the roots of the remaining adjacent teeth (Fig. 267). Consequently, at a later time there is a risk of accidentally opening the sinus during the extraction of one of these remaining teeth. If a single molar remains in the maxilla for a long time after the loss of the neighboring teeth, downward extensions of the maxillary sinus may occur mesial and distal to this tooth. If force is applied in extracting such a tooth, the tooth and the base of the alveolus (the floor of the sinus) may be removed together rather than the tooth being removed from its alveolus.

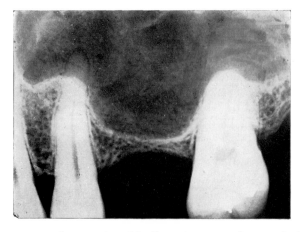

Fig. 267. Roentgenogram of upper jaw. Maxillary sinus extends toward alveolar crest after loss of first molar.

Among possible sequelae of the accidental removal of the floor of the maxillary sinus in the process of tooth removal is the persistence of an unhealed antraoral fistula.[1] With this persistent communication between the oral cavity and the antrum, the fistulous canal becomes lined with epithelium.[3]

Another circumstance that may contribute to accidental communication [1] between the oral cavity and the maxillary sinus is the presence of hypercementoses on the roots of maxillary molars.[1] Lack of proper surgical procedure in the removal of these teeth may result in the removal of the sinus floor along with the teeth.

References

1. Archer, W. Harry: Oral Surgery, Philadelphia, 1956, W. B. Saunders Co.
2. Bauer, W. H.: Maxillary Sinusitis of Dental Origin, Am. J. Orthodont. & Oral Surg. **29:** 133, 1943.
3. Christiansen, G. W.: The Mouth as a Factor in Maxillary Sinus Disease, J. A. D. A. **22:** 1926, 1935.
4. Ennis, L. M., and Batson, O.: Variations of the Maxillary Sinus as Seen in the Roentgenogram, J. A. D. A. **23:** 201, 1936.
5. Hofer, O.: Dental Diseases and Their Relation to Maxillary Antrum, J. D. Res. **17:** 321, 1938. (Abst.)
6. Kohsaka, T.: Studies of the Ciliated Epithelial Cells of the Mucous Membrane of the Maxillary Sinus by Phase Contrast Microscopy, J. Oto-rhino-laryngological Soc. Japan, **61:** 1, 1959.
7. MacMillan, H. W.: The Relationship of the Teeth to the Maxillary Sinus; Anatomic Factors Underlying the Diagnosis and Surgery of This Region, J. A. D. A. **14:** 1635, 1927.
8. Schaeffer, J. P.: The Sinus Maxillaris and Its Relations in the Embryo, Child and Adult Man, Am. J. Anat. **10:** 313, 1910.
9. Schaeffer, J. P.: The Nose, Paranasal Sinuses, Nasolacrymal Passageways and Olfactory Organ in Man, Philadelphia, 1920, P. Blakiston's Son & Co.
10. Sedwick, H. J.: Form, Size and Position of the Maxillary Sinus at Various Ages Studied by Means of Roentgenograms of the Skull, Am. J. Roentgenol. **32:** 154, 1934.
11. Zuckerkandl, E.: Normale und pathologische Anatomie der Nasenhöhle and ihrer pneumatischen Anhänge (Anatomy of the Nasal Cavity), Leipzig, 1893, W. Braumüller.

Chapter XV • HISTOCHEMISTRY OF THE ORAL TISSUES*

INTRODUCTION

This chapter deals with a relatively new area of study. Microscopic histo-chemical techniques may be considered as extensions of routine staining pro-cedures. True histochemical procedures, however, have a known chemical basis. Use of these techniques, most of which have been evolved during the past ten years, enables direct microscopic visualization of sites at which chemical re-actions occur. Although such reactions are not quantitative from a strict nu-merical standpoint, they, nevertheless, enable the histologist to detect with precision, for example, sites of high or low enzyme activity in individual cells. Thus, the great advantage of microscopic histochemistry lies in accuracy of localization even at the cytological level.[18, 21, 22, 26a, 46, 61]

As with some other tissues of the body, those of the oral cavity contain both connective tissue and epithelial components. Significant chemical constituents of these tissues are mucopolysaccharides, mucoproteins (glycoproteins), mucins (mucoids), and enzymes.

Structure and chemical composition of connective tissue. Connective tissue, which is derived from the mesenchyme, consists of specialized cells, fibers, and an amorphous ground substance.[33, 40] The last two may form distinct structures such as in bone and cartilage. Although the specialized connective tissues exhibit morphologic diversity, they have many chemical similarities in common.

Specific cell types appear to be implicated in the production of intercellular fibers and ground substance components. Fibroblasts and osteoblasts for example,

---

*By M. S. Burstone.

352

are associated with the formation of collagenous fibers and mucopolysaccharides of the ground substance.[33, 40] The latter are hexosamine-containing polysaccharides. Ground substance also has proteins which contain carbohydrates, and these are referred to as glycoproteins. Mucopolysaccharides, the acid type of which is widely distributed in nature, are of primary significance in connective tissue and presumably act as binding and protective agents. The acid mucopolysaccharides of the ground substance are polymers containing acetylated amino sugars and hexuronic acids. Among the best-known mucopolysaccharides are hyaluronic acid and chondroitin sulfuric acid. Hyaluronic acid forms viscous gels that are hydrolyzed by the enzyme hyaluronidase. Relatively little is known about the state of mucopolysaccharides in tissue from a biochemical standpoint. This is an area which may be elucidated by histochemical techniques.

As previously indicated, glycoproteins are protein complexes containing protein, mucopolysaccharide, and, in specific instances, hexuronic acid. Histochemically, glycoproteins stain with basic stains such as hematoxylin. They also stain metachromatically with dyes such as toluidin blue. This dye, which ordinarily stains tissue components blue, will stain certain tissue components a red-violet shade (metachromatic reaction). Among the tissue components that stain metachromatically are mast cell granules and the intercellular substance of cartilage. The metachromatic reaction is believed to be related to the formation of aggregates of dye molecules upon glycoprotein complexes. Fibroblasts are known to be involved in the production of a series of acid mucopolysaccharides.

Relatively little mucopolysaccharide is found in bone and dentin upon chemical analysis.[57, 64] The amount is usually less than 1 per cent. The remaining organic fraction of bone consists of approximately 93 per cent collagen, 5 per cent "resistant" protein, and 1.7 per cent citrate.[34] Dentin is stated to contain 0.5 per cent of chondroitin sulfate. A chrondroitin sulfuric acid-protein complex is known to occur in cartilage.

Although fibroblasts are known to synthesize collagen, the mechanism by which fibers are produced is still under study.[52] The connective tissue fibers are embedded in the ground substance in varying proportion and thus give tissues certain gross characteristics. The vitreous humor of the eye contains few fibers, whereas the dermis of the skin and the lamina propria of the gingiva have large numbers of collagenous fibers. Many fine fibers (reticulin) associated with a ground substance form the basement membranes of epithelial surfaces and parenchymatous organs. These fibers, which characteristically stain with silver, are also found in developing connective tissue.[67] Biophysical and chemical studies have shown that reticulin of the basement membrane is a collagen in close association with a carbohydrate and lipid component.[84] Two types of reticulin have been distinguished to date.

Elastin is a relatively ill-defined protein characterized by its extreme insolubility.[51] It is not considered to be an important constituent of the final product of tissue repair. From the histochemical standpoint, considerable caution should

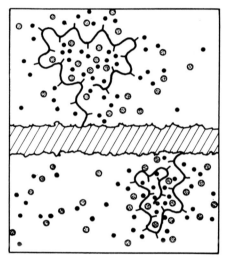

Fig. 268. Diagram of protein-mucopolysaccharide complex in connective tissue. Center core represents protein. Wavy line represents polysaccharide chain. Solid dots are sodium ions, and stippled dots are chloride ions. Background is water of the milieu. (From Dorfman, A.: J. Chron. Dis. **10:** 403, 1959.)

be exercised in interpretations of the staining reactions of fibrous elements based upon the use of nonspecific staining procedures.

As previously indicated, another group of conjugated proteins is exemplified by the glycoproteins, which play an important role in the structure and function of connective tissue (Fig. 268). Coiled chains of mucopolysaccharide are attached to a central protein core. Each repeating disaccharide unit has two negative charges representing sulfate and carboxyl groups.

The so-called nucleoproteins also form an important class of conjugated proteins. The latter are combinations of protein and a prosthetic or addition group. Nucleoproteins, for example, are composed of basic proteins in combination with nucleic acids. The latter are complexes of purine and pyrimidine bases, sugar and phosphoric acid. Nucleoproteins constitute a major portion of nuclear chromatin. Desoxyribonucleic acid (DNA) may be visualized by the so-called Feulgen method.[46]

Epithelial tissues and derivatives. Details of the histochemical characteristics of the oral epithelium, the epithelial components of the tooth germ, and the salivary glands will be considered in another section of this chapter. Salivary glands contain the so-called "mucins" or "mucoids." The definition of this group is a chemical one from the biochemical standpoint and a morphologic-tinctorial one in some respects from the histochemical viewpoint. Histochemical detection of mucins generally is based upon their acid mucopolysaccharide content, which affects certain staining reactions. The acidic nature is due to the presence of glucuronic acid, sulfate, or sialic acid. Recent histochemical work has shown that a number of acid mucins lack sulfate esters.[72, 73]

Ground substance in normal and abnormal conditions. Alterations in ground substance in various physiologic and pathologic states have been stressed by Gersh and Catchpole.[40] One concept suggests that depolymerization of mucopolysaccharides is reflected in a number of physiologic and pathologic changes. It is also possible that enzymatic hydrolysis of the protein component of the polysaccharide complex may be responsible for tissue alterations. The proteolytic enzyme plasmin has been found to hydrolyze the protein that binds acid mucopolysaccharide in cartilage.[54]

Enzymes. Enzymes may be considered as "living" molecular catalysts. They are proteins that catalyze a series of vital complex chemical reactions at body temperature.[75] Among these are synthetic, hydrolytic, and molecular transfer processes. Although over fifty enzymes have been obtained in the crystalline state, the biochemical knowledge as to their mechanism of action is incomplete.

Histochemistry has enabled the histologist to detect the actual sites of cellular and even intracellular enzyme activity. The topographic distribution of enzymes may be ascertained by the quantitative microchemical techniques developed by the Linderstøm-Lang group,[43] or by techniques that result in the formation of visible dyes in tissue sections prepared for microscopic examination. The latter approach has been referred to as microscopic histochemistry, and it is the approach that will be considered in this chapter. During the last twenty years great advances have been made in the development of histochemical techniques for the demonstration of enzymes. The first histochemical enzyme technique was developed by Gomori in 1939 and demonstrated alkaline phosphatase.[46] During the last ten years new methods for the demonstration of aminopeptidase, succinic dehydrogenase, and cytochrome oxidase have been developed. The application of these techniques offers broad implications in the study of oral tissues in normal and pathologic conditions.

HISTOCHEMICAL TECHNIQUES
Fixation procedures

Routine fixation procedures employing formalin or Zenker-formol solutions (see Chapter XVI) are generally of little or no use in histochemistry. The same is true of decalcification with strong acids. These procedures not only inactivate enzymes but also denature proteins and thus alter the availability of their reactive groups. Therefore special methods of fixation had to be devised for use with histochemical techniques.

One of the simplest histochemical fixation procedures employs cold acetone or neutral formalin at 0° C. The low temperature obviates some of the deleterious effects of the fixative and at the same time facilitates mild protein denaturation.[18, 46] In the case of some enzyme systems (e.g., cytochrome oxidase), unfixed tissues must be employed because of the labile nature of the enzyme. Although unfixed frozen sections retain high enzymatic activity, they are not generally recommended for histochemical procedures because the lability and solubility of the tissue constituents may give rise to serious diffusion artifacts.

One of the best types of fixation is the freeze-dry process originally devised by Altmann and subsequently developed by Gersh.[42] Tissues are frozen rapidly at low temperature, usually in liquid nitrogen. The frozen tissues are then placed in a refrigerated vacuum chamber where the ice in the tissues is removed by sublimation, i.e., by direct transformation into vapor without going through a liquid phase. This is the same process by which powdered human blood plasma is prepared. Following dehydration in vacuo, the specimens are embedded in paraffin and sectioned employing a standard microtome. Under optimal conditions, frozen-dried tissues exhibit excellent histologic characteristics and do not show shrinkage artifacts so commonly seen with aqueous fixatives. More important is the high degree of preservation of enzyme systems.[15, 16, 18]

Of greatest interest to the oral histologist and the pathologist are histochemical studies of teeth and bone in health and disease. As previously indicated, routine fixation plus decalcification of hard tissues may make any final chemical interpretation of a staining reaction difficult if not impossible. Frequently the overanxious beginner will perform histochemical stains on routinely fixed and decalcified hard tissues, with questionable results. In specific cases, however, carefully controlled decalcification in cold buffered solutions may be of value.[48] Fortunately, techniques have been developed that make it possible to section certain types of frozen-dried undecalcified tissues.[22] In other cases ground sections may be prepared of undecalcified material.[14]

Specific histochemical methods

The histochemical techniques that have been primarily employed in the study of oral tissues may be classified as (1) protein and lipid methods, (2) polysaccharide and mucin methods, and (3) enzyme methods. They are all characterized by a direct staining reaction or by the formation of an insoluble dye or precipitate at the reactive site.

The mucopolysaccharide, mucoprotein, and mucin methods depend upon the use of nonspecific stains (e.g., Alcian blue) or semispecific stains (e.g., periodic acid-Schiff) that, under defined conditions, react to identify the chemical complex being studied.

Protein group methods are more specific and usually are based upon known classical reactions of protein chemistry. They employ reagents such as dinitrofluorobenzene or ninhydrin in reactions that give rise to insoluble colored products.[19]

Lipid methods employ nonspecific stains that have empirically been found to possess a strong affinity for fats.

The enzyme techniques utilize several different principles.[26a] The Gomori method for alkaline or acid phosphatase uses phosphoric esters of glycerol, glucose, or adenosine. The enzymatically liberated phosphate ion is converted into an insoluble salt, and this is subsequently visualized by transformation into a cobalt compound.[46] Another procedure, originally developed by Menten, Jung, and Green, is referred to as the azo-dye technique.[58] It employs a naphthol phosphate or other type of ester. The enzymatically released naphthol is coupled in situ with a diazonium salt to form an insoluble dye. With regard to the original glycerophosphate technique, it has been shown that calcium phosphate, one of the reaction products, may diffuse and give false localizations on developing bone.[44] The tendency for this to occur is most likely in the pH range between 7.2 and 8.4. Because of this and other considerations, the azo-dye phosphatase techniques are probably the best for the study of teeth and bones.[21, 22] Sophisticated new substrates for use with the azo-dye technique have been developed in recent years. They facilitate precise microscopic localization of alkaline and acid phosphatases as well as esterases.[22, 24] Aminopeptidase can also be detected by an azo-dye method.[16] Recently the demonstration of phosphatase activity by ultraviolet fluorescence has been reported.[24]

There is little question that the future of histochemical research is primarily dependent upon the development and synthesis of new organic reagents for the visualization of intracellular chemical substituents. One of the important areas of research is the application of histochemical techniques to electron microscopy.

PROTEIN AND LIPID HISTOCHEMISTRY OF ORAL HARD TISSUES

The ground substance of the oral tissues, including bone, stains with a number of histochemical procedures. Among these are techniques for the demonstration of carbohydrate groupings, the best known of which is the periodic acid-Schiff (pa-S) technique.[45] The chemical basis of this method lies in the fact that periodic acid oxidizes glycols with vicinal hydroxyl groups to aldehydes, which in turn are revealed as a colored dye by leukofuchsin. This colorless reagent thus results in formation of a red dye when reacted with aldehydes formed in tissues.

The periodic acid-Schiff method is believed to demonstrate under specific conditions the carbohydrate moiety of a glycoprotein complex.[40] This technique probably has been employed more than any other in studying the ground substance of teeth and bones.[14, 31, 36] The ground substance of normal mature bone and dentin exhibits little or no reactivity with the pa-S technique (Fig. 269).[14, 36] However, resorbing bone or dentin is intensely stained.[14] Newly formed bone and dentin are also quite reactive.[14, 55] This staining reaction has been interpreted to indicate changes in the submicroscopic state of organization of the ground substance.[41] However, more definitive studies are needed in order to confirm this hypothesis. Interglobular less calcified dentin exhibits a distinct pa-S reaction (Fig. 269), as does the abnormal poorly calcified dentin matrix in dentinogenesis imperfecta and in odontomas (Plate 4, *B*).

Enamel matrix is essentially nonreactive with the pa-S method. However,

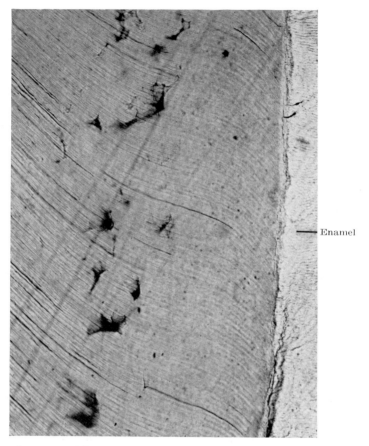

Enamel

Fig. 269. Ground section of human tooth showing periodic acid-Schiff reactivity of inter-globular dentin. (×143.)

enamel lamellae are intensely stained in ground sections (Fig. 270). In some areas the rod interprismatic substance exhibits some reactivity.

Specific protein methods identify certain amino acids or their groupings (e.g., amino, carboxyl).[19] Only a few of these techniques have been applied in the study of teeth and bone. Of interest are the dinitrofluorobenzene (DNFB) and ninhydrin-Schiff methods. The DNFB reagent combines with alpha-amino groups of proteins in tissue sections to form a pale yellow complex. An intense reddish color is subsequently revealed by a reduction and diazotization technique which results in the formation of an azo-dye (Plate 4, A). The pattern of staining is essentially the same as seen with the pa-S method in both normal and abnormal dentin. The ninhydrin-Schiff method is specific for amino acids and is based on the classical ninhydrin reaction of protein chemistry.

Some of the previously discussed techniques have found application in the study of dental caries and bone and dentin resorption.[14, 36, 74]

Biochemical studies indicate a rather low lipid content of the organic matrix

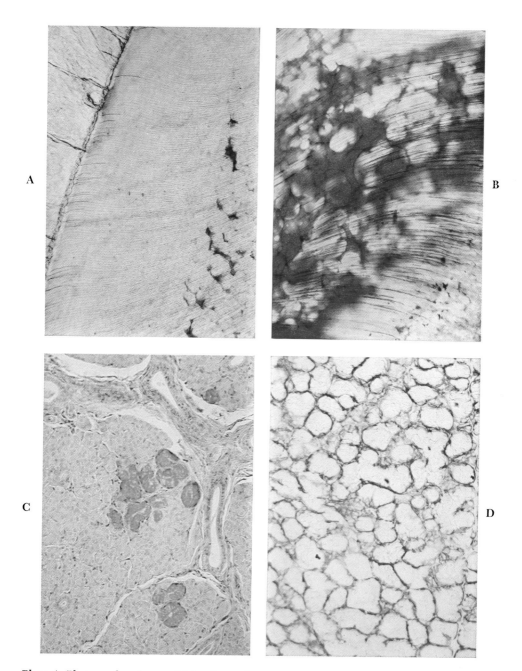

Plate 4. Photographs of several histochemical reactions. **A,** Ground section of human dentin. Dinitrofluorobenzene (DNFB) technique reveals reactive protein groups of interglobular areas. (×143.) **B,** Ground section of human odontoma, showing periodic acid-Schiff reaction of poorly calcified dentin. (×85.) **C,** Alcian blue staining of isolated group of mucous cells in dog parotid gland. Mucicarmine counterstain. (×143.) **D,** Alkaline phosphatase activity of basement membranes of rat sublingual gland. (×143.)

Fig. 270. Ground section of human enamel. Lamella stains with periodic acid-Schiff method. (×143.)

of dentin.[50, 63, 71] Histochemical studies have demonstrated the presence of lipids by the sudanophilic reaction in the odontoblastic processes and enamel rod sheaths.[70] More recent work has shown a fairly widespread lipid distribution throughout the developing tooth, with a distinct sudanophilia in the basal zone of the ameloblasts.[77] This reactive ameloblastic zone is also believed to delineate phospholipid associated with enamel matrix formation.

POLYSACCHARIDE, PROTEIN, AND MUCIN HISTOCHEMISTRY OF ORAL SOFT TISSUES

Polysaccharides. The previously discussed pa-S reaction, when used in conjunction with specific tests, is a highly accurate method for the demonstration of glycogen. Carmine, a dye, has also been used to demonstrate glycogen, but it is not as specific as the pa-S method. Epithelial glycogen is known to increase during inflammation and repair.[12, 32, 69, 79] Human attached gingiva, which is variable in keratinization, exhibits a variable glycogen content. On the other hand, the nonkeratinized alveolar mucosa virtually always contains glycogen.[83]

Of interest are animal experiments that also demonstrate an increase in glycogen in benign and malignant epithelial proliferations.[1]

The so-called "mast cells" were first reported by Ehrlich in 1879. They are readily found in various connective tissues throughout the body. Mast cells appear most prominently in acute, less so in chronic, inflammation. Mast cells are also known to contain histamine, thus further implicating them in the inflammatory processes.[65] Their staining with metachromatic dyes and certain biochemical features indicates the presence of a sulfated mucopolysaccharide.[38] Mast cells in the human gingiva have been studied in normal and pathologic states.[30] It was found that the number of mast cells decreases adjacent to the gingival sulcus. In acute necrotizing gingivitis there is a lack of mast cells.

Proteins and protein groups. Glycoproteins in human gingiva have been studied by means of the periodic acid-Schiff method.[37] The reticular fibers comprising the basement membrane are discretely stained. The lamina propria exhibits reactive elements that include collagenous, reticular, and elastic fibers. The amorphous ground substance also exhibits a variable degree of staining in suitably fixed material (e.g., frozen-dried). Study of gingiva with newer definitive protein group and amino acid methods should be undertaken.[19]

Keratinization is one of the important characteristics of the epidermis and some areas of the oral epithelium in normal and abnormal conditions. The mechanism by which cells of the malpighian layer are altered to form keratin has been only partly elucidated. The disulfide bridges in keratin are believed to result from the oxidation of sulfhydryl groups of cysteine.[82] Histochemical study of sulfhydryls and disulfides of gingiva has been reported.[80] However, further work is required to determine the precise changes of these groups in normal and pathologic states.

Mucins. Mucins found in saliva function to form a protective coating on the oral mucous membranes and also act as a lubricant. Mucins (mucosubstances) contain high molecular weight protein-carbohydrate compounds known as glycoproteins, which are capable of forming viscous fluids and water-soluble gels. Of interest is the fact that few enzymatic properties can be attributed to them. Two types of glycoproteins occur in the mucus of salivary glands. One contains L-fucose as its primary carbohydrate component and has been called fucomucin.[8] The other predominating type of mucin glycoprotein contains sialic acid in conjunction with an N-acetylhexosamine, and it is referred to as sialomucin.[9] Both fucomucins and sialomucins are found together in secretions, with one usually predominating over the other. Submandibular glands contain high sialomucin content.[56] Sialic acid is believed to confer acidity upon certain mucins. For purposes of definition, sialic acid refers to the acetylated derivatives of neuraminic acid.[10]

The use of histochemical techniques has greatly added to our knowledge of the histologic and cytologic localization of salivary gland mucins and their specific chemical constituents.[13, 72] From a histochemical standpoint mucins

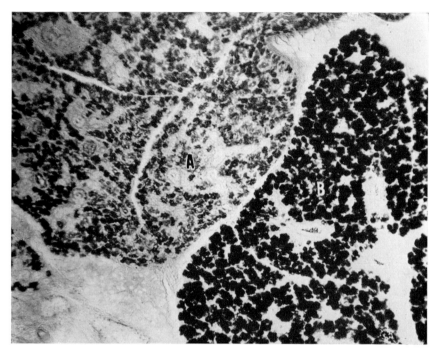

Fig. 271. Frozen-dried mouse submandibular, **A**, and sublingual, **B**, glands showing periodic acid-Schiff reactivity of mucins. (×140.)

may be identified on the basis of either nonspecific stains or by the use of reactions that have a known chemical basis. A nonspecific but highly useful reaction may be obtained with the dyes mucicarmine or mucihematin. Salivary gland mucins can also be stained by the use of the pa-S reaction (Fig. 271), aldehyde fuchsin, colloidal iron, and Alcian blue (Plate 4, *C*).[47] However, the staining reaction is variable, and species differences can be observed. Only recently have careful studies been undertaken to elucidate the chemical basis of such staining differences.

ENZYME HISTOCHEMISTRY OF ORAL HARD TISSUES

As previously mentioned, enzymes are considered to be the biologic catalysts that control the rate of chemical reactions in bone as well as in other tissues. Definitive study of enzymes in hard tissues by means of routine *biochemical* procedures presents certain technical problems, since calcifying tissues are nonhomogenous systems containing different types of cells and intercellular substance. On the other hand, *histochemical* techniques offer excellent possibilities for visualizing specific enzymes of the cellular elements in bone and dentin.

Until recently, alkaline phosphatase was given foremost consideration in histochemical studies. This is due primarily to the impetus given to modern microscopic histochemistry by the original phosphatase technique of Gomori.

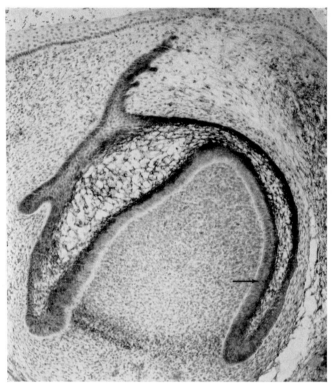

Fig. 272. Alkaline phosphatase reaction of tooth of monkey embryo. The ameloblastic layer (arrow) is nonreactive. (×87.)

Application of this technique in the study of calcifying tissues has been reviewed in the text edited by Bourne.[11] More recently, histochemical localization of a number of hydrolases associated with the development of hard tissues has been reported.[21, 22] The azo-dye methods are the most desirable for studying undecalcified hard tissues since they are not affected by the presence of inorganic bone salts.

Alkaline phosphatase. This enzyme, which has a pH optimum of around 9, is capable of hydrolyzing a number of naturally occurring as well as synthetic phosphoric acid esters. The function of alkaline phosphatase has been implicated in the synthesis of fibrous proteins and also in the passage of metabolites across cell membranes. No studies of this enzyme in human dentinogenesis have been reported. However, in animal material a marked enzymatic reaction is observed to be associated with dentinogenesis as well as osteogenesis (Figs. 272 and 273). The cytoplasm and cytoplasmic processes of osteoblasts stain intensely. The same sharply delineated reaction is also observed at neutral pH and pH 7.5. No enzyme activity is found in bone or dentin matrices per se except at the very periphery. However, fibers entering the matrix are active. Of interest is the fact that nuclear staining is never observed with the azo-dye methods.[21, 22, 76] Intramembranous bone formation reveals enzymatic activity of endosteum, periosteum, and osteocytes. In the case of intracartilaginous bone, high activity is associated with the matrices and cells of the hypertrophic and provisional zones of calcification. The active perichondrium is selectively and strongly stained. (Table 7.)

In the developing molar, as well as in most of the incisor, activity is limited to the stratum intermedium, odontoblasts, and subjacent pulp (Fig. 273). Staining of Korff's fibers is also observed. No ameloblastic enzyme activity is apparent. The staining reaction in the incisors of rodents is similar with one important exception. This consists of a reaction of ameloblasts and reduced enamel organ at the incisal end of the tooth. (Table 7.) The remaining ameloblasts, as in the molar, are unstained. The possible existence of alkaline phosphatase activity of dentin has been investigated by several workers.[7, 53] There appears to be definite evidence of phosphatase activity of dentin matrix, although the activity is relatively low.

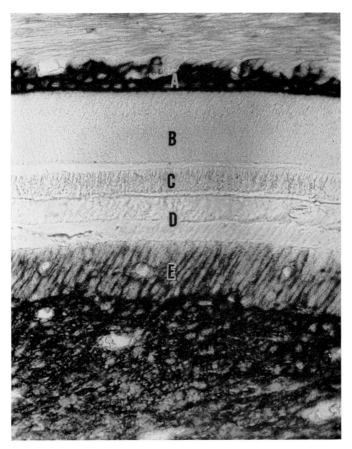

Fig. 273. Frozen-dried undecalcified incisor of hamster. **A**, Stratum intermedium. **B**, Ameloblasts. **C**, Enamel matrix. **D**, Dentin matrix. **E**, Odontoblasts. Note alkaline phosphatase reactivity of Korff's fibers and subjacent pulp. (×87.)

Acid phosphatase. Acid phosphatase is less widely distributed than its alkaline counterpart (Table 7). The optimal pH lies in the range of 5.0 to 6.0. Osteoclasts exhibit a striking acid phosphatase reaction.[18, 21, 22, 64] (Fig. 274.) It is of interest that phagocytic cells (e.g., macrophages) also show high acid phosphatase activity. This suggests that osteoclasts may be biochemically related to foreign body giant cells. In vivo uptake of radioactive plutonium by osteoclasts has been reported.[2] This finding further suggests a possible phagocytic function. It is important to note that the high activity of two distinct enzymes, acid and alkaline phosphatase, is associated with osteoclasts and osteoblasts, respectively.[22] This tends to confirm the view that tissues endowed with intense alkaline phosphatase activity are practically devoid of acid phosphatase activity.[68] Tissue sections of bone and dentin matrices are capable of hydrolyzing phosphate esters at an acid pH. The reaction is diminished by known acid phosphate inhibitors.

Table 7. Phosphatase activity of cellular elements associated with calcification (short incubation)*

	Alkaline phosphatase	Acid phosphatase
Bone		
Osteoblasts	+	0
Osteocytes	+	0
Osteoclasts	0	+
Cartilage		
Active perichondrocyte†	+	0
Resting chondrocyte	0	0
Hypertrophic chondrocyte	+	0
Tooth		
Stellate reticulum	+	0
Stratum intermedium	+	0
Ameloblasts‡	0	0
Odontoblasts, fibers, and subjacent pulp	+	0

0 = No reaction. + = High activity.
*From Burstone, M. S.: Hydrolytic Enzymes in Dentinogenesis and Osteogenesis. In Sognnaes, R. F. (editor): Calcification in Biological Systems, Washington, D. C., 1960, American Association for the Advancement of Science, p. 217.
†From perichondrium.
‡Ameloblasts at incisal end of rodent incisor show high enzymatic activity.

Esterase. Esterases, according to histochemical definition, are enzymes which hydrolyze simpler fatty acid esters (e.g., acetates and butyrates). They also exhibit certain inhibitory preferences as contrasted with the enzymes (lipases) that hydrolyze more complex fatty acid esters.[46]

Most histochemical techniques for the demonstration of esterases reveal no reactivity of tooth and bone structure. However, one specific type of ester substrate is rapidly hydrolyzed by developing bone and dentin matrices.[3] Of interest

Fig. 274. Acid phosphatase reaction of osteoclast in Howship's lacuna. Frozen-dried undecalcified alveolar bone of hamster, nuclear counterstain. (×750.)

is the fact that certain ester substrates are also hydrolyzed by proteolytic enzymes.

Considerable esterase activity has also been found in the cells and microorganisms associated with the formation of deposits on teeth (calculus).[13]

Aminopeptidase. Aminopeptidases are proteolytic enzymes that hydrolyze certain terminal peptide bonds. In recent years an azo-dye technique has been developed for the histochemical demonstration of the enzyme, employing L-leucyl-β-naphthylamide or DL-alanyl-β-naphthylamide as synthetic substrates.[16, 18] Osteoclasts in the human being exhibit an intense staining reaction, whereas those of other species (rodents) are unstained.[22] In the developing rodent dentition there is a distinct reaction of the stratum intermedium and the odontoblasts. There is some staining of the periosteum. Chondrocytes as well as the perichondrium are also reactive.

The biochemical function of aminopeptidase is not clear. It is of interest, however, that macrophages show intense activity, as do certain sites associated with breakdown of connective tissue.[18] It has been reported that osteoclasts in vivo have strong proteolytic abilities and are capable of liquefying a plasma clot.[49]

Cytochrome oxidase. This enzyme is widely distributed in living organisms.[75] It is an iron-porphyrin-protein compound that enables cells to utilize molecular oxygen. Cytochrome oxidase is found in mitochondria. Cardiac and skeletal muscle, which are known to exhibit high oxygen consumption, likewise show high cytochrome oxidase activity (Fig. 275).

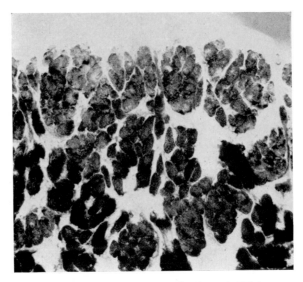

Fig. 275. Cytochrome oxidase activity of tongue muscle of rat. (×100.)

In 1885, Ehrlich found that if α-naphthol and N,N-dimethyl-p-phenylene-diamine were injected into living tissue, a blue dye was formed in vivo. This is referred to as the "nadi" reaction from the first two letters of *naphthol* and *diamine*. Unfortunately, the "nadi" reaction is not adequate for microscopic localizations because the blue dye formed diffuses badly, is fat-soluble, and fades. During the last few years, new definitive histochemical techniques for the demonstration of cytochrome oxidase have been developed.[20, 23] These enable microscopic localization of the enzyme even at the mitochondrial level. Both osteoclasts and osteoblasts show activity, with the staining of the former predominating (Fig. 276).[21] This certainly suggests high metabolic activity of osteoclasts associated with physiologic bone resorption. The stratum intermedium of both molars and incisors also exhibits high oxidase activity.

Succinic dehydrogenase. Succinic dehydrogenase is an enzyme that is closely associated with cytochrome oxidase in cell mitochondria. Succinic dehydrogenase is one of a series of enzymes widely distributed in animal tissues which catalyzes the removal of hydrogen. In order that the reaction be continuous, the liberated hydrogen has to be constantly removed by so-called "acceptors" or "carriers." Succinic dehydrogenase dehydrogenates succinic acid to fumaric acid in the presence of a hydrogen acceptor.[75]

This enzyme usually is demonstrated by the use of colorless compounds called tetrazoles, which are changed by reducing sites (dehydrogenase) into a colored dye (formazan).[46]

In hard tissues, high dehydrogenase activity is found in osteoclasts but not in osteoblasts.[21] The stratum intermedium and the odontoblasts in developing

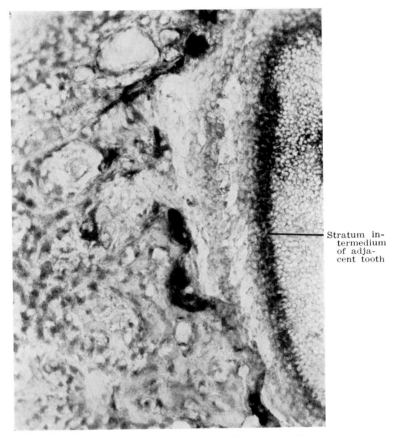

Stratum in-
termedium
of adja-
cent tooth

Fig. 276. Cytochrome oxidase activity of osteoclasts in jaw of hamster. (×110.)

teeth are also stained. The distribution of cytochrome oxidase and succinic dehydrogenase in oral tissues is essentially similar.

Summary. The enzymatic cellular components associated with bones and teeth are summarized in Table 8.

It is interesting to note that sites of high activity involving a number of different enzymes are to be found in the same structure (e.g., stratum intermedium). As new enzyme techniques are developed, the state of our knowledge of the cytochemistry of oral tissues in normal and pathologic conditions will be enhanced considerably.

ENZYME HISTOCHEMISTRY OF ORAL SOFT TISSUES

Alkaline phosphatase. In human gingiva alkaline phosphatase has been observed in the capillary endothelium of the lamina propria (Fig. 277).[81, 85] Phosphatase activity ascribed to collagenous fibers may be genuine or may be a staining artifact. A staining reaction of the epithelium per se is the result of diffusion of the enzyme reaction products. On the other hand, polymorphonuclear leukocytes exhibit a genuine activity.

Table 8. Enzyme activity of cells associated with bones and teeth

	Alkaline phosphatase*	Acid phosphatase*	Amino-peptidase†	Cytochrome oxidase†	Succinic de-hydrogenase†
Bone					
Osteoblasts	++	0	+	+	+
Osteocytes	++	0	+	+	+
Osteoclasts	0	++	?	++	++
Cartilage					
Active peri-chondrocyte	++	0	++	++	++
Resting chondrocyte	0	0	+	+	+
Hypertrophic chondrocyte	++	0	+	+	+
Tooth					
Stellate reticulum	++	0	+	+	+
Stratum intermedium	++	0	+	+	+
Ameloblasts (molar)	0	0	0	0 or +	0
Odontoblasts	+ or ++	0	+	+	+

0 = No staining. + = Less active. ++ = More active.
*Frozen-dried paraffin-embedded tissues.
†Fresh-frozen tissues.

Fig. 277. Alkaline phosphatase activity of capillaries of lamina propria of human gingiva revealed by ultraviolet fluorescence. (×80.)

The oral epithelium of the rat exhibits an increased alkaline phosphatase activity during the estrous cycle, which also can be correlated with phosphatase changes in the vaginal epithelium.[66] Although alkaline phosphatase may be related to keratinization, its precise role cannot be ascertained until more is known about the function of this enzyme.

The basement membranes associated with salivary gland acini exhibit high alkaline phosphatase activity (Plate 4, *D*).[26]

Phosphatase activity of taste buds of several species has also been observed.[4, 6]

Acid phosphatase. Our knowledge of the distribution of acid phosphatase in human gingiva is incomplete. Studies with the glycerophosphate method indicate a primary staining reaction in the superficial layers, with the exception of the keratinized zone.[27] This pattern appears to correspond with that observed in the skin.[59] High activity is seen in macrophages in chronic inflammation (Fig. 278). Further studies of this enzyme with newer histochemical techniques are obviously desirable.

Esterase. Little information is available on the esterase activity of human gingiva. A reaction is usually observed in the more superficial layers of the gingival epithelium including the keratinizing zone.[86]

High esterase activity is found in salivary gland ducts and also in demilunes of the sublingual gland (Figs. 279 and 280).[15] A similar activity is observed in the taste buds of several species and has been related to gustatory discrimination.[4, 5]

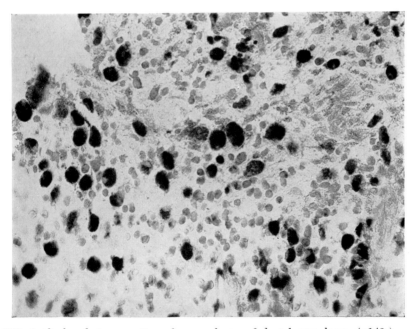

Fig. 278. Acid phosphatase reaction of macrophages of dental granuloma. (×143.)

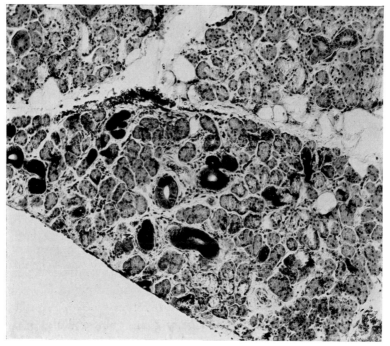

Fig. 279. Esterase activity of ducts of frozen-dried human parotid gland (nuclear counterstain). (×110.)

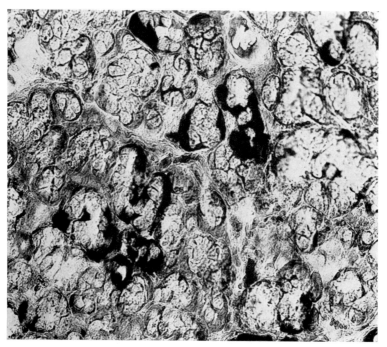

Fig. 280. Esterase activity of demilune cells of frozen-dried human sublingual gland. (×210.)

Aminopeptidase. The activity of the enzyme in human gingiva is low, with the exception of that found in polymorphonuclear leukocytes.

The enzyme aminopeptidase is also found in human salivary gland ducts.[16] With the development of newer, more sensitive methods, significant information on the distribution and role of proteolytic enzymes in the oral tissues should be obtained.

β-glucuronidases. This term represents a group of enzymes that are capable of hydrolyzing the β-glycoside linkage of a number of naturally occurring and synthetic glucuronides. β-glucuronidase is found in all animal tissues, but highest activity is found in the liver, kidney, and spleen. The enzyme is believed to have three roles: the conjugation of steroid hormones, the hydrolysis of conjugated glucuronides, and a role in cellular proliferations.[39]

Activity is observed in the basal cell layers of the oral tissues of man and rat, suggesting a possible role in cellular proliferation.[28, 29]

Cytochrome oxidase and succinic dehydrogenase. Studies of this enzyme in

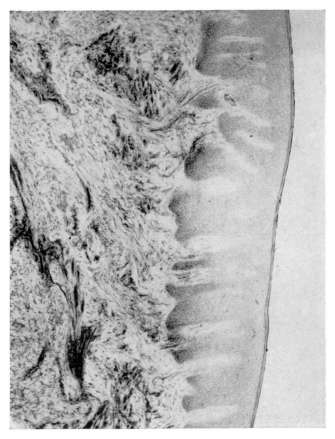

Fig. 281. Human attached gingiva showing cytochrome oxidase activity of basal cell layer and in connective tissue of the lamina propria.

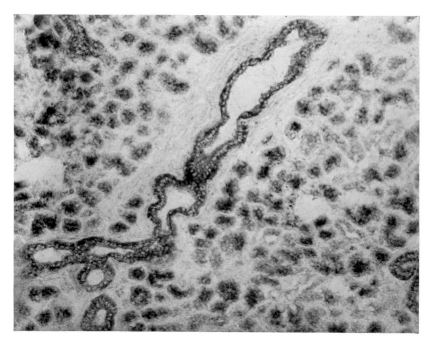

Fig. 282. Cytochrome oxidase activity of human parotid gland. (×143.)

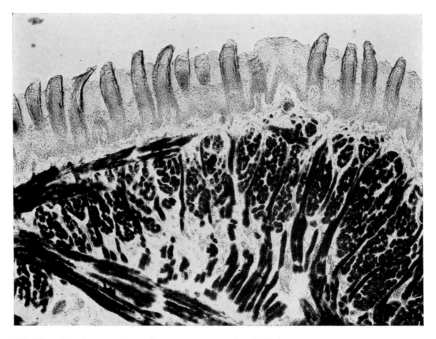

Fig. 283. Phosphorylase activity of rat tongue muscle. (×70.)

human gingiva have been made using primarily biochemical methods, and activity has been found to be relatively low.

With the application of new histochemical techniques, the precise sites of oxidase activity in normal and inflamed gingiva have been observed.[21] With these techniques, cytochrome oxidase activity was also found to be low and was observed in the crevicular epithelium, epithelial attachment, and basal cell layer of the free and the attached gingiva (Fig. 281). In chronic gingivitis, a striking increase in activity is manifested in the epithelium from the free gingival groove through the epithelial attachment. The underlying connective tissue stroma exhibits a variable increase.

Biochemical studies have shown rather high oxidase levels in the salivary glands.[62] With histochemical methods, the ducts exhibit predominant staining (Fig. 282).[20, 23]

Studies of succinic dehydrogenase have been made primarily with biochemical techniques. From the histochemical standpoint, the basal cell zone of human gingiva exhibits the highest reducing activity.[35] Salivary gland ducts exhibit a distinct staining reaction with the tetrazole histochemical techniques.[60]

Phosphorylases. Phosphorylase or amylophosphorylase, is a transferase, i.e., an enzyme that catalyzes the transfer of radicals such as phosphate or acetyl. In the case of phosphorylase, tissue glycogen undergoes an esterification reaction to form glucose-l-phosphate. When phosphorylase is demonstrated by histochemical means, skeletal muscle is intensely stained (Fig. 283).[75, 78]

References

1. Argyris, T. S.: Glycogen in the Epidermis of Mice Painted With Methylchol-Anthrene, J. Nat. Cancer Inst. **12:** 1159, 1952.
2. Arnold, J. S., and Jee, W. S. S.: Bone Growth and Osteoclastic Activity as Indicated by Radioautographic Distribution of Plutonium, Am. J. Anat. **101:** 367, 1957.
3. Baer, P. N., and Burstone, M. S.: Esterase Activity Associated With Formation of Deposits on Teeth, Oral Surg., Oral Med., & Oral Path. **12:** 1147, 1959.
4. Baradi, A. F., and Bourne, G. H.: Gustatory and Olfactory Epithelia. In Bourne, G. H., and Danielli, J. F. (editors): International Review of Cytology, vol. 2, New York, 1953, Academic Press, p. 289.
5. Baradi, A. F., and Bourne, G. H.: Histochemical Localization of Cholinesterase in Gustatory Epithelia, J. Histochem. & Cytochem. **7:** 2, 1959.
6. Baradi, A. F., and Bourne, G. H.: New Observations on Alkaline Glycophosphatase Reaction in the Papilla Foliata, J. Biophys. & Biochem. Cytol. **5:** 173, 1959.
7. Baumgärtner, F., and Cremer, H. D.: Verschiedene Methoden zur Bestimmung der Phosphataseaktivität in Rinderzähnen, Arch. Oral. Biol. **1:** 8, 1959.
8. Blix, G.: Neuere Forschungsergebnisse über tierische Glykoproteide und mucopolysaccharide, Angew. Chem. **62:** 171, 1950.
9. Blix, G., Svennerholm, L., and Werner, I.: The Isolation of Chondrosamine From Gangliosides and From Submaxillary Mucin, Acta Chem. Scand. **6:** 358, 1952.
10. Blix, G., Gattschalk, A., and Klenk, E.: Proposed Nomenclature in the Field of Neuraminic and Sialic Acids, Nature **179:** 1088, 1957.
11. Bourne, G. H. (editor): The Biochemistry and Physiology of Bone, New York, 1956, Academic Press.
12. Bradfield, J. R. G.: Glycogen of the Vertebrate Epidermis, Nature **167:** 40, 1951.
13. Burstone, M. S.: A Cytologic Study of Salivary Glands of the Mouse Tongue, J. D. Res. **32:** 126, 1953.

14. Burstone, M. S.: The Ground Substance of Abnormal Dentin, Secondary Dentin, and Pulp Calcification, J. D. Res. **32:** 269, 1953.
15. Burstone, M. S.: Esterase of the Salivary Glands, J. Histochem. & Cytochem. **4:** 130, 1956.
16. Burstone, M. S., and Folk, J. E.: Histochemical Demonstration of Aminopeptidase, J. Histochem. & Cytochem. **4:** 217, 1956.
17. Burstone, M. S., and Keyes, P. H.: Studies on Calcification. I. The Effect of Inhibition of Enzyme Activity on Developing Bone and Dentin, Am. J. Path. **33:** 1229, 1957.
18. Burstone, M. S.: The Relationship Between Fixation and Techniques for the Histochemical Localization of Hydrolytic Enzymes, J. Histochem. & Cytochem. **6:** 322, 1958.
19. Burstone, M. S.: Histochemical Methods for Protein Detection, Handbuch der Histochemie, bk. 3, pt. 2, Stuttgart, 1959, Gustav Fischer, Verlag.
20. Burstone, M. S.: New Histochemical Techniques for the Demonstration of Tissue Oxidase (Cytochrome Oxidase), J. Histochem. & Cytochem. **7:** 112, 1959.
21. Burstone, M. S.: Histochemical Observations on Enzymatic Processes in Bones and Teeth, Ann. New York Acad. Sc. **85:** 431, 1960.
22. Burstone, M. S.: Hydrolytic Enzymes in Dentinogenesis and Osteogenesis. In Sognnaes, R. F. (editor): Calcification in Biological Systems, Washington, D. C., 1960, American Association for the Advancement of Science, p. 217.
23. Burstone, M. S.: Histochemical Demonstration of Cytochrome Oxidase With New Amine Reagents, J. Histochem. & Cytochem. **8:** 63, 1960.
24. Burstone, M. S.: Postcoupling, Noncoupling, and Fluorescence Techniques for the Demonstration of Alkaline Phosphatase, J. Nat. Cancer Inst. **24:** 1199, 1960.
25. Burstone, M. S.: Histochemical Study of Cytochrome Oxidase in Normal and Inflamed Gingiva, Oral Surg., Oral Med., & Oral Path. **13:** 1501, 1960.
26. Burstone, M. S.: Histochemical Demonstration of Phosphatases in Frozen Sections With Naphthol AS-Phosphates, J. Histochem. & Cytochem. **9:** 146, 1961.
26a. Burstone, M. S.: Enzyme Histochemistry and Its Application in the Study of Neoplasms, New York, 1962, Academic Press, Inc.
27. Cabrini, R. L., and Carranza, F. A.: Histochemical Distribution of Acid Phosphatase in Human Gingiva, J. Periodont. **29:** 34, 1958.
28. Cabrini, R. L., and Carranza, F. A.: Histochemical Localization of β-Glucuronidase in Stratified Squamous Epithelium, Naturwiss. **22:** 553, 1958.
29. Cabrini, R. L., and Carranza, F. A.: Histochemical Distribution of Beta-Glucuronidase in Gingival Tissue, Arch. Oral Biol. **2:** 28, 1960.
30. Carranza, F., and Cabrini, R. L.: Mast Cells in Human Gingiva, Oral Surg., Oral Med., & Oral Path. **8:** 1093, 1955.
31. Cobb, J. D.: Relation of Glycogen, Phosphorylase, and Ground Substance to Calcification of Bone, A. M. A. Arch. Path. **55:** 496, 1953.
32. Dewar, M. R.: Observations on the Compositions and Metabolism of Normal and Inflamed Gingiva, J. Periodont. **26:** 29, 1955.
33. Dorfman, A.: The Biochemistry of Connective Tissue, J. Chron. Dis. **10:** 403, 1959.
34. Eastoe, J. E.: The Organic Matrix of Bone. In Bourne, G. H. (editor): The Biochemistry and Physiology of Bone, New York, 1956, Academic Press.
35. Eichel, B.: Oxidative Enzymes of Gingiva, Ann. New York Acad. Sc. **85:** 479, 1960.
36. Engel, M. B.: The Softening and Solution of Dentin in Caries, J. A. D. A. **40:** 284, 1950.
37. Engel, M. B., Ray, H., and Orban, B.: The Pathogenesis of Desquamative Gingivitis, a Disturbance of the Connective Tissue Ground Substance, J. D. Res. **29:** 410, 1950.
38. Fisher, E. R.: Tissue Mast Cells, J. A. M. A. **173:** 171, 1960.
39. Fishman, W.: β-Glucuronidase. In Sumner, J. B., and Myrbäck, K. (editors): The Enzymes: Chemistry and Mechanism of Action, vol. 1, New York, 1950, Academic Press, p. 635.
40. Gersh, I., and Catchpole, J.: The Organization of Ground Substance and Basement Membrane and Its Significance in Tissue Injury, Disease, and Growth, Am. J. Anat. **85:** 457, 1949.
41. Gersh, I.: Ground Substance and the Plasticity of Connective Tissues, Harvey Lectures, Series XLV, Springfield, Ill., 1949-1950, Charles C Thomas, Publisher.
42. Gersh, I., and Stephenson, J.: Freezing and Drying of Tissues for Morphological and Histochemical Studies. In Harris, R. J. C. (editor): Biological Applications of Freezing and Drying, New York, 1954, Academic Press, p. 329.

43. Glick, D.: Techniques of Histo- and Cyto-Chemistry, New York, 1949, Interscience Publishers, Inc.
44. Gomori, G.: Sources of Errors in Enzymatic Histochemistry, J. Lab. & Clin. Med. **35:** 802, 1950.
45. Gomori, G.: The Periodic Acid-Schiff Stain, Am. J. Clin. Path. **22:** 277, 1952.
46. Gomori, G.: Microscopic Histochemistry: Principles and Practice, Chicago, 1952, University of Chicago Press.
47. Gomori, G.: The Histochemistry of Mucopolysaccharides, Brit. J. Exper. Path. **35:** 377, 1954.
48. Greep, R. O., Fischer, C. J., and Morse, A.: Alkaline Phosphatase in Odontogenesis and Osteogenesis and Its Histochemical Demonstration After Demineralization, J. A. D. A. **36:** 427, 1948.
49. Hancox, N.: The Osteoclast. In Bourne, G. H. (editor): The Biochemistry and Physiology of Bone, New York, 1956, Academic Press.
50. Hess, W. C., Lee, C. Y., and Peckham, S. C.: The Lipid Content of Enamel and Dentin, J. D. Res. **35:** 273, 1956.
51. Jackson, D. S.: Some Biochemical Aspects of Fibrogenesis and Wound Healing, New England J. Med. **259:** 814, 1958.
52. Jackson, D. S., and Smith, R. H.: Some Aspects of the Biosynthesis of Collagen. In Recent Advances in Gelatin and Glue Research, New York, 1958, Pergamon Press, p. 54.
53. Kreudenstein, S.: Ueber den Phosphatasennachweis im Dentin, Deutsche Zahn-, Mund- u. Kieferheilk. **26:** 100, 1957.
54. Lacks, C. H., and Rogers, H. J.: Action of Plasmin on Cartilage, Nature **182:** 948, 1958.
55. Laskin, D. M., and Engel, M. B.: Relation Between the Metabolism and Structure of Bone, Ann. New York Acad. Sc. **85:** 421, 1960.
56. McCrea, J. F.: Studies on Influenza Virus Receptor-Substance and Receptor-Substance Analogues. I. Preparation and Properties of a Homogeneous Mucoid From the Salivary Gland of Sheep, Biochem. J. **55:** 132, 1953.
57. McLean, F. C., and Urist, M. R.: Bone: An Introduction to the Physiology of Skeletal Tissue, Chicago, 1955, University of Chicago Press.
58. Menten, M., Jung, J., and Green, M.: A Coupling Histochemical Azo-Dye Test for Alkaline Phosphatase in the Kidney, J. Biol. Chem. **153:** 471, 1944.
59. Moretti, G., Adachi, K., and Ellis, R. A.: Regional Differences in Acid Phosphatase and Between Esterase Activity in the Epidermis of the Chimpanzee and the Macaque, J. Histochem. & Cytochem. **8:** 237, 1960.
60. Nachlas, M. M., Tsou, K. C., DeSouza, E., Cheng, C. S., and Seligman, A. M.: Cytochemical Demonstration of Succinic Dehydrogenase by the Use of a New p-Nitrophenyl Substituted Ditetrazole, J. Histochem. & Cytochem. **5:** 420, 1957.
61. Novikoff, A. B.: Intercellular Localization of Chemical Constituents. In Mellors, R. C. (editor): Analytical Cytology, ed. 2, New York, 1959, McGraw-Hill Book Co., Inc.
62. Person, P., and Burnett, G. W.: Dynamic Equilibria of Oral Tissues. II. Cytochrome Oxidase and Succinoxidase Activity of Oral Tissues, J. Periodont. **26:** 99, 1955.
63. Pincus, P.: Enamel Protein, Proc. Royal Soc. Med. **32:** 513, 1938.
64. Putschar, W. G. J.: General Pathology of the Musculo-Skeletal System, Handb. allg. Path. **3:** 363, 1960.
65. Riley, J. F.: The Mast Cells, London, 1959, E. & S. Livingstone, Ltd.
66. Ring, J. R., and Levy, B.: Changes in Alkaline Phosphatase Activity of Rat Oral Epithelium During the Estrous Cycle and in Response to Administered Estrogen, J. D. Res. **29:** 817, 1950.
67. Robb-Smith, A. H. T.: What Is Reticulin? In Council for International Organization of Medical Sciences, Symposium on Connective Tissue, Oxford, 1957, Blackwell Scientific Publications, p. 177.
68. Roche, J.: Phosphatases. In Sumner, J. B., and Myrbäck, K. (editors): The Enzymes: Chemistry and Mechanism of Action, vol. 1, New York, 1950, Academic Press, p. 486.
69. Rothman, S.: Physiology and Biochemistry of the Skin, Chicago, 1954, University of Chicago Press, p. 468.
70. Sognnaes, R. F.: Microstructure and Histochemical Characteristics of the Mineralized Tissues, Ann. New York Acad. Sc. **60:** 545, 1955.
71. Soyenkoff, R., Friedman, B. K., and Newton, M.: The Lipids of Dental Tissues: A Preliminary Study, J. D. Res. **30:** 599, 1951.

72. Spicer, S. S.: A Correlative Study of the Histochemical Properties of Rodent Acid Muco-polysaccharides, J. Histochem. & Cytochem. **8:** 18, 1960.
73. Spicer, S. S., and Warren, L.: The Histochemistry of Sialic Acid Containing Muco-proteins, J. Histochem. & Cytochem. **8:** 135, 1960.
74. Steinman, R. R., Hewes, C. G., and Woods, R. W.: Histochemical Analysis of Lesions in Incipient Dental Caries, J. D. Res. **38:** 592, 1959.
75. Sumner, J. B., and Somers, G. F.: Chemistry and Methods of Enzymes, ed. 3, New York, 1953, Academic Press.
76. Symons, N. B. B.: Alkaline Phosphatase Activity in the Developing Teeth of the Rat, J. Anat. **89:** 238, 1955.
77. Symons, N. B. B.: Lipid Distribution in the Developing Teeth of the Rat, Brit. D. J. **105:** 27, 1958.
78. Takeuchi, T.: Histochemical Demonstration of Branching Enzyme (Amylo-1, 4 $\rightarrow$ 1,6-Transglucosidase) in Animal Tissues, J. Histochem. & Cytochem. **6:** 208, 1958.
79. Turesky, S., Glickman, I., and Litwin, T.: A Histochemical Evaluation of Normal and Inflamed Human Gingiva, J. D. Res. **30:** 792, 1951.
80. Turesky, S., Crowley, J., and Glickman, I.: A Histochemical Study of Protein-Bound Sulfhydryl and Disulfide Groups in Normal and Inflamed Human Gingiva, J. D. Res. **36:** 255, 1957.
81. Vallotton, C.: Etude bio-histologique de la phosphatase dans la gencive humaine normale et dans les gingivites, Schweiz Monatschr. Zahnh. **52:** 512, 1942.
82. Van Scott, E. J., and Flesh, P.: Sulfhydryl Groups and Disulfide Linkages in Normal and Pathological Keratinization, A. M. A. Arch. Dermat. & Syph. **70:** 141, 1954.
83. Weinmann, J. P., Meyer, J., and Mardfin, D.: Occurrence and Role of Glycogen in the Epithelium of the Alveolar Mucosa and of the Attached Gingiva, Am. J. Anat. **104:** 381, 1959.
84. Windrum, G. M., Kent, P. W., and Eastoe, J. E.: Constitution of Human Renal Reticulin, Brit. J. Exper. Path. **36:** 49, 1955.
85. Zander, H. A.: Distribution of Phosphatase in Gingival Tissue, J. D. Res. **20:** 347, 1941.
86. Unpublished data.

Chapter XVI • TECHNICAL REMARKS*

INTRODUCTION

This chapter is intended to give the student a general idea of the preparation of microscopic slides rather than to cover fully the subject of microscopic technique. For detailed information, specialized textbooks should be consulted.[2, 11-13] The various processes to which a tissue is subjected from the time it is taken from the body until it is ready to be examined under the microscope are termed microtechnique. Its object is to prepare the specimen for examination of its microscopic structure.

PREPARATION OF HISTOLOGIC SPECIMENS

Dissection. Dissection is the first step in the preparation of a specimen; the material may be secured by a biopsy (excision during life) or at an autopsy (post-mortem examination). Pieces of tissue are cut as small as possible to insure satisfactory fixation and impregnation. A very sharp knife should be used to prevent tissue structures from being distorted and squeezed.

Fixation. Immediately after the specimen is removed and the surface washed free of blood, it is placed in fixing solution. The object of fixation is to preserve the tissue elements in the same condition in which they are at the moment the reagent acts upon them and to harden or so affect them that they will not be altered by the processes of dehydration, embedding, staining, clearing, and mounting. The amount of the fixing solution should be at least 20 times the volume of the tissue. The fixing tissue coagulates the protein content of the cells, thus preventing decomposition.

There are several fixing agents in general use, the most common of which are formalin, formalin-alcohol, Zenker-formol solution, and Bouin's fluid. A good and rapidly penetrating fixative for small specimens is Zenker-formol solution, a

---

*First draft submitted by Joan Launspach, research technician of the Foundation for Dental Research, Chicago College of Dental Surgery. Revised by Dorothy Permar.

mixture of 9 parts of potassium bichromate and bichloride of mercury with 1 part of neutral formalin. Formalin (5 to 10 per cent) is used for large pieces of tissue, e.g., jaws. It does not deteriorate, and it penetrates very rapidly. Formalin-alcohol fixes and dehydrates simultaneously, and it is used mostly for surgical specimens. Bouin's fluid is a solution of picric acid and formalin; it is especially applicable in studying cell outlines but is rather slow to penetrate.

The length of time necessary for a fixing agent to act upon a tissue varies according to the size of the specimen and the penetrating power of the fixative. Generally, it should be just long enough for the agent to saturate the piece thoroughly without allowing it to become brittle. Small pieces of tissue, e.g., gingiva, are left in Zenker-formol solution only four to eight hours, whereas larger pieces, such as jaws, may be left in formalin for days. In order to obtain good fixation of pulp in an intact tooth, the surface of enamel and dentin is ground away to a thin layer of dentin around the pulp. This process not only ensures rapid and through penetration of the fixing agent but also reduces the time of decalcification and permits a thorough impregnation with celloidin. When fixing biopsy specimens, the solution should be at approximately body temperature.

After the specimens are thoroughly fixed, they are washed in running water for twenty-four to forty-eight hours to remove all acids and reagents. Occasionally, however, special treatment is required to remove the precipitates caused by certain agents; for example, specimens fixed in Zenker-formol solution are treated with Lugol's (iodine) solution and sodium thiosulfate, and specimens fixed in formalin are placed in a mixture of potassium hydroxide before staining. However, there is no need of this if neutral formol is used.

Decalcification. Animal tissues may be classified as hard and soft or calcified and noncalcified. The dental histologist is particularly interested in the hard tissues, namely, the enamel, dentin, cementum, and bone. These are impregnated with a variable quantity of mineral salts and cannot be sectioned on the microtome unless decalcified.

Decalcification of a tissue is the removal of its mineral content by an acid such as nitric, hydrochloric, trichloroacetic, formic, or sulfosalicylic. The length of time a specimen remains in the decalcifying agent is influenced by the choice and concentration of the acid and the size of the specimen; however, the shorter the time the better is the staining. A 5 per cent solution of nitric acid seems to be most satisfactory and is, therefore, widely used. It acts quickly without causing swelling of the tissue or any other undue changes in its elements; it does not interfere with the staining process to any marked degree.

While tissues are being decalcified, they should be suspended in a large quantity of the fluid in order that the salts dissolved may sink to the bottom of the jar. Occasional stirring or gentle agitation of the specimen and warming of the acid may hasten the process of decalcification, but great care should be taken not to injure the tissues.

To ascertain whether the inorganic salts have been removed completely, the specimen can be pierced with a sharp needle or pin; when no gritty substance is detected, the decalcification is sufficient. Roentgenographic check-up can also be employed and has the advantage of avoiding injury of the specimen. After decalcification, a tooth should be as pliable as a piece of cartilage. The enamel disappears almost entirely owing to its low percentage of organic matter. The decalcifying agent may also be tested for calcium. This is done by placing in a test tube 5 or 6 ml. of the acid in which the specimen had been standing and then adding 1 ml. of concentrated ammonium hydroxide and several drops of a saturated aqueous solution of ammonium oxalate. A precipitate will form when any appreciable amount of calcium is present. If the precipitate forms, the acid covering the specimen should be changed, and the test for complete decalcification should be repeated in a couple of days. If no precipitate is detected after the test tube has stood for an hour and after several additions of ammonium oxalate, it may be assumed that the specimen is nearly completely decalcified. It should be allowed to remain in the same acid for forty-eight hours longer and the test repeated.

Decalcification has been achieved lately by chelating agents.[16] A chelating agent is any chemical which removes a specific mineral ion from another molecule by preferential molecular combination, to form a soluble mineral complex. Specifically, such compounds as the dicarboxylic-ethylene-diamines comprise this group of agents. This activity may take place at a mildly acid, neutral, or mildly basic pH.

Following decalcification the specimen is washed thoroughly in running water for at least twenty-four hours. For this point it is treated as a soft tissue and is ready for the embedding process. It is possible, however, to embed hard tissues first and decalcify them later—the specimen is run through the solutions in routine fashion; after it is blocked, the excess celloidin is cut away, and the tissue is suspended in acid until decalcified. This takes much longer than the usual procedure, and the results are often uncertain.

In order that a tissue may be sectioned on the microtome, it has to have a certain rigidity to offer sufficient resistance to the cutting edge of the knife. This may be accomplished by freezing the tissue or, as is more commonly done, by using an embedding medium that fills the interstices of the tissue. The freezing technique is employed when immediate investigation of the specimen is required, as in the course of a surgical operation. Some substances (fat, lipoids, etc.) are dissolved during embedding; tests for such substances can be made only in frozen sections.

Embedding. Embedding is a much more lengthy process, but results are more satisfactory. Before the specimen is embedded (i.e., impregnated with a suitable substance such as paraffin or celloidin), the water has to be removed from the tissues. Paraffin embedding is more rapid and is used for small pieces, usually soft tissue, as decalcified pieces become brittle during the heating that is necessary in using this method. Celloidin embedding takes longer but causes less shrinkage.

This technique is more commonly used in dental histology when large blocks of decalcified material have to be sectioned.

Dehydration is accomplished by placing the specimens in ascending alcohols (50, 70, 95, 100 per cent) for approximately one day each; the length of time depends on the size and permeability of the specimen. Two consecutive changes of absolute alcohol are used. Because paraffin or celloidin is not soluble in alcohol, it has to be replaced by a fluid that is a solvent for the embedding medium.

When paraffin is selected as the embedding medium, the absolute alcohol is replaced by xylene or oil of cedar wood. The specimens are placed in the solvent twelve to twenty-four hours and are then placed in liquid paraffin in the incubator (56° C.) for several hours. Finally, the specimen is placed in a form filled with molten paraffin and quickly cooled. Attention must be given at this point to the orientation of the specimen so that it will be cut in the desired plane. A good plan is to place the surface to be cut first toward the bottom of the form. The paraffin block is now attached to a holding block, with the side to be cut first on top, by passing a warm spatula between paraffin block and holding block. The paraffin block is now attached to the holding block by passing a warm spatula between the bottom of the paraffin block and the holding block. The mounted paraffin block is trimmed so that the edges are parallel and so that there is about one-eighth inch of paraffin surrounding the tissue on all sides. The specimen is now ready to be sectioned on a microtome.

If celloidin, a solution of nitrocellulose in absolute alcohol and ether, is selected as the embedding medium, a mixture of equal parts of ether and alcohol is used as a solvent in which the tissue remains for twelve hours. It is then carried through a thin (6 per cent) and medium (12½ per cent) into thick (25 per cent) solution of celloidin. The length of time that is necessary for each of the solutions to penetrate the specimen depends upon size and permeability of the tissue. Soft tissue is well infiltrated with celloidin after three weeks, whereas decalcified specimens require at least six weeks; to ensure thorough impregnation, it is wise to leave teeth longer in the lower concentration of celloidin and a somewhat shorter time in the stronger concentration. When it is necessary to "rush" a specimen, the tissue in thin celloidin may be placed in a 50° C. oven in a tightly stoppered container; the embedding period is thus shortened to two or three days. This method causes considerable shrinkage. Small pieces of tissue may be placed directly on a fiber block and left to harden in a desiccator filled with chloroform vapor. Large pieces of tissue, e.g., jaws, are placed in an evaporating dish filled with celloidin that is allowed to harden down slowly. When the celloidin has reached the desired degree of hardness, blocks are cut out; after being softened in thin celloidin for a few minutes, they are placed on fiber blocks, allowed to air dry, and then are placed in 70 per cent alcohol for storage or sectioning.

Sectioning. Tissues are sectioned by means of a microtome, a machine equipped with a knife. There are three different types of microtomes, the freezing, the rotary, and the sliding, the use of which depends on the kind of tissue and embedding medium used. Each is a heavy, specially designed machine, precisely constructed, and capable of slicing prepared tissues into exceedingly thin sections. The knife is wedge-shaped and made of heavy steel to afford the greatest possible rigidity; it must have a very keen edge as the slightest nick would tear a section. Sharpening a microtome knife is one of the most important, as well as one of the most difficult, tasks of a technician. Larger nicks are removed on a coarsely grained stone, and a fine edge is achieved by grinding the knife on a fine hone. The final cutting edge is obtained by stropping on a finishing leather microtome strop. A much more rapid method, and one equally as satisfactory, that has been developed recently is the use of a grinding machine consisting of an ebony wheel mounted on a rotary motor. A strop, dusted with abrasive powder, is used to put the finishing edge on the knife. The possibility of making good sections depends upon the type of tissue, its preparation, and the condition of the knife. Sections of 5 to 15 microns ($\frac{1}{1000}$ millimeter equals 1 micron) are considered thin.

The importance of the freezing technique in preparing surgical specimens has been mentioned. It is well known that by exposing tissues to an extreme degree of cold they become hard and can be sectioned easily with the freezing microtome. The cold is generated by means of carbon dioxide that is sprayed onto the stage holding the specimen; rapid evaporation produces the required temperature.

The rotary microtome is used only for sectioning paraffin blocks; the knife is immovably fixed at a right angle to the block, which is carried past the sharp edge of the knife by turning a wheel. With this machine it is possible to cut long ribbons of serial sections. The ribbons are placed in lukewarm water where the wrinkles are removed as the paraffin becomes soft. The desired sections are then floated onto slides lightly smeared with egg albumin and placed in a 37° C. oven for a few minutes. Before staining, the paraffin is dissolved in xylene, the slides rinsed in absolute alcohol, and the sections carried through descending concentrations of alcohols into distilled water; then they can be stained by water-soluble dyes.

A celloidin block is sectioned by a different method. For this purpose the sliding microtome, a heavy sledgetype instrument, is used. The longitudinal angle of the knife is adjusted to each specimen so that the entire cutting edge is used in sectioning. The angle of the cutting edge of the knife should be changed according to the hardness and density of the material. To obtain the most satisfactory results, the knife should be in an almost horizontal position for large decalcified pieces and at an acute angle for soft tissue. During sectioning, both specimen and knife are continually moistened with 70 per cent alcohol; the sections are placed in distilled water before staining. The celloidin usually is not removed from the section as the stain penetrates the tissues in spite of this embedding medium. However, it has to be removed from the section in the case of specific stains, i.e., Mallory, azure-eosin, etc. For this procedure, the section is mounted on a slide covered with egg albumin and is flooded with oil of cloves to dissolve the celloidin; the slide is rinsed in 95 per cent alcohol and is placed in 70 per cent alcohol until ready for staining.[12] When serial sections are desired, sections are mounted on glass slides that are then blotted and flooded with a very thin solution of collodion. After a coating is formed, the slides are marked with a diamond pencil or India ink and stored in 70 per cent alcohol until ready for staining.[20]

Some special staining methods can be applied only to sections of undecalcified teeth and bone. To obtain such sections, mature enamel has to be removed from the teeth. The tissue impregnated with celloidin is placed in a shallow dish and covered with celloidin. The solution is allowed to evaporate slowly until the celloidin is very hard (two to four weeks). A very hard knife, which has been sharpened and stropped, should be used; when checked under the microscope, it has deep and even teeth and should be clamped in the microtome at a 13 degree angle.

Staining. Dyes used to stain specimens for microscopic examination may be classified as basic or acid, according to their affinity for different cellular elements. Basic dyes, sometimes called nuclear dyes, primarily stain nuclear chromatin, basic substance of cartilage and mucus; the more commonly used are hematoxylin, methylene blue, safranine, and carmine. Acid dyes color the cytoplasm of the cell, uncalcified bone and dentin matrix, and some connective tissue fibers; eosin and phloxine are representative of this group. By using combinations of the two groups, because of their different affinities, a marked differentiation of the cellular elements of the specimen is possible.

Sections may be stained on the slide or floating in dishes; in the latter case, better differentiation is afforded. Although the steps of the various staining methods differ considerably, they may be arranged in the following order: staining, differentiating, decolorizing, dehydrating, clearing, and mounting.

Hematoxylin and eosin is one of the most commonly used combinations of stains because it is the simplest to handle. For the differentiation of more specialized tissues, the following are recommended: Mallory stain[11] or Heidenhain's azan,[11] a modification of Mallory's stain, for connective tissue (the latter is more brilliant and has greater capacity for differentiation); silver impregnation, a modification of Foot's stain by Gomori, for connective tissue fibers and nerve elements[2]; Van Gieson's stain, a counterstain to hematoxylin, for differentiation of white connective tissue[12]; and Weigert's stain, for elastic tissue.[12]

After sections of tissues have been stained and differentiated, they are dehydrated and then passed through a medium that will mix with the dehydrating fluid as well as the reagent in which the sections are to be mounted. These intermediary fluids are called clearing agents because they have a high refractive index, thus rendering the sections more or less transparent.

For celloidin sections a variety of clearing agents is used: terpineol (lilacin), carbolxylene, oil of cloves, oil of cedar wood, oil of Origanum, and beechwood creosote; for paraffin sections usually only two are used: xylene or toluol.

After clearing, the sections have to be placed in some medium that will preserve the stain and prevent the tissue from drying. Such solutions are termed mounting agents. Among the most common are gum dammar, Canada balsam, and Clarite. Loose celloidin sections are floated onto the slide and straightened out with the aid of a fine camel's hair brush; they are blotted carefully and covered with a drop of mounting medium and a coverslip. Weights may be placed on the coverslips to prevent the formation of air bubbles. When dry, they are cleaned carefully with xylene and labeled with India ink.

Altmann-Gersh technique. The Altmann-Gersh freezing and drying technique for special microchemical studies should also be mentioned. The tissues are frozen instantaneously when placed in a tube of isopentane in a liquid air container and are dehydrated under vacuum while still frozen, thus avoiding a redistribution of minerals. Fixation, alcohol dehydration, and clearing are omitted as the dehydrated tissue can be immediately infiltrated with paraffin and sectioned according to the usual methods. This technique has proved valuable in the preparation of tissues for microincineration and for special microchemical reactions.

PREPARATION OF GROUND SECTIONS

Ground sections are prepared by using abrasive stones upon a tooth or bone until the tissue is reduced to translucent thinness. It is the principal method of examining the enamel, which has so little organic material that it disappears almost entirely when the teeth are decalcified by ordinary methods. Therefore, this technique should complement the decalcification method.

To prepare a ground section of a tooth, it is first ground down on one side on a carborundum stone that rotates at high speed on a laboratory lathe. It is important that the tooth be kept wet constantly with cold water to lessen the heat produced by friction and to prevent the section from drying. If it is allowed to dry, its organic constituents will shrink and present a picture untrue to the conditions during life. The tissue is likewise more apt to crack and break up during preparation if it becomes dry. When the desired level is reached and the ground surface is perfectly plane, this surface is polished on wet ground glass and, finally, on an Arkansas stone. The other side of the specimen is then ground down until the section is sufficiently translucent. This second side is also polished in the above described manner, to remove the gross scratches produced by the carborundum stone. The finished ground sections should have an average thickness of 25 to 50 microns and, if desired, may be stained before they are dehydrated, cleared, and mounted.[13]

For surface staining of ground sections, the surface is well polished and the section is covered with 0.25 per cent HCl to decalcify it slightly; then it is stained lightly with hematoxylin.[15] By this method only the surface of the ground section is stained, and the stained layer can be viewed with high-power lenses as it is only a few microns in thickness. This method, however, causes slight decalcification of the enamel, making a marked differentiation of rods from sheaths and cementing substance, a condition not representative of normal enamel. Enamel that has been partially decalcified by caries or a poorly formed enamel has this appearance.

If it is necessary to investigate an undecalcified tooth with the surrounding soft tissue, ground sections can be made by using the petrifaction method. The specimen is embedded in Kollolith-chloroform solution or in Canada balsam,[13, 15] where it is left until it is sufficiently hard before it is ground down to a desired thickness. Thin "serial" ground sections of teeth and jaws may be cut in one operation by infiltrating the specimen with a plastic material and using a cutting device made up of steel wheels set at various distances.[18]

PREPARATION OF ORGANIC STRUCTURES IN THE ENAMEL

The routine decalcification of whole teeth in an aqueous solution of acid usually destroys the enamel completely. At most, merely shreds of the organic structures remain near the cervical areas in a tooth of a young person.

The organic structures may be demonstrated by Bodecker's celloidin decalcifying method.[4] When dentin is included in the specimen, sections are rarely satisfactory because this tissue becomes very brittle as a result of the many media through which it passes. It is necessary only for study of the organic structures in the enamel under high magnification. In general, this method is erratic, and a high percentage of failures must be expected.

The Cape-Kitchin modification[3, 5] of Bodecker's method is quite simple and gives satisfactory results if the structures of the matrix are not magnified more than about 500 diameters.

Frisbie, Nuckolls, and Saunders[7] recently developed a technique for the successful recovery of the enamel matrix. The fresh specimen is immediately fixed in neutral formalin for a long period of time (six months); most of the dentin is then removed with a dental bur, and the tooth is placed in the fixative again for a shorter period of time, depending on the penetrability of the specimen. The completely fixed enamel is decalcified by placing the specimen on gauze stretched over a platinum wire frame and immersing it in a 5 per cent solution of nitric acid in 80 per cent alcohol for twenty-four to forty-eight hours. Dehydration is begun with 70 per cent alcohol without preliminary washing. The specimen is infiltrated with celloidin at 56° C. for two weeks and then allowed to harden down slowly at room temperature until the block is very hard. Sectioning is done with a sliding microtome at 3 to 4 microns.

An aqueous decalcification of enamel under a coverglass is the simplest but the least satisfactory method for its study. It is sufficient to show enamel lamellae, cuticle, tufts, and can be used to demonstrate gross differences in quantity of organic structures of enamel in recently erupted teeth and in teeth of old persons.

However, the disadvantages are that only low magnifications up to 100 diameters are possible and that the specimens are not durable.

Another method of differentiating the organic from the inorganic content of the enamel is by incineration. It has been shown that the heating of sections of human adult enamel up to 800° C. causes a destruction of the organic content but leaves enamel rods intact.

PHOTOMICROGRAPHY

Photomicrographs are photographs of microscopic sections, made with the aid of a microscope. Most of the illustrations in this book are such photographs. Transmitted light is the most commonly used method of illumination as it permits the sharpest differentiation of details and the highest magnification of tissue structures in stained decalcified sections.

Reflected light is used in oral histology in photomicrographs of ground sections of enamel and dentin. These sections should be ground perfectly smooth. There is no need for extreme thinness because the specimen is viewed only from the surface from which the light is reflected.

Polarized light also is useful in the study of the dental tissues. It vibrates in a single known plane and requires special equipment and technique. By this means it is possible to determine details of the submicroscopic structure of tissues, due to the differences in optical properties of various elements. Polarized light is particularly useful in the study of calcified tissues, but it is not confined to these because fibrous and keratinized structures also yield information when studied by this method.

Grenz rays are a form of exceedingly soft roentgen rays. When ground sections of teeth are photographed in this way, slight variation in calcification may be defined, thus rendering this method useful in the study of calcified structures.[1, 13]

A method has been developed recently by Gurney and Rapp[8] for studying the fine structural details of tooth surface by adapting the Fax Film technique used for study of metallographic surfaces. Microimpressions are made of the specimen, using a plastic film that may then be mounted on a glass slide for a permanent preparation. Scott and Wyckoff[17] obtained similar results by shadowing collodion replicas with vaporized metal in a high vacuum, a more complicated method. The effect of chemical agents on tooth structure and the changes in tooth surfaces (caries) may be observed using these methods. When examined under the electron microscope, many submicroscopic structures are visible.

Ultraviolet light technique[4] and fluorescent light microscopy likewise have been applied in special studies of dental tissues but have not yet attained wide use.

References

1. Applebaum, E., Hollander, F., and Bodecker, C. F.: Normal and Pathological Variations in Calcification of Teeth as Shown by the Use of Soft X-rays, D. Cosmos **75:** 1097, 1933.

2. Bensley, R. R., and Bensley, S. S.: Handbook of Histological and Cytological Technique, Chicago, University of Chicago Press.
3. Bodecker, C. F.: Cape-Kitchin Modification of Celloidin Decalcifying Method for Dental Enamel, J. D. Res. **16:** 143, 1937.
4. Bodecker, C. F.: Enamel of Teeth Decalcified by Celloidin Decalcifying Method and Examined by Ultra Violet Light, D. Rev. **20:** 317, 1906.
5. Cape, A. T., and Kitchin, P. C.: Histologic Phenomenon of Tooth Tissues Observed Under Polarized Light, With a Note on Roentgen Ray Spectra of Enamel and Dentin, J. A. D. A. **17:** 193, 1930.
6. Cowdry, E. V.: Microscopic Technique in Biology and Medicine, Baltimore, 1943, Williams & Wilkins Co.
7. Frisbie, H. E., Nuckolls, J., and Saunders, J. B. de C. M.: Distribution of Organic Matrix of Enamel in Human Teeth and Its Relation to Histopathology of Caries, J. Am. Coll. Dentists **11:** 243, 1944.
8. Gurney, B. F., and Rapp, G. W.: Technic for Observing Minute Changes on Tooth Surfaces, J. D. Res. **25:** 367, 1946.
9. Guyer, M. F.: Animal Micrology, Chicago, 1943, University of Chicago Press.
10. Hotchkiss, R. D.: Microchemical Reaction Resulting in Staining of Polysaccharide Structures in Fixed Tissue Preparation, Arch. Biochem. **16:** 131, 1948.
11. Loosli, C. G.: Outline of Histological Methods, Chicago, University of Chicago Press.
12. Mallory, F. B.: Pathological Technique, Philadelphia, 1938, W. B. Saunders Co.
13. McClung, C. E.: Microscopic Technique, New York, 1937, Paul B. Hoeber, Inc., pp. 353-401.
14. McLean, F. C., and Bloom, W.: Calcification and Ossification. Calcification in Normal Growing Bone, Anat. Rec. **78:** 133, 1940.
15. Meyer, W.: Die Anfertigung histologischer Schliffe (Preparation of Histologic Ground Sections), Vrtljschr. f. Zahnheilk. **41:** 111, 1925.
16. Nikiforuk, G., and Sreebny, L.: Demineralization of Hard Tissues by Organic Chelating Agents of Neutral pH, J. D. Res. **32:** 859, 1953.
17. Scott, D. B., and Wyckoff, R. W. G.: Shadowed Replicas of Tooth Surfaces, Pub. Health Rep. **61:** 697, 1946.
18. Sognnaes, R. F.: Preparation of Thin Serial Ground Sections of Whole Teeth and Jaws and Other Highly Calcified and Brittle Structures, Anat. Rec. **99:** 133, 1947.
19. Sognnaes, R. F.: The Organic Elements of the Enamel, J. D. Res. **27:** 609, 1948; **28:** 549, 558, 1949; **29:** 260, 1950.
20. Willman, M.: Technique for Preparation of Histological Sections Through Teeth and Jaws for Teaching and Research, J. D. Res. **16:** 183, 1937.
21. Wolf, J.: Plastische Histologie der Zahngewebe (Plastic Histology of Dental Tissues), Deut. Zahn-, Mund- u. Kieferheilk. **7:** 265, 1940.

INDEX